Shell Connections 2004

NEW PLAYS
FOR YOUNG PEOPLE

Shell Connections 2004

NEW PLAYS
FOR YOUNG PEOPLE

A copy of
Shell Connections 2003
and
Shell Connections 2004
has been placed in every secondary school
in the UK through the generous support of
The Foyle Foundation

faber and faber

First published in 2004
by Faber and Faber Limited
3 Queen Square London WC1N 3AU

Typeset by Country Setting, Kingsdown, Kent CT14 8ES
Printed in England by Mackays of Chatham plc, Chatham, Kent

A CIP record for this book is available from the British Library

0-571-22447-4

2 4 6 8 10 9 7 5 3 1

Contents

Introduction

The plays in this anthology are a result of the National Theatre's new writing programme for teenagers, and have already been performed by hundreds of schools, colleges and youth theatres around the world (the companies that premiered the work are listed at the back of this book). Now the plays have been put together in one sparkling collection for you to try out. And if you'd like to join the programme, I'll tell you how in a minute. But first, the plays.

You'll find cast sizes vary enormously and that many of the works offer scope for flexibility. Settings include a derelict East End tower block, a terrible city in a terrible country, a Bed and Breakfast in Bloomsbury, Moscow, China and Walthamstow. There's a tale of alien abduction set in the past, of memory and a search for self-identity, and of a plot to capture the royal princes. The plays are packed with contemporary resonances and, above all, have been written by some of the best writers around with teenagers in mind.

Moonfleece by Philip Ridley might be described as an East End *Hamlet*. In it, fourteen-year-old Curtis has arranged a secret meeting in a flat with fellow members of the right-wing political party which he leads. Things, however, do not go as planned when one of the two squatters now occupying the flat begins to tell a story that will change Curtis's life for ever. Shakespearean references don't end here. *Discontented Winter: House Remix* by Bryony Lavery starts, pauses, fast-forwards and sometimes rewinds in a world in which everyone's fighting for the remote and the action happens in mangled TV-speak and replays of old TV plots. Ronan, a latter-day Richard III, hatches a plot to kidnap one of the royal princes as Serena, a posh Sloanie, schemes to snatch the other. In a nearby tower block, anoracky Cheviot wants to quit her world and assume her rightful position as commander of a starship. Meanwhile, one of the princes is falling in love with a slapper, while the other prepares to lead the youth of the country in over-throwing the government

Bedbug – the Musical, adapted by Snoo Wilson with music from Gary Kemp and Guy Pratt, is a wonderful and dangerous fable. Ivan Varlet, a boozy mechanic and pro-letarian Party member, is marrying a hairdresser in a self-improving effort to join the bourgeois class. Catastrophe strikes at the wedding, however, when the guests set fire to the house, the fire brigade is too drunk to save them, and everyone dies – save Ivan, who is washed into the cellar and frozen in a block of solid ice, only to be thawed alive fifty years later and put on display as a specimen of what humanity was like before the glorious Revolution.

In Patrick Marber's brilliant new comedy *The Musicians*, the members of the UK's Ridley Road School Orchestra are to give the most important concert of their lives in just over two hours' time, playing Tchaikovsky's Fourth Sym-phony to an audience of cultural bigwigs in Moscow. There's just one small problem: they have no instruments. Luckily for them, Alex, the Russian boy who cleans the hall in which they are to play and is a devout *Pinball Wizard* fan, comes up with a plan that saves everyone.

The poet Simon Armitage's *Eclipse* is set in Cornwall in August 1999, on the day of a total eclipse of the sun. Six friends are called to the police station to give evidence about the appearance and disappearance of the strange Lucy Lime, whom they met out on the beach beneath the cliffs that day. One or all could be culpable.

Dead End, by Letizia Russo, tells the story of what appear to be two separate groups of teenagers. The first is a community who live under the dictatorial role of Sirius, whom they believe to be God. The second comprises two schoolmates, Kent and Kris, who are on a long journey to meet Sirius. While Kris is always friendly, Kent is hiding a dark secret; and when Kent and Sirius finally meet, we discover the past they share and witness the playing out of their battle over who is to rule as God.

In 1830, a British Admiralty ship at anchor off Tierra del Fuego has one of its landing boats stolen by natives. In reprisal, the Captain takes four tribal teenagers hostage, brings them to England, and converts them to Christianity, planning to return them in three years' time to run a trading station. In *Boat Memory* Laline Paull shows the Fuegians' arrival at their new home in Wathamstow, and how their intital compliance turns to alienation under the influences of village racism, teenage hormones and the pangs of first love, enforcing the Fuegians' premature return.

The Willow Pattern is a wonderful retelling by Judith Johnson of the ancient Chinese legend popularised in this country by its traditional use in the design of tableware. A rich Mandarin has a much cherished daughter, Knoon-She, who, despite her father's lavish gifts, defies his plans for her marriage, and is forced to flee the palace with her lover Chang. The Mandarin is so devastated by his daughter's desertion that he pursues the lovers and, in a fit of fury, burns down the house in which they are sleeping. The spirits of the two lovers rise up in the form of two doves, and fly off to the Realm of Eternal Happiness.

Headstrong, by April De Angelis, takes place mainly on an opium clipper in the China Sea. Because Rose's mother once set fire to a field of crops in protest at the industrialisation of agricultural work, Rose has become a ward of the state, and has been sent to live with a religious family as a servant. When she joins Lila and her mother on a journey to meet Lila's prospective groom, her father's new business partner in the opium trade, Rose sees first-hand the destruction that the drug can cause, and finally understands what her mother has been fighting against.

Spoilt for choice? Finally, in *Where I Come From: Scenes from Abroad, by Mike Williams*, written by Richard Nelson, a young man tells us his story, beginning in the sitting room of a London Bed and Breakfast in 1987. Here, a group of American high-school students has just completed a week of visits to mostly boring museums and mostly boring plays. On the final night of their stay, finding themselves alone in the B. and B. and fortified by music and raging emotions, they stay up all night, confronting their wounds, dancing, and creating the most unforgettable of evenings.

All the plays are accompanied by interviews with the writers and notes based on workshops run by the National Theatre that involved all the teachers and youth theatre directors who premiered the plays. These workshops took place over a long weekend in Keswick, Cumbria, and gave the directors an opportunity to work with the writer of the play that they'd chosen and other leading artists. The notes comprise a summary of responses to the questions asked, along with staging suggestions and exercises tried out at the retreat. I hope you'll find these useful, too.

The plays were premiered in March, and each production received a visit and show report from a National Theatre assessor. Most productions were then going on to one of a series of festivals at leading venues. The programme culminates in a six-day festival at the National in July.

Shell Connections is a continuous programme which is open to anybody who works with eleven-to-nineteen-year-olds. If you would like more information on how you can participate in premiering the next series of plays, just visit our website (shellconnections.org.uk).

SUZY GRAHAM-ADRIANI
National Theatre
March 2004

BEDBUG – THE MUSICAL

Book adapted by Snoo Wilson
from the play *The Bedbug*
by Vladimir Mayakovsky

Music by Gary Kemp and Guy Pratt

Lyrics by Snoo Wilson
with additional lyrics
by Gary Kemp and Guy Pratt

For the musical score to *Bedbug*
please apply to Steve Dagger,
Dagger Entertainments, 14 Lampton Place,
London, W11 2SH

Characters

Ivan Varlet
also known as Ivor Violet, Party member,
former worker, now the fiancé of

Elzevir Bornagin
manicurist and cashier of a beauty parlour

Rosalie Bornagin, her mother

David Bornagin, her father

Zoya Byrioshka, a working girl

Oleg Bard, an eccentric female life-stylist

V. Mayakovsky, poet and narrator

Market Vendors
Button Seller, Fruit Seller, Doll Seller,
Herring Seller, Lampshade Seller, Bra Seller

Bookseller
Balloon Seller
Barefoot Youth
2nd Youth
Inventor
Cleaner
Intellectual Girl
Solo Mechanic
Accountant
Chief of Police
Policemen
Professor of Cryogenic Unit
Zoo Director

Fire Chief
Revolutionary Fire Brigade
Future Fire Brigade
Usher
Choreographed Stenographers
Doctor
Best Man
Reporter
Hairdressers
Mechanics
Reporters
Paperboys
Lurve Girls
Zoo Steward
Workers
Chairman of City Soviet
Orator
Reporters 1–7
High-School Students
Master of Ceremonies
Members of Presidium of City Soviet
Children
Future Man and Woman
Vets
Historian
Zoo Keepers
Old People
Animals
Animated Voting Machine

PROLOGUE AND SCENE ONE

Enter the author, Mayakovsky, in an explosive fashion.
Everything that Mayakovsky does is performed outsize.
The wild-eyed, cloth-capped poet harangues the audience
confidently, revolver in hand. He is wielding a pair of
pistols, bursts through a screen which is showing a
collage of Russian images from the twentieth century:
everything from the storming of the Winter Palace to
babushkas selling wooden Gorbachev dolls in Red
Square and queues outside the Moscow McDonald's.

Mayakovsky
    'In my end is my beginning.' Who am I? A poet. Right.
    My first poem was 'Mayakovsky, a Tragedy',
    I am Vladimir Mayakovsky, come from the dead.
    Like other visitors from the nether world, my time here
        is brief.
    Relax, I explain everything. The only brains blown out
        tonight will be mine.
    For those who have not read their programmes yet
    This prologue is pronounced by the shade
    Of the former author – who long ago shot himself.
    Some say I Mayakovsky knew
    My time was up: Stalin was always behind a bad
        review.
    My advice to you is, enjoy tonight! It could be your
        last, and any artistic shock
    Could be a trembling prelude to delight.

    The Bedbug, work of genius, begins in a street market
        after that false dawn of the assassination of the Tsar,
        the Russian Revolution ushering in

A brief and comically deluded season of hope.
Audience! Do your best. If not moved, pretend. To be
    alive
Is not always to be sincere; unless you are a genius.
You might say I foresaw
The revolution would turn to ashes, and burnt straw.
I left a note, to be found beside my brains. 'The love
    boat has crashed.'
Hell's devils tell me it loses everything, in translation.
(But they would, wouldn't they?)
The poetic heart is subject to perturbation.
My love life was not in tip-top condition, plus
I was subject to arrest by Comrade Stalin
And the condemned man calls in vain for pen and
    paper.
I had a flair for gesture that enabled me to pinch out
My own deathless flame – and what can I tell you?
Darkness! No more taper.

My pen, you will observe, skewers many hearts;
I wield it like a stake, to drive through the hypocritical
    left ventricle of all later Stalinist, Socialist-Realist,
    fear-beshitted so-called 'art'!
A glowing Futurist electron storm returns
To illuminate the tundra of the Russian soul!
I hereby conjure up before your eyes
A Russian state department store
In front of it here, a People's Market.
Begin my play, and
Unfold here, its lethal prophecy.

*He fires pistols, and exits through broken screen. Scene
begins. The cries of the street vendors all overlap in
a scene-setting panorama. The sellers begin a market
number, each pitching their wares, building the song
to a choral crescendo.*

Button Seller
Dutch press studs,
Dutch press studs,
Better than buttons are Dutch press studs.
Dutch press studs, Dutch press studs,
Twenty-four-hour control. (*Repeats.*)

Doll Seller
Dancing dolls, dancing dolls,
Light as a feather are dancing dolls,
Dancing dolls, dancing dolls,
Ready and willing are dancing dolls. (*Repeats.*)

Fruit Seller
No kiwis, no melons,
We got Socialist bananas,
Not twenty, not eighteen,
Fifteen's all I'm asking.
Bargain bananas
Are yours for the gobbling –
Put the best Russian manhood to shame! (*Repeats.*)

Herring Seller
Herrings! Non-Tsarist herrings!
And herrings! Republican herrings! (*Repeats.*)

L'shade Seller
Lampspshades, lampshades! (*Repeats.*)

Bra-seller
Lovely brassieres trimmed with mink,
Ladies, you never seen anything like it.
Not just thermal, decorative too.
Be surprised what your husband'll do. (*Repeats.*)

*Singing continues under dialogue. Balloon Seller is
making up animals with long thin balloons.*

Balloon Seller What am I doing? I'll tell you. With these
all-socialist balloons at five kopecks, you can make

7

animals – see – like a sweet little post-monarchist sausage dog – you try.

He gives an untied balloon to a small Boy. Boy lets go and balloon deflates.

Balloon Seller You got to hold on tight to its arse. Have another try now. Thing is, even with with socialist balloons, it all whooshes out. That's right – whoops –

Balloon flies out of Boy's hand again.

Bookseller Books, books. 'How to' books on all subjects. This one – special offer – *How to Commit Adultery*, a spicy rib-tickler by ex-Count Leo Tolstoy, full of practical hints –

All
A modern souk, a new bazaar,
Though not the first, the best by far.
You'll be surprised, you'll be amazed,
Amazement is our stock in trade.

You might presume the state provides,
But you don't need to shop inside.
Unless you take that foolish step,
The choice is yours, selection wide.

It's every Russian's right to choose
State or private enterprise.
We can obtain in any size
If you supply a crate of booze.

You want some cheese, you want a hat,
A bit of this, a bit of that.
A dream come true, we promise you –
The marketplace is where it's at.

Marxists all, in Marx we trust,
He will prevail when we are dust.

But even Lenin will admit,
It's only fair to earn a crust.

Music fades under dialogue. Enter Varlet and his future mother-in-law, Rosalie Pavlovna, and Oleg.

Varlet I say, look at these aristocratic nightcaps! Is it real fur?

Varlet puts a bra from a stall on his head.

Bra Seller Real? Is this lovely fur real? Was Cleopatra a snake fancier? Feel that silkiness. It's from the inside legs of the animals. But there wasn't no suffering involved. These little minks were sleeping on silk, crammed with cream, before they finally sacrificed themselves for the Soviet people's comfort.

Rosalie Comrade Violet, I wouldn't advise trying to put your head in one of those. There are two, see?

Varlet Away with you, foolish creature. I always have two of everything that catches my fancy.

Rosalie But they're not for your sort. They're for supporting parts of outstanding female Party members.

Varlet What nonsense. After I marry your daughter Elzevir, these trinkets will dress what comes to pass.

Rosalie Get away! You're not one of them cross-dressers, are you? And I thought he was an honest prole, not a decadent capitalist!

Varlet I'm talking about what comes to pass exactly nine months after. I know they will make superior hats for your future grandchildren. They can put them on when they go out together in the park.

Rosalie They'll have to be twins if they're going to put their two heads into one brassiere!

Varlet Of course we'll have twins – because I am going to have two of everything I want in the future. It is written! You just have to read Comrade Marx.

Oleg I think what the former Ivan Varlet, now known as Ivor Violet here, is doing is bringing an innocent proletarian eye to bear on everyday creations, and transforming their use-value with his incisive intelligence, don't you?

Rosalie I didn't realise that union with the proletariat meant that my grandchildren will have to go round for ever with their heads crammed into one fur-trimmed brassiere as if they were Siamese twins.

Oleg Rosalie, don't provoke His Working Classness – don't forget, with your kind of background, you need to get that HWC union card in your front room.

Doll Seller (*background*) Dancing dolls, dancing dolls, light as a feather, ready and willing in all kinds of weather.

Oleg If he wants two of everything, it's his by right! We've had the revolution, the proletariat are the men of the hour!

Varlet (*to Doll Seller*) Hither, fellow. (*Examines dolls.*) 'The fruit of the proletarian loom must be able to step out of its cradling, into culture and elegance.'

Rosalie You'd better have two of them, too, then.

Varlet No. I don't just want two, I want a whole regiment of those.

Rosalie But Comrade Violet!

Varlet Don't comrade me in public till after the marriage. For now, you are still unredeemed bourgeoise, so watch what you say.

Oleg How about Future Comrade as a correct form of address and you can call her future mother-in-law?

Rosalie I take your point, Future Comrade Violet, but for the money we're spending, we could smarten up any number of your compatriots – shave and shampoo a dozen of the grottiest proles. If the wedding's going to go off with a bang, we're going to need to budget for some booze.

Varlet Do you imagine I would forget to order drink? Of course not.

Oleg That is so true! The trouser pockets of Future Comrade Violet, however repellent, contain within them the socialist horn-of-plenty! As the wedding is the promised union of the working and bourgeois classes, the Future Comrade has committed to several bottles of vodka already for the occasion.

Herring Man Finest post-Tsarist herrings! Essential accompaniment to all kinds of vodka!

Rosalie (*brightening*) You hear that? Salted herrings are the very thing for a wedding! Out of my way, young prole-gentleman. (*looking*) Oh dear, how disappointing.

Oleg Let me carry them – I won't charge a penny –

Rosalie How much do you want to get rid of these horrid little stunted sardines?

Herring Man I can't let these salmon go at under two roubles sixty. They weigh a full kilo each.

Rosalie Two-sixty for a piddling minnow like that?

Herring Man That's no minnow, that's an apprentice sturgeon! Look at the fat on those gills!

Rosalie Sturgeon? More like a twiglet fish.

Music stops.

Well, I'm not standing here arguing, we've had a revolution in case you haven't heard. I'm going to get some decent fish from the Soviet State Co-op!

Herring Man Pull the other one!

Rosalie Don't you try to stop me bypassing the private sector!

Exit Rosalie.

Herring Man Go ahead, go on, see what they've got in there. It's rubbish. You'd be lucky to find a fish head that hasn't gone off.

Oleg Oh, this is all so upsetting and unnecessary. Future Comrade Violet, why let your dear future mother-in-law get involved in tasteless street polemics when, if you refer to me, I can personally guarantee the most luxurious and stylish wedding that you'll ever have in your life! (*to Varlet*) Fifteen roubles and a bottle of vodka, how about it?

Varlet Others are going to be handling the petty-bourgeois details. I don't care to be involved.

Oleg Alright, then have you thought of having your nuptials conducted along the lines of the ancient Rites of Eleusis? Eleusis of the ancient world, the fountain of our culture, where sacred drama and religion both drank from the same stream? We can reconstruct the rites for your ceremony. When the wedding procession advances, holding sheaves of corn in front of the bride, I will sing in praise of Hymen.

Varlet Hymen? Hymen who?

Oleg Hymen's the ancient goddess of marriage and fertility.

Varlet No no. I want an honest to goodness modern Red wedding, with no decadent foreign trimmings.

Oleg Then the wedding will obey our socialist dramatic unities – I refer to the coming unities, of class . . . let's see . . . a Red . . .

Romantic music begins.

We envision the red-dressed Red wife-to-be stepping out of her carriage as she arrives on the arm of the Red accountant, the universal proxy father-in-law, representing the state. She's looking pretty steamed up, but he's ooh, red as a beetroot. And then the Red red groom is ushered in by the Red ushers, and the red tablecloth is covered with bowls of steaming borscht and juicy red hams.

Music stops.

How does that envision for a start?
Varlet I like it. How does it go on?

Enter Zoya, circles them suspiciously.

Oleg Very well.

Music begins again.

The blushing guests tear the Red red tops off the vodka
  bottles with sweaty fingers and pour the proper vodka
  down their red throats, and when they look down at
  you again to draw breath, they shout, 'Kiss, kiss!' and
  your brand new encarminated red-hot spouse with her
  tongue weaving like a red cobra inside her mouth
  comes towards you closer and closer till her panting
  embouchure closes succulently on your own rosy face
  sphincter, sploosh! – recipe for mutual rapture. All
  taking place exactly as modernity stipulates, in a
  divinely atheistic ambience, you note.
Zoya Just a minute. Ivan!

Music stops abruptly.

What's this old cow going on about? What wedding?
  Who's getting married?
Varlet Nothing's happened yet, Zoya. But as clear as the
  recent triumph of the working class, we cannot continue
  our romantic acquaintance.
Zoya Why not? What are you two talking about?
Varlet Nothing that concerns the objects of my previous
  affections.
Oleg We are discussing the impending rubicund nuptials
  between Elzevir Davidovna Bornagin, and this
  eminently titled prole-gentleman here, His Working
  Classness Ivor Violet.
Zoya His name is plain Ivan Varlet, and he is engaged to
  me! Or was. What's going on? What about me, Ivan?

Varlet Ivan? Who he? Ivan exists only in memory. Enter
Ivor, the new man!

Varlet's Song.

So sorry, Zoya,
If I destroy ya
Hopes for the future, but you're an annoyance.
Class credentials take a battering,
Pinstriped pants prove more flattering.

All (*except Zoya*)
The bourgeoisie's the new norm,
This is how proles should reform.

Varlet
Ivan is dreaming his dream of advancement,
Turning his previous fiancé down flat.
Changing his name, his cap for a top hat,
Drink up to that, brothers, drink up to that.

All (*except Zoya*)
Destiny beckons and Ivan's arising,
He's got the bridegroom's right answer down pat –
I do, I do, and the bride says, I do too,
Drink up to that, brothers, drink up to that.

The bourgeoisie's the new norm,
This is how proles should reform.

Varlet
Call me a fool, say that I will fall hard
But the ace in this game is my red Party card.

Zoya
Dumped at the altar – world-shattering,
No thought for me, not a smattering.
Carry on joking and chattering,
This poor heart's taking a battering.

All (*except Zoya*)
> The bourgeoisie's the new norm,
> This is how proles should reform.
>
> Ivan is dreaming his dream of advancement,
> Turning his previous fiancé down flat.
> Changing his name, his cap for a top hat,
> Drink up to that, brothers, drink up to that.
>
> Destiny bekons and Ivan's arising,
> He's got the bridegroom's right answer down pat –
> I do, I do, and the bride says, I do too,
> Drink up to that, brothers, drink up to that.

Varlet
> I do, I do, and the bride says, I do too,
> Drink up to that, brothers, drink up to that.

Zoya You're not that different!

Varlet I am too! Ivan drank like a fish, as if his life depended on it, and his wretched guitar was the extent of his cultural horizons. He's gone, I have disinvented him.

Music stops.

Zoya Ivan! You once said Ivan and Zoya belonged together for ever, like pork and beans!

Varlet That wretch Ivan would say anything to have his way with a girl.

Zoya Ivan – you once said our hearts beat as one. And that we would work for the good of our class together for ever . . . Don't tell me it's over, Ivan.

Varlet Our former love which you wish me to recall has been liquidated, citizen. I shall summon the people's trusty law enforcers if you try to obstruct my heart's new direction with your plebeian fisticuffs. All that is behind me.

Re-enter Rosalie.

Rosalie The bleeding fishmonger was right, the fish I saw in there are even smaller . . . (*Sees Zoya.*) Just a minute, what's going on? Who's this little slut?

Rosalie starts to pull Zoya, who is holding on to Varlet. A crowd gathers, cheering.

Zoya Piss off! Who are you?

Rosalie Has she got her hooks into you, Future Comrade Ivor? Piss off yerself, you little tart, he's going to be my son-in-law!

Zoya His fate is tied to mine. Irreversibly.

Rosalie Aha! You mean you're pregnant and you want money. Alright, fair's fair, I'll pay you off here and now.

Zoya You lot can only think of money!

Rosalie Not true! When I've paid you off I'm going to split your nostril in the bargain, you little slut. Come here!

The Policeman's Song.

Police
Citizens! Please stop this ugly scene!
Admit the law must throw itself between.
We arrest every action underhand
And if you're drunk we'll put you in the can.
Citizens! Please stop this ugly scene.

Girls
Now we know there is no God
Post-revolutionary mode.

Boys
We seek the higher things in life,
Come with us up the red red road . . .

Transformation to:

SCENE TWO

Previous scene dissolves as Mayakovsky enters.

Mayakovsky (*to audience*) Another scene: familiar
grubby dormitory of unhygienic hostel for young
inner-city workers. The stereotyped occupants of its
dirty bunks are familiar failures from other socialist-
realist plays. (*Identifies.*) The failed would-be inventor.
The craven floor cleaner. One girl in spectacles – that is
right, she is an intellectual who thinks for herself. And
a member of proletarian brotherhood who has
somehow lost his shoes.

Music stops. Barefoot Youth screams and runs around.

Barefoot Youth Oi! Me grass shoots!

Intellectual Girl Yer wot?

Barefoot Youth Some capitalist swine's nicked me daisy
roots again! The last time, I tried to leave 'em in hand
luggage at the railway station, last thing, but they say
they won't take anything that ripe. What am I
supposed to do, sleep with the effing cheesers on?

Cleaner I meant to tell you. Ivan Varlet's borrowed them
to see that bourgeois cow he's going to get hitched
with. He was effing and blinding trying to get them on.

Barefoot Youth I'll effing blind him if he ruins 'em, the
poxy class traitor! What does he think he's doing in
my shoes?

Cleaner Moving up the social ladder!

Barefoot Youth Can you see it working out? I know he's
trying to improve, you just have to look at all the crap
he leaves around – before it was old sardine tins and
empty beer bottles and dog-ends, now it's bottles of
aftershave in amazingly poncy wrapping paper. Effing
ponce.

Cleaner Now now, stop that or the warden'll –

Barefoot Youth Ponce, ponce, that's what all class traitors are.

Intellectual Girl Class traitor, arse traitor. Just because he's got a flash new tie an' gear you're going on like he was a poncing enemy of the people.

Barefoot Youth He is a poncy bloody enemy of the people. I'm the people, aren't I? I told him not to take my boots and look what he done. But you know, he's not going to fool anyone into thinking he's not still a prole. He's so thick, when he tightens his tie, it stops any blood getting to his brain at all.

Inventor As a matter of fact, he's not so stupid after all – seems to have reinvented himself. Seen this box of calling cards? (*Shows them round.*)

All (*mocking*) Ivor Violet! Wooooo!

Displays of extravagant and contemptuous mirth. Inventor takes bottle of aftershave.

Barefoot Youth 'Ere, are you nicking that?

Inventor 'Ivor Violet' won't need aftershave. He sounds like he smells good enough already! I'm sure I could use it in one of my inventions.

Barefoot Youth Leave it, mate, it's got class contamination written all over it! Go on, pour it away!

Intellectual Girl You can mock, but he's started a one-man cultural revolution in the domestic sphere, from right here in the hostel! He's made an effort to change himself.

Barefoot Youth I agree he's recently been smarming this horrible-smelling stuff all over his sideboards. They hang off the side of his face like something nasty off a dog's behind. No wonder they call 'em buggers' grips.

Inventor (*surprised*) Oh, is that why sideboards was invented? There's a reason for everything in this world.

Intellectual Girl Lotsa movie stars have sideburns now.

Barefoot Youth But Ivan's not a movie star. He makes steering wheels. He's a factory mechanic, third-class!

Enter greasy Mechanic.

Mechanic Not any more. That's all in the past. Comrade Ivan Varlet came in and chucked his job in today. I saw him as he was leaving the gates. Said factory work was incompatible with his new life and new wife.

Intellectual Girl Who is this lucky girl, then?

Barefoot Youth Not you, obviously.

Intellectual Girl Piss off! Just 'cos I'm not against him for trying to better himself! I'm curious, that's all!

Mechanic A posh hairdresser's daughter is what he's landed. Yep. The poodle-fancying class, hearing a genuine card-carrying member of the proletariat was available, threw out a lure, and the lucky girl is reeling her prize in now. She'll sort his new side-whiskers out for free in the salon by day, and then, come the night, his proletarian short an' curlies will get a seeing-to. From any angle, Ivan will be unrecognisable.

Intellectual Girl Lucky for him.

Mechanic Yeah, but it doesn't alter the fact that marriage across class lines is deeply decadent. Take me for instance. I'm a socialist. To build a new state, with occupations and living space for everyone, I know you gotta stick to your guns.

Barefoot Youth The war's over. It stopped being 1917 a while back. The revolution's finished, dad! Anyone who can afford it can get as many new pairs of shiny shoes as they like!

Enter Oleg. Ivan, wearing new shoes and clothes, throws the boots to Barefoot Youth.

Barefoot Youth Thanks for nuffin'!

Oleg The new couture is the middle, not the end of the transformation. We need a dancing lesson to accompany your striking new outfit. Meinheer Ivor will complete the schooling for admission to your new class. We'll do it right here in the hostel. Music, ho!

Dance music.

When you leave this squalid boarding house for your red wedding, you will truly have been transformed into a new graceful creature. Head up now. Now, follow my instructions. At the nuptial climax of your modern wedding, the seductive rhythm of the foxtrot will insinuate itself into the guests' consciousness. And we will all . . . step out onto the dance floor!

Varlet These new shoes are playing Old Harry with my corns. Can't I take them off?

Oleg Certainly not! This rehearsal should be in full dress. Step up, sir, imagine your bride-to-be standing here and one, two, three and off!

Varlet dances.

Barefoot Youth Class traitor!

Oleg Very nicely, sir! Now, Monsignor Violet, the moon is riding high, filling your soul with longing and passion – the nightscented stock fills the air with heavy perfume, and what are you doing? Imagine you are weaving dreamily back from a well-stocked taverna. The Rites of Eleusis were always concluded with a dance. Don't wiggle your rear end, you're supposed to be leading your lovely partner, not carrying a sack of spuds. Too high! Watch that hand!

Varlet It won't stay up!

Oleg Alright, well, just locate the lovely lady's brassiere, and hook your thumb in it; easy for you, and it's very pleasant for the lady too. Now you can experiment with the other arm. What on earth are you doing with your shoulders?

Ivan's dance gets wilder and wilder.

That's not a foxtrot. It's something greater! You have a talent and no mistake. You're too big for this country! You should break into Europe and astonish them all! Beyond socialism! The song of the body beautiful! More, more! Encore! Bravo! Magnificent!

Varlet falls over. Music stops.

Oleg I was thinking, the Moulin Rouge will never be the same after you conquer Paris! But I must go and finish off the preparations – if I don't keep the ushers off the booze we'll never get there. Tuck your shirt inside your trousers but not inside the underpants. That is, provided you have underpants . . .

Oleg leaves.

Barefoot Youth Oy, dog's dinner! What's going on then?

Varlet Etiquette would say, none of your business, respected Comrade. But I will tell you. I have fought for the good life, and I have won. Furthermore, I'm doing my class, the proletariat, a favour by raising the average standard of living. What do you say to that?

Gunshot, off. Enter Youth.

Second Youth 'Ere! You know Zoya, Ivan Varlet's rejected fiancée? Well, she gone all demented with romantic woe and shot herself! I don't know how she's going to explain herself at the next Party meeting!

Voices Help! First aid! Help! First Aid!

Zoya is carried in by an excited crowd.

Man Someone phone for an ambulance!

Mechanic There's no phone here!

Crowd (*enthusiastic*) Find a phone! Emergency! Find a phone! Emergency! Find a phone! Emergency! Emergency!

Crowd exits, leaving Zoya on the floor. Music stops.

Man Missed the heart, thank God – only shot herself through the tits! Did they say you knew her?

Varlet I knew her once, but my past is behind me.

Varlet steps over Zoya and comes downstage to hail cab.

Varlet Cabbie! Seventeen Lunacharsky Street, otherwise known as Hairdresser Hall. Don't forget my baggage! Farewell to poverty, lice and cheap propaganda – (*as he exits*) – hello to relaxed summer evenings with trivial chatter upon the veranda.

Exits, leaving Mechanic alone with body of Zoya. Mechanic kneels, weeping, to hold her hand. The crowd comes back and surrounds them.

Mechanic Don't die, my love!

Zoya (*faintly*) To think I tried to kill myself over a greasy worthless jerk like Ivan. There's nothing stupider than misplaced love.

Mechanic I know what you mean. (*Cloth cap off, hand on heart, he sings.*)

The Mechanic's Song.

The road towards Utopia
Is paved with blood and stone.
There's many with me, comrades,
I know I'm not alone.
The godless Party promises
A heaven for our eyes,
But who will pay for this?
We're paying with our lives.

We've been building a road to a better world
For nigh on seven years,
But now the mists have moved away

To show the path we steer –
The road to Utopia leads straight to a wall,
And our work was in vain,
'Cos the wall don't want us,
The wall don't us,
The wall don't want us at all.
See how sleek our masters get
While we sit in our dirt and sweat.
Still it isn't finished yet,
Our Utopia.
Our Utopia.

Hark to what our masters said,
'Swing your hammer, swing with dread.
Hit that rivet on the head.'
But the dream will fall,
But the dream will fall.

And the wall don't want us,
The wall don't want us,
The wall don't want us at all.

SCENE THREE

Music stops. Enter Mayakovsky, Elzevir Bornagin, Best Man, Accountant and Matron of Honour, Accountant's wife. Oleg is Mistress of Ceremonies.

Mayakovsky Beauty parlour is the site for the Red Wedding attended by friends of bride, all hairdressers, and friends of groom, all mechanics. Both are eyeing bottles of vodka, and food.

Elzevir I think we could start, Ivor darling, don't you?

Varlet Not so fast!

Elzevir What's the matter? Don't you want to get married after all?

23

Varlet You bourgies have a thing or two to learn about protocol in this new world! On these important occasions of inter-class mingling, protocol has to be strictly observed. In addition to the Best Man, the Accountant and Matron of Honour, his regularly fulfilled wife, the Secretary of the Committee of our glorious steering-wheel factory has graciously accepted our invitation. And look, here he comes!

Guest runs in.

Elzevir Oh, is Mr Steering-Wheel the guest of honour? Some sort of super-prole? I see. Alright, I'm sure that will be convenient.

Varlet Deigning graciously to illuminate our nuptials with his working-class brilliance and repartee – the highest representative of socialised motor vehicle assembly, Comrade Lassalchenko! (*Pause.*) But you're not Comrade Lassalchenko, are you?

Guest Party greetings and apologies for absence from Comrade Lassalchenko's message reads – (*Reads.*) 'Tomorrow I can go anywhere – even into a church. Today, however is a Party day, and like it or lump it, I have to report to my Party committee in full.' Message ends. (*Exits.*)

Varlet So that's that. Apologies having been tendered, we should move on to the next item on the agenda.
(*Opens champagne bottle and sprays it over Elzevir.*)

Elzevir Just a minute – what sort of celebration is this? You're ruining my dress!

Varlet I hereby declare this wedding – open!

Cheers and the guests rush for the food.

Rosalie Comrades, proles, nuptial sponsors of the hour from all sexes – please help yourselves from the generous buffet. I've been saving the ham for a rainy day ever since the end of the war. It's impossible to find porkers tasting like they do nowadays. They just don't feed piggies the right food.

Eating: a musical interlude, during which everyone eats furiously.

Best man Next item – drink!

All stop eating, rush to drinks, take and raise bottles. Music stops.

Best Man And now, the smooch that proclaims the twin fleshes one inseparable for ever more till divorce do 'em part!

All Kiss! Kiss!

Elzevir and Varlet kiss.

Kiss! Kiss!

Elzevir kisses Varlet with passion. He returns kisses stolidly.

Best Man We witness here the historic embrace of the broad masses, by the bourgeois! C'mon let's hot it up! We Russians know how to celebrate – We celebrate Shakespeare's birthday – an' Beethoven – in fact we celebrate 'em both, all day, every day –

Oleg Now about this union we are celebrating. I predict it will be a reconciliation of the two classes and all their inherent contradictions, for ever and a day.

Applause.

All Kiss – kisss!

Oleg And there's something about this union that we should not forget when we see a twinkle in both the bride and groom's eye. I predict we will soon hear the patter of tiny feet around the beauty salon! Tiny socialist hands raised to be manicured!! What is happening here is the rebirth of family life which over the years has been so damaged by the economic savagery of the marketplace.

All Shut up, you old windbag. Get them to kiss! Kiss! Kiss!

Oleg Not Marx, not Engels, could have dreamed in a thousand years that what we are witnessing could ever take place – Labour and Capital together. What a winning combination! Neither lived to see the heroic class, then obscure, if promising, rise up and seize the reins of history. They never dreamt that in a dramatic development, the conquering hero, Labour would take such a shine to Capital – now dethroned but clearly, enduringly alluring.

Usher Who's that trying to make off with a case of vodka over there! Come back!

Guest I was just putting it somewhere safe, honest.

Oleg Well spotted, comrade usher. But no need to bust a blood vessel, just get everyone to relax – (*Calls out.*) Attention please, everyone!

Guests finally fall silent as Usher holds the vodka-thief (the Accountant) by the lapels.

Usher You're one of those bleeding bourgies, aren't you?

The two sides – hairdressers and mechanics – divide and square up for a fight.

Oleg People, listen to me! We shouldn't be getting snooty about occupations! 'She's a hairdresser and he's a mechanic, so they can't get on!' One look at the bride and groom would dispel that nonsense. (*to bride and groom*) I think that if the hairdressers could all find a mechanic to demonstrate their art on, then both classes will discover exactly why the bride and groom are going to live happily ever after.

A pairing off of hairdressers and mechanics, mutually suspicious. Tension. The hairdressers begin to do the mechanics' hair, against their wishes.

The Hairdressers' Song.

Oleg

There's a class of persons present, maligned, misunder-
    stood,
Who in this dawning new age can still do simple good.
I sing in praise of hairdressers all around the world –
It's an international movement –
Let's hear it for them, girls!

Hairdressers

We like to chat a little bit, it helps us pass the hours,
You won't believe the stories that we hear under the
    dryers.
Oh, don't you think we raise the tone
And we deserve a union of our own.
Don't you think we raise the tone
And we deserve a union of . . .

Oleg

Hairdressers can change a woman's thoughts about
    herself,
Her hair done right, she'll never stay fore'er upon the
    shelf.
Why should Mother Nature rule and make us all
    unchanged?
Now the revolution's come, dear,
Men! don't be ashamed.

Hairdressers

Admittedly beside the gossip other passion pales.
We follow fashion fearlessly
And do each other's nails.
Attending weddings is our bliss,

27

We'll give the bride a loving kiss.
Oh, don't you think we raise the tone
And we deserve a union of our own?
Don't you think we raise the tone
And we deserve a union of our own?
Don't you think we raise the tone
And we deserve a union of our own?

The men fight off the hairdressers. Brawls break out.
A stove is knocked over and smoke starts to fill the
stage. Smoke increases. The hairdressers are winning,
pinning mechanics down in the mêlée to perm their
hair with monstrous combs and spraycans of lacquer,
as the stage darkens and pandemonium breaks out.

All (*variously*) Kiss! Kiss! / Where's the bride and groom –
/ can't see them – / We're on fire! / Who said fire? / Fire
brigade! – It's out of control! / Heeelp!

Blackout.

SCENE FOUR

Music stops. Firemen inspect rows of charred corpses.
Enter Fire Chief, with further group of firemen, officials.

Chief Alright, what's going on? Twelve hours I hear it
took you to come to a blazing hairdresser's salon.
Twelve hours, from ten streets away. You lot should
have rescued at least some of these hapless folk,
innocently celebrating what was to have been the
happiest day in the life of the bridegroom.

Fireman 1 There was nothing we could do, Chief. Like,
when we arrived, the whole bleeding place was like an
oil refinery. Vodka musta been feeding the flames.

Fireman 2 What a bloody barbecue, eh?

Chief But a hundred per cent casualties! It's not going to look good in the records. Dear oh dear. We better do an inventory. What have we got here, anyway?

They review the corpses, pulling back the shrouds and dropping them in place again.

Fireman 1 One bod, bonce all spoiled, probably falling beam . . .

Fireman 3 One charred bod, sex NK, hairdressing tongs in hand . . .

Fireman 4 One female bod, with wire thingummyjig fried tight on her upper bonce.

Chief Spare us the details, sonny. I've just had me tea.

Fireman 2 giving charred notes to Fire Chief.

Fireman 2 One, back of the site, criminal and pre-revolutionary build, was found with a cash register in his hands.

Chief (*pockets notes*) Something for the firemen's ball at last. Check the cellar too.

Fireman 2 Can't get down there. It filled up with our water straight off, and froze solid. We did manage to rescue this.

Fire Chief examines a blackened box, then opens it. It is a case of vodka. Bottles of vodka from the case are handed out to firemen, and they line up for their drinking song.

Chief What you see when you clear up afterwards is enough to drive anyone to drink. But I'm amazed you lot can even take any more. You were all pissed out of your heads when you left the fire station and drove off the wrong way!

The Firemen's Song.

Chief

Traditional! The marriage feast
Which ends in Armageddon,
It's quite surprising anyone survives
A Russian weddin'.
And you firemen are so legless
That you cannot point a hose.
Proof alcohol's a killer, avoid the dreaded dose!

Hear my dreadful warning, people,
Hear it loud and clear –
With each and every cork that pops
Rehearse it in your ear.
If you like a drink you well may think
That it won't end in tears,
But you're risking full combustion
When your liver changes gear.

Firemen

Oy! Oy! The red-nosed fireman strives in vain
To douse the flames
We cannot get the ladder up,
We call each other names.
Oy! Oy! It's never too late to celebrate!
As the flames go higher, the flames go higher,
What was once a bride and groom
Becomes a funeral pyre.

Ding dong, the bells all clang, emergency,
We're coming soon
But if at first we don't arrive
You still can hear our tune.
Ding dong, it's best to drown your sorrows first.
As the flames go higher, the flames go higher.
What was once a bride and groom
Becomes a funeral pyre!
Om tiddly om tiddly om, oy! oy! (*Repeats.*)

Firemen exit. Enter Mayakovsky, with pistol.

Mayakovsky It is I, Mayakovsky. With a wedding that leaves Ivan in a state of cryogenic suspension, he is forgotten for half a century as socialism re-engineers men's souls and the promised Utopian world paradise is forged.

Shoots pistol. Music stops.

On, to 1975!

SCENE FIVE

Mayakovsky (*continues*) Futuristic conference hall with crazy Futurist electronic voting system.

Gestures to actors as they set up the scene.

An old worker and his apprentice are polishing bits of machinery – very feebly. (*Exits.*)

Old Man It's a vital vote, this one today, young shaver. Oil the Agricultural Zone's voting apparatus. We don't want no little mistakes again.

Youth Yeah the Central Zones were a bit off as well, and the Smolensk apparatus was coughing a bit.

Old Man Are we forgetting, sonny, that all this grew from a socialist blueprint? Everything works, more or less. Just needs a drop of oil. Urals factories are go, Kursk metalworks sections is spanking new with sealed bearings. Runs with 'all the smoothness of a military operation'.

Youth I thought you must remember military operations, Vlad, 'cos you're so bloody Jurassic and wrinkly.

Old Man Nah. I was a baby when they had the revolution. I'm not that old. I do remember in the old days, just after the revolution, people voting by hand. My mother had to hold me in her arms. And the whole hall was filled with a thousand and one people, and there was all this argy-bargy, and they was split down the middle, exactly on the vote. My mother couldn't vote, of course, she was carrying me in her arms and this stopped her.

Youth That could never happen now with this modern voting equipment.

Old Man Exactly. In the old days, some people stood at the back and waved a cut-out and pretended they had twelve hands; that can't happen nowadays.

Enter Orator.

Here comes the President of the Institute for Resurrection. I say!

Youth What's he doing here?

Old Man I'd guess there must be something of great national importance to be made public in the resurrection department! What can it be?

Orator Citizen functionary mechanic and apprentice – plug in the interactive response registers for all the federation zones! We have an urgent consensus to hold.

Old Man and Youth hurry to their places.

Old Man Yes suh! Green Register go!

Young Man Green Register on!

Old Man Red Register on!

Young Man Red Register go. All systems go!

Orator Testing testing. One, one, one.

Old Man Test transmission verified, President, transmission commencing forthwith!

Orator (*coughs, announces*) Now hear this! At the corner of 62nd Street and 17th Prospect in the town of Tambov, a building brigade working at a depth of seven metres has unearthed an ice-filled cellar of a previous building. Visible in the midst of the ice is a free-floating, frozen human figure. In the opinion of the Institute for Human Resurrection, this individual, who froze to death very rapidly in the immediate post-revolutionary era, could be reactivated. This motion has been circulated by telegram and discussed and we will now proceed to register the different opinions on this proposal. Remember, the Institute for Resurrection reminds you that the life of every worker must be used until the last possible instant. What we have found is definitely a worker – the hands are callused, and this is the distinguishing mark of workers around the decade of his entombment. I would also remind you that after the wars that swept over the world, and led to the creation of our World Federation, human life was declared inviolable by decree. But we should note the objections to resuscitation, from members of the Institute of Prevention of Disease, who fear a renaissance of many of the bacilli and bacteria known once to have infested the inhabitants of what was formerly Russia. But remember, comrades, I cannot emphasise this too strongly, we are voting for a human life here!

Lights, bells, buzzers.

In order to further anthropo-cum-archaeological comparative studies into the age in question, the Resurrection Institute itself votes for resurrection! (*Orator reads message.*) 'A warning from the sanitary inspection stations in the Don Basin. The hazard to humankind of reviving these archaic bacteria is great, so the sample must remain in a deep frozen state for ever!'

Hubbub.

The Siberian Agricultural Zones request that the defrosting indeed take place, but only after harvest in

33

the autumn so that the Tractorate who have naturally
all heard of the monster on their cab radios while
harvesting, can be witnesses to this prodigious event.
I can take no more amendments, before voting. All in
favour of immediate action, raise hands!

A forest of steel hands goes up.

Orator Voting on the Siberian amendment?

Two hands only.

The Assembly of the Federation hereby accepts the
motion for full and immediate resuscitation.
All Resurrection! Resurrection! Resurrection NOW!

Stage floods with reporters.

Reporter Eskimo *Isvestia*? Clear the front page. It's
resurrection!
Second Reporter Vladivostok *Pravda* – news desk.
Conference has voted for resuscitation – pictures by
wire to follow –
Third Reporter Berlin and Warsaw *Komsol Pravda* –
Resurrection confirmed as predicted –
Fourth Reporter Chicago Soviet *Isvestia* – it's go for
resurrection –
Fifth Reporter *Red Gazette* of Rome – resurrection gets
green light –
Sixth Reporter Shanghai *Weekly Pigeon-Fancier* – it's go
for resurrection –
Seventh Reporter Los Angeles *Weekly Embalmer* – shock
horror decision on near-corpse. Ex-guitarist to swear
and smoke again.

The Reporters' Song.

First Reporter
Despite the risks, it's been decreed,
Early man is to be freed.

34

Will he be vermin free?
Tune in tomorrow to know. (*Repeats.*)

Second Reporter
This just in! This just in!
We're witness to history! This just in! (*Repeats.*)

Third Reporter
The state has decided,
Although he's retarded,
Homo vulgaris, with archaic virus,
Suspended in block-ice,
This Cro-Magnon man
May put our best Russian bridegrooms to shame.
(*Repeats.*)

Fourth Reporter
Danger, ignoring the danger.
Danger, from yesterday's stranger. (*Repeats.*)

Fifth Reporter
Bedbug bovver-boys, booze and vice!
We'll be bringing you an exclusive.
Read it first in *Izvest-ia* . . .
He may just be your caviar! (*Repeats.*)

Newsboys come on with papers.

Newsboys
Resurrection! Resurrection! Resurrection! Resurrection!

All
Our brave new world will set him free,
The white heat of technology.
When he awakes this will all seem
The perfect futuristic dream.

Science shows us how to feel,
How to vote and how to heal.

Science plays the starring role –
Reanimates the humble prole.

*As they sing, Zoya, much older, comes on and buys a
paper, reads the news.*

Zoya Oh no! They can't be! They're bringing him back
to life! No! No!

*Screams. Music ends. Continuous action as ice-block is
revealed.*

SCENE SIX

*Zoya waving newspaper at Professor, who is working in
the Cryogenic Unit with a frozen ice-block containing
Varlet.*

Zoya (*panting*) Comrade! Comrade Professor! Don't go
through this! Don't pull the lever or the bleeding
shenanigans will start all over again.

Professor Shenanigans . . .? Comrade Zoya, in your
excitement you appear to have slipped back into a
language unknown to today's scientists. Excuse me.
(*Takes up dictionary.*)

Zoya Oh, you know what I mean!

Professor I'm afraid to say I don't. Modern life has a
very different language, and we have no use for these
old words. Slobberchops . . . Shibboleth . . . Here we
are. Shenanigans. 'Useless occupation or activity that
prevents anything being done.'

Zoya Exactly! Fifty years ago, this 'shenanigans' which
you are about to unfreeze caused me to attempt
suicide! (*She mimes shooting herself, graphically.*)

Professor Suicide? What's that? You've got me guessing
again, comrade. (*dictionary*) Suppositious . . . Swabber

... Suppository ... Suspender ... (*Pause.*) Suicide. (*Reads.*) Oh dear. I suppose they were turbulent times in those days, and we understand there were injustices. Did you try to shoot yourself after receiving a court order from a misguided tribunal, perhaps?

Zoya No. I acted entirely alone.

Professor Then it must have been an accident. It is irrational to end life before it stops being of use to the Party.

Zoya I acted out of disappointed love, comrade.

Professor Oh, that is impossible. It is well known that love for the Party means we have children and railway bridges and tractors, and so forth.

Zoya I can't stay if you continue with the reverse cryogenic programme.

Professor But I can't let you go, if you know it! There is specialised information which we in the Party may need from you to ensure his survival. To survive the trauma of awakening after all these years.

Zoya I think I am going to try and kill myself again.

Professor I beg you to submerge your personal feelings for the good of the Party.

Zoya He's going to be extremely dangerous to bring back. All the vodka inside him could ignite when you run the defrosting current through him.

Professor goes to phone.

Professor Good point. People's Fire Brigade? Prepare to saturate Resuscitation Room 451 area with carbon dioxide.

Zoya What's so wonderful that's he's got that needs to be brought back?

The Fire Brigade, completely modernised with extinguishers, all arrive at the back, at the double, very brisk and efficient.

Professor The past, comrade, is a puzzle that modern
   socialism seeks to explore, for the further enlightenment
   of mankind.

Professor Switch on the current when I say.

Doctor Alternating current standing by.

Professor Now!

Professor Bring up the temperature to 98.6 Fahrenheit
   with fifteen-second bursts.

Doctor Fifteen seconds and counting!

Professor Have the oxygen ready.

Doctor Surgical oxygen cylinder and mask ready to go!

Professor Replace the ice with air pressure as you draw
   off the melt-water, and I want a full description for the
   Institute of every physical change he goes through –

   *Choreographed stenographers, taking down the
   narrative.*

Sixth Doctor Natural colour returning . . . Subject
   appears almost ice-free . . . Chest movement now
   perceptible! But some very unusual manual spasms
   now apparent!

Professor That's a trapped sensory-reflex from the time
   he was frozen. Musical, probably: unimportant. They
   had things which they used to strum with one hand
   like that, didn't they?

Zoya Oh no, he's coming back with his bloody guitar as
   well!

First Doctor Temperature 98.6

Second Doctor Pulse is 68 per minute.

Sixth Doctor Breathing regular.

Professor Stand back, gentlemen! Observe the triumph of
   science!

   *Varlet comes to life, dishevelled. He rises up, clutching
   his guitar, bending over it, retuning it, croaking along
   in a broken, cracked voice.*

Varlet
  The Party went over the top,
  Then someone musta shouted stop . . . (*Twang.*)

I think we're in a police station, me old guitar! I musta have slept it off. I'm starting to feel rough. I'd prefer by far to be in a bar. (*Twang.*)

The firemen surround him and put an end to the song with a burst of dry ice. Music stops.

Professor Comrade Neanderthal, this is not a police station.

Varlet faces Professor.

Varlet What?

Professor Drunk tanks are no longer necessary. This is Reverse Cryogenic Room 451 in the Institute for Resurrection where specimens can be thawed out under scientific conditions.

Varlet Specimens?? I'm a person – I've got documents to prove it! Come off it! You're pissed! You're all pissed! I know doctors – they're never far from the surgical spirit, and – it's glug, glug, glug all the time with them . . . what's the date?

Professor The tenth day of the revolutionary month Blossomy.

Varlet Not Blossomy, already? I musta been asleep for . . . What year is it then?

Professor Revolutionary year fifty-nine!

Varlet You're kidding. Don't tell me it's fifty-nine years . . .

Professor That's exactly what we are telling you.

Varlet Oh no! I'd better get the wife a bunch of flowers. She's going to be really pissed off.

Professor You do not have a wife, specimen.

Varlet I don't have a wife!? Look, here's my marriage certificate. (*Searches.*) Oh no! Where the bloody hell is it? I can't find it –

Doctor What's it doing now?

Varlet's hands go in and out of pockets faster and faster, trying to find the documents.

Professor Dictionary, please. We may be able to get a clue from its speech-patterns. (*Consults dictionary.*) What you are witnessing, comrades, is a slice of biological history. Deprived of its partner, the male creature is resorting shamelessly to decadent pre-revolutionary self-pleasuring. Extremely unhygienic. Stop it immediately.

Two doctors move forward with a straitjacket and try to put it on Varlet.

Varlet Oy! Lemme alone, you wankers!
Professor Dictionary again, please!

Varlet frees himself from the jacket and throws it down.

Varlet There's a woman out there, waiting for me – She's been waiting there for fifty years!
Professor The creature acts as if still trapped in fantasy. Comrade Zoya, see if you can obtain the animal's trust, alone.

Zoya steps forward to be recognised by Varlet. He stares at her. The rest of the doctors and the Professor step back .

Varlet Who's this? Just a minute, don't I know you?

Lighting change. 'The Loveboat Theme.'

Zoya and Varlet approach each other.

Varlet Blow me down, it's got to be the ex-girlfriend's mother. If not you're the spitting image –
Zoya Fifty years have passed, comrade.

Varlet You're not Zoya, are you?

Zoya Yes, I am Zoya. I was Zoya. What a fool Zoya was to care about you.

Varlet Tell me it's not fifty years on.

Zoya Find out for yourself.

Music stops. Zoya throws open a huge door, and traffic noise and fumes pour in and fill the stage. Varlet, dazzled by the light, peers out into the new world.

Varlet There's not a horse in sight. Cars cars cars! It's inhuman! Where am I? What's going on? Is this Moscow, Paris or New York?

The door closes, and the noise and fumes die away abruptly.

Zoya You'll never survive in the modern world. They should never have unfrozen you.

Varlet That's a cruel thing to say, Zoya. But then you always had a cruel, sarcastic side to you.

Zoya Cruel? I was the one who was given the push by you! (*Exits.*)

Varlet I don't know what I remember any more. This is all so confusing. I don't like this modern world. It's all machines. And the people have turned into machines too. Just a moment, here's a little animal friend I recognise! A bedbug! Perhaps you can you take me to 17 Lunacharsky Street, little bedbug? Take me back in time again, to where there is singing and dancing, and people there, admittedly drunk, stupid, laughing – but alive.

The Klop Song.

Varlet (*sings to bedbug, with guitar*)
Little bed, little bug,
Where you go, my heart goes with you.

Little bed, little bug,
So familiar to me.

*The cast come on to take up the refrain en masse as
the scene changes.*

Cast
Little bed, little bug,
Where you go, my heart goes with you.
Little bed, little bug,
So familiar to me.

Varlet
You don't complain, you make your home
Where'er your little legs may roam.
Hot or cold, you'll survive,
You remind me I'm alive.
I once had dozens, now there's one,
Will you be my only one?
Little Klop, in the seams
Of my trousers and my dreams.

Cast
Little bed, little bug,
Where you go, my heart goes with you.
Little bed, little bug,
So familiar to me.

SCENE SEVEN

Enter Mayakovsky.

Mayakovsky Scene Seven: a future city street where
pedestrians are borne effortlessly along. When hungry
they can pause and refresh themselves with all the
different kinds of fruit that grow from the trees that
overhang the moving pavements. But all is not well,

suddenly, fifty years after the glorious revolution. This city is suddenly full of rumours. (*Exits.*)

A Man and a Woman move around, as if on conveyer belts, holding newspapers. A Reporter eating a slice of melon walks in.

Woman What's going on with these diseases spreading everywhere?

Man I dunno. Nothing in the world newspapers!

Woman It's scary! Who can you trust?

Reporter Pssst! You will know that as First Reporter I always have access to the finest class of information – so here it comes! If you step off your pedestrian travellators, comrades, and come under the shade of our civic omni-arborials, I can tell you more, in confidence, of the worrying situation that has followed on the vote to thaw out the sub-human.

Points to men hurrying across stage, each with a black bag with a dog's head wearing a stethoscope sticking out of the bag.

We have three epidemics now raging in the town.

Epidemic Dances.

See that? Those men are vets. This particular epidemic started when the resurrected early mammal made contact with some of our advanced domestic animals – and now the dogs don't bark any more, they don't play, they only go around on their hind legs, smirking, winking and generally ingratiating themselves with diners in restaurants, and then – they bite. The doctors say that anyone who is bitten by one of these animals will develop all the symptoms of infection before going on to bite someone else.

All Disgusting! Outrageous!

Reporter Now look at this! Disease number two!

A Fireman rolls by, drunk.

Fireman 1
Walk backwards with me to the good old days,
You could get legless in so many ways.

Firemen 1 *and* **2**
With a chum on each arm, and a bottle in hand . . .

Chief
Boys, keep down the noise, you know it's bin banned.

All Firemen
No reading or writing, just fighting, fart-lighting.
Liver on fire, heart's desire.
Cast not the first stone, we're merry,
And the effects are revolutionary.
I'm tiddly, I'm . . . oh, oh.
I'm tiddly, I'm . . . oh, oh. (*Repeat.*)

Reporter See that? He's done for as well! There are
already one hundred and seventy-five workers infected
just like him.

*Several firemen take up the tune and hum softly as
they weave backwards and forwards, all over the
stage.*

They say this one may be even more contagious.

Historian This is dreadful! How on earth did it start?

Reporter To revive the unfrozen early mammal, a
fermented mixture you may have heard of was used,
called 'beer'. During the preparation great care was
taken, but some has escaped and been accidentally
ingested. Five hundred and twenty workers have been
hospitalised and the numbers are growing every day!

Historian As an historian, I know about this 'beer'.
I predict the mysterious illness can only be conquered
if enough volunteers come forward – and for the good

of the people, I will put myself forward immediately as a test case to be inoculated!

Applause from the crowd. Firemen stop singing. Man bows and exits. Enter Girl, dancing by herself.

Reporter This is the third variety of plague the subhuman has brought. Any women who live within earshot of the crazed infected mammal hear him at night, when the town is silent, hear the plunk of his horny plectrum on his depraved instrument through the thin walls – finally this noise becomes too much for our girls – they go out of their minds –

Man This I do not believe! How can this be? Does this illness yet have a name?

Reporter Provisionally. Infection rates of 'Lurve', as it is known, are running at over seventy-five per cent of all within earshot!

All 'Lurve' microbes are poisoning every cubic centimetre of our air!

The single Girl is joined by several others, inhaling imaginary roses and swooning about the stage. They swoop around, to music, humming in a trance.

Reporter At a certain stage, 'Lurve' victims respond to a further set of stimuli. They come together on a hidden signal, and somehow the parasitic infection synchronizes all infected legs, in a low parody of decadent bourgeois art!

Suddenly the girls come together to do high kicks, in an intense, professional-looking, insect-like conga.

Man (*amazed*) How on earth is that done??

Reporter We don't know yet, but the epidemic is reaching crisis proportions! It's as if some sort of depraved primitive consciousness is taking over the world!

Enter Zoo Director, with a magnifying glass. The girls keep dancing in conga round him.

Zoo Director Attention please!

Music stops.

I am your Zoo Director. A search party has reported that the precious sole living example of the unique blood-sucking creature, the Klop, or bedbug, has been sighted here a quarter of an hour ago, heading for the fourth floor, with a top speed of one and a half versts per year it won't be far away – comrades, search the premises immediately!

Everyone searches while the girls dance through them.

Reporter You'll never find it this way. The only way to capture a bedbug is to lay out some bait –
Voice Put a naked man on a mattress in every window!
Voices Don't shout, you'll frighten it away!
Director Anyone who finds it is warned not to try to secrete it about their person. This bedbug is state property and a severe fine will be levied if it is found on any person!
Voice Here it is! Here it is!

Spotlight on one spot on stage. The girls stop dancing.

Director Yes, that's it.

Music stops.

Firemen, over here!

Charade with drunken firemen, trying to trap it in helmet, and ladders.

Director It's over here now! Bastard got away! Never fear, quick –
Fireman Got it!

46

Director Don't let it fall – it'll kill itself! Do not crush the insect's legs! Careful!!

Voices Got it, hurrah!

Director Careful, now – the capture, using the highest technology in a previously undreamed of combination, has been resoundingly successful. Now you be quiet, folks, please. It has crossed its legs and wishes to rest! Thank you, comrades, for your struggles, which will I'm sure enhance our scientific knowledge. This is an unique specimen of Bugus Normalis, extremely popular at the beginning of the revolutionary era and believed extinct subsequently. Now our city Zoological Gardens will be the first to exhibit it and, if we're not on the tourist map after this, I'll eat my tricycle. I invite all present, including gentlemen of the press, to a formal inauguration of Bugus Normalis' new life in captivity.

The Klop Song Reprise.

Chorus
Little bed, little bug,
Where you go my heart goes with you.
Little bed, little bug,
So familiar to me.

Exit all, to music, as Bedbug is taken off ceremonially, on a velvet cushion.

SCENE EIGHT

Cryogenic ward. Varlet strums 'The Klop Song' on his guitar.

Varlet Can we liven up this cryogenic ward please? Professor, c'mere – gimme some more hair of the dog, will you? The drink you gave me just now doesn't have a chance in hell of curing a hangover. What about a litre of vodka?

Professor I could not be responsible for giving you a lethal dose.

Varlet If a litre was lethal I'd have been dead years ago. Did I ask to be sober when I was resurrected? No! If you can't get me what I want, freeze me back! (*slurred*) What 'smatter? Scared?

Professor The state acknowledges that the life of each worker is sacred.

Varlet But your charter doesn't have to include me. I'm not working here, am I? I'm just waiting by a hatch for my rations like an animal. So what is sacred about a research animal? Gimme a proper drink, or put me out of my misery.

Enter Zoya with books.

Professor Comrade Zoya, please explain to the animal we are not empowered to act against the collective vote.

Varlet A collective vote which took none of my feelings into account!

Professor exits. Varlet turns To Zoya.

Get me a drink!

Zoya They won't allow it here at the Institute. But I've got some books for you. I don't know whether they are what you want, the ones we talked about. Nowhere carries books about 'Lurve' nowadays, for us it's a new, frightening disease. I couldn't find anything on daydreams, and the closest I could get to roses was a textbook on horticulture.

Varlet Am I alone in finding this glorious future unacceptably sanitised? Do you remember what it was like, Zoya?

Zoya I remember. But, in the collective, regret has no part to play.

The Loveboat Has Crashed.

Varlet
This is why I would rather die –
What did we fight for in the old days?
Memory's in short supply,
Censored, sanitised.
All the chips were stacked on red,
We took our chances with the gun,
We danced and sang, we thought we'd won.
What happened?

Why did you let it go,
Sweet proletariat?
A beautiful plan, the perfection of man –
I would have died for that.

Zoya
How can you blame me now?
You never worked for this.
Didn't you feel that our noble ideal
Was more than hypothesis?

Varlet *and* **Zoya**
I would have died for that,
Now we're all out of time.

Varlet
We were afloat on dreams,

Varlet *and* **Zoya**
But the loveboat has crashed.

Zoya
We're out of step with love,
Time hasn't been our friend.

Varlet
The world's lost its passion
Now feelings are rationed,

Varlet *and* **Zoya**
But we can't start again.

Why did we let it go,
Sweet proletariat?
A beautiful plan, the perfection of man –
I would have died for that.

I would have died for that,
Now we're all out of time.

Varlet
We were afloat on dreams,

Varlet *and* **Zoya**
But the loveboat has crashed.

The past is ashes now,
We are both out of time.
Feelings are rationed here
Now the loveboat has crashed.
The loveboat has crashed.
The loveboat has crashed.

Enter Doctor and Professor of the Cryogenic Institute.

Doctor The Professor of this Cryogenic Resuscitation
Unit tells me you are not satisfied with your existence
in our modern state, but here's an old tradition you'll
like we have kept alive. Dancing! Tomorrow, you can
watch twenty thousand male and female workers
celebrating the collective harvest with a dance around
a thousand-tractor rally in the people's arena.

Varlet (*contemptuous*) Aw, I can't wait. It's pretty obvious
that you haven't the faintest idea what to do with me
here. I'm redundant. (*Pause.*)

Professor (*to Zoya*) There is a sort of sub-human logic to
what he is saying. We just don't have the resources to
provide the beast's natural environment.

Varlet starts throwing books.

Varlet Crap, crap, and more crap! These are some of the most boring bloody books I've ever had the misfortune to open. What's this leaflet advertising?

Zoya I'd freeze him again without a second's regret, if it was my decision.

Varlet has found a flyer in the books that Zoya brought in.

Varlet Zoya – explain – please. What's this about?

Zoya (*reads*) 'Situations vacant.' It's a jobsheet. They give them out on the streets. The city is committed to full employment. I must have picked one up . . .

Varlet But have you read it, you dumb woman? It's the way out. It says, look, 'Human being wanted.' Human being! That's me. None of the rest of you are qualified any more, are you?

Zoya (*reads*) Job at . . . Civic Zoo??

Varlet 'Ordinary human being wanted!' See – someone wants me! Get on the blower now and call this number, you brain-dead oaf!

Professor If you are sure this is suitable for you –

Professor goes to phone.

Varlet I could do this! I could do this job!

Professor (*on phone*) Zoo Director? This is the Institute for Resurrection. We think we may have a candidate who would fit your advertisement. Right away. No, he won't need to be tranquillised for conveyance to you – he wants to go.

SCENE NINE

The stage fills with animal imitations. Elephants, giraffes.

Steward This way, foreign comrade – journalists! Next to the platform, leave room for the Brazilians – their airship is landing at this moment in the central airport. Sun-blessed comrades, kindly mix in with the pigmentally challenged Scandinavian visitors, that way we can get a memorable and striking effect.

Music stops.

Oh, it looks a picture. You high-school students, over to the left, listen up. Four veterans from the Union of Centenarians have elected to supplement the Professor's lecture with thrilling eye-witness examples of the old time, fresh – culled from their memory banks.

Happy old people come forward in a dense clanking phalanx Zimmer frames.

Old Man Oh! I remember it like it was now.

Old Woman No, it's me who remembers it like it was now!

Second Old Man You remember like it was now, but I can remember what it was like before now.

Old Woman Oh, I can remember before that, before before now. I can remember a very long time ago.

Old Man Oh, I remember that time, but also what it was like before that! All of which I remember like it was yesterday! What day is it today?

Steward Thank you, veterans! Right now we've got the distilled experience of beardless youth to hear – by the right, quick march!

Children enter, marching.

Take these, now, children.

Steward hands out drinks and cigarettes.

These smelly slops used to be called drink. Your school has been chosen to feed the latest acquisition. These are animal nutrition units, products specifically created by the Central Medical Institute for one special creature. The white tubes are called cigarettes, which the animal sets fire to and inhales the smoke which has no known calorific value, though research is continuing.

Varlet holds out hand to them from behind screen.

Look, he wants to be fed. But first, hear the greetings of the all-important chairman and committee of the City Soviet who will explain the importance of your zoo studies!

Enter Chairman.

The Committee Song.

Committee
We send fraternal greetings to the workers of the zoo.
We Soviet city workers all applaud what you do.
Heroes of labour, with rhinos for neighbours!
We send fraternal greetings to the workers of the zoo.
Oy!

Chairman Comrades, children, welcoming committee, other species. Since external mishaps have been mini-mised in our modern society, there is time now for us to develop interest in spectacle. However extravagant the world of appearances may be, it contains significant scientific and historic truths which can be unlocked by study of kindred species. We can spend hours staring at the multicoloured and inflamed posteriors of baboons, and we can link the sight with a deeper understanding of the past struggles of the world proletariat. The latest arrival is easily as baffling and finally instructive as any of the droll creatures we have here already. Mr Zoo Director, we applaud you, and I hand over the chair.

All
Oy!

Music ends. Applause. Director goes up to podium.

Director If it had not been for the kind offer of my colleague, the Professor at the Institute of Resurrection, these – two – specimens of a bygone era, present here, would not be available for our edification tonight. Initially, we were only aware of one. We first caught Bedbugus Normalis, it was on its own, but we knew we would need a Homo Sapiens feedsource to keep the specimen alive. But how? We have evolved far beyond them. I put out an advertisement, and to my utter astonishment a mammalian specimen was made available. When the specimen arrived at the zoo, we discovered that it was Bourgeoisius Vulgaris, not noble Homo Sapiens. However, Bedbugus Normalis is not too choosy, thankfully, and both have settled into their little routine quite happily. Bourgeoisius Vulgaris, in the era this specimen is from, affected horrid passions for what was called 'culture'. It was not possible to avoid Bourgeoisius's cultural droppings filling the insteps of your shoes, wherever you stepped.

Carefully, keepers sweep round Varlet's draped cage.

In the past, it was disgusting and contagious but today we have a system which continuously removes any culture that the animal deposits so you are all quite safe. Comrades and comradesses, Bedbugus Vulgaris and Bourgeoisius Normalis in an exact replica of their natural habitat. Behold!

Curtains fall away to show Varlet on a bed with a bottle and guitar. Crowd approach. Varlet plucks guitar listlessly. Director steps into the cage, puts on rubber gloves, draws gun and turns a listless Varlet round for the visitors.

Come closer, comrades, don't be frightened. It's quite tame. Look, this is something you won't have seen before. It's going to have a 'smoke'.

Voice Disgusting! The children shouldn't be allowed to contribute to the fire risk!

Director And then – this part is for strong stomachs only – it's going to have some 'booze'.

Voice This is cruel – watching animals take poison! We shouldn't be tormenting it!

Director Would you like to come for a little walkies, Bourgeiosius? Come on! See, it knows its name. Come on, leave your little chum under the bed and come for walkies. Bourgeoisius dropped a whole lot of culture after his breakfast before you arrived – he generally only does that once a day. So you have nothing to fear in the way of impromptu missiles from that quarter.

Director opens the cage door and retreats. Slowly Varlet comes out and peers around.

Say hello to the nice people!

Director slowly backs away from Varlet, who looks at the crowd, disinterested, then turns back to the theatre audience, and starts to peer at them, excited for the first time. Recognition.

Varlet Hey – just a minute – citizens! Hundreds of them. Brothers! My own, my very own people! People like me! How did you get in here? So many of you? When were you all unfrozen? Oh, this is marvellous – but why am I kept all alone in the cage when there are so

55

many of you? We could have a party. Come and join me please, immediately! All of you! (*Yells.*) I'm so lonely – it hurts to be alone. So alone! Do you know what it's like to be alone?

Varlet sinks to his knees.

I'm sad, so sad, sad, sad. Life has cheated me . . . Join me . . . Why am I suffering like this?

Children scream again.

Varlet Touch me. Come closer! (*Sobs.*)
Director Comrades, you are witnessing an anomaly. The bright lights must have caused it to hallucinate. How unfortunate and pathetic. Please remain calm and wait for it to return to its cage. Remain still, children, and none of you will be in danger; it will not attack unless provoked.

Behold the Noble Prole.

Varlet
   The road towards Utopia
   Was paved with blood and stone –
   We were so great in number
   How could we have known?

   I am the myth incarnate,
   Your liver and your soul;
   And I've come back to haunt you –
   Behold the noble prole.

   We were building a road to a better world,
   Free of want and fear,
   But now the mists have moved away
   To show the path we steered –
   The road to Utopia leads straight to a wall,
   And our work was in vain,
   'Cos the wall don't want us,

The wall don't us,
The wall don't want us at all.

See how sleek our masters get
While we sit in our dirt and sweat.
Still it isn't finished yet,
Our Utopia.
Our Utopia.

Hark to what our masters said,
'Swing your hammer, swing with dread.
Hit that rivet on the head.'
But the dream will fall,
But the dream will fall.

And the wall don't want us,
The wall don't want us,
The wall don't want us at all.

All

Marxists all, in Marx we trust,
He will prevail when we are dust.
A dream come true, we promise you . . .

As the song ends, it's as if Varlet can't see the audience any more. He retreats into his cage, watched by all.

End.

A Hideous Mockery of Social Engineering

Snoo Wilson interviewed by Jim Mulligan

Snoo Wilson wrote his version of *Bedbug* for the first
National Theatre *Connections* Festival in 1997. It is not
a literal translation, rather an adaptation that tries to stay
true to the nature of the original.

> The original play by Vladimir Mayakovsky was
> produced in 1929 at a time when Russia was supposed
> to be sorting out the problems of society for ever, and
> Mayakovsky makes a hideous mockery of this social
> engineering. He shows us a ridiculous future where
> love and romance don't exist. I think he's a prophet
> showing us the hollowness of the promises of the
> Russian Revolution.

The 2003 version of the play has two major changes from
Wilson's original. There are now two musical collabora-
tors: this is a full musical, written in seven 'panels', with
revised lyrics and a score. The text of the play is relatively
short, so the music and songs give emotional colouring.
The second change is the introduction of Mayakovsky
as the ringmaster.

> Politically Mayakovsky was ambiguous. He saw himself
> as a poet of the people, a son of Russia, a revolutionary
> who rose through the masses. But in fact his father
> was a downwardly mobile landed gentleman who
> ended up in Georgia. It must have been exhilarating for
> Mayakovsky to arrive in pre-revolutionary Moscow
> and then serve it as its poetic voice.

Bedbug now starts with Mayakovsky addressing the
audience and explaining that he has come from the dead,

that he shot himself, that some people say he knew his time was up, that he was about to be arrested by Comrade Stalin. His suicide, he says, was a gesture, pinching out his 'deathless flame'.

Mayakovsky was a prominent figure and the Revolution was devouring its own children, particularly the artists. The same thing happened in the French Revolution. There is a terrible vertiginous realisation that you can't stop the thing, the carpet keeps rolling up and trapping people inside it. So the choice he made was a very Russian one. He shot himself. A clean end, but the suicide always leaves a terrible burden for the family and society to carry.

In a sense *Bedbug* is a heavy political play about a period that will probably be unknown to the people who are performing or watching it. But beneath the politics there is a very strong story about an arranged marriage. Both parties enter into it with unrealistic hopes, as we see Ivan, the grotesque proletarian and the grasping survive-at-all-costs plebeian, ditching Zoya, the girl he is supposed to love, in favour of the wealthier Elzevir.

The first part of *Bedbug* is farcical in a grim, gritty and realistic setting. There is a riotous wedding party that ends in a fire in which everyone except Ivan dies. Mayakovsky then comes on stage again to bring the play up to 1975, telling us that Ivan has been discovered frozen in a block of ice, in a state of cryogenic suspension. During the fifty years he has been in suspended animation the socialist state has been forging a utopian paradise. The world that Ivan now enters is sanitised and controlled. He is still uncouth and loud-mouthed, and the only thing he can find that is a familiar comfort is a solitary Bedbug Vulgaris that has been frozen with him. The only contribution he can make to the 'brave new world' is the release of three microbes – the very ones that destroyed the Revolution. The first microbe infects the dogs, which then walk on their hind legs smirking and infecting anyone who is bitten with the 'sycophant disease'; the second microbe is the drunkenness that is part of the Russian temperament; and the 'lurve virus' is a reflection on the early attempts of the Revolution to subjugate human relationships to the common good.

We have to remember here that the original play was performed when Mayakovsky was still alive and when the audience had no idea where the Revolution was going. And here was this poet suggesting that it would all end in disaster. It is difficult to comprehend what the audience might have thought or what reports the secret police would have relayed to Stalin. Mayakovsky must have known the writing was on the wall. Surely, this was his final statement or gesture of contempt.

> Young people should relate to this play. After all, Mayakovsky is laughing at greed, vanity and believing that you are better than you are because you have money and position. There are more than enough examples of that kind of corruption in our society for young people to ponder on.

By bringing in Mayakovsky as a character after he has committed suicide Snoo Wilson makes us reflect on what the individual should do in the face of dictators.

> I don't think there are easy answers. Should he have hung or gone into exile? It's a dilemma that has faced and is facing millions. I think a lot of my passion is a historic indignation about what savages we've been in Europe over the past hundred years. We seem to be a bloody society. We're in a terrible ongoing blood-bath where we can't deploy gentleness and compassion to solve political problems.

The conclusion of *Bedbug* is a powerful invitation to the audience to compare Mayakovsky's nightmare future with the realities of our society. The Zoo Director brings a pathetic Ivan out of his cage to be gaped at by the audience on the stage. But Ivan peers out at the real audience and for the first time becomes animated. He sees hundreds of his brothers: 'Why am I kept all alone in my cage when there are there so many of you? We could have a party.' In other words, do you, members of the audience, want to be human and flawed like me? Or do you choose to live in this mad society? Snoo Wilson gives no answer. Ivan is led back to his cage with the Director calming his audience with the words, 'It will not attack unless provoked.'

Production Notes

Possible stagings are many and varied, but the designs from Meyerhold's first production at his own theatre in 1929 may suggest a springboard. The various crowd scenes mean that a minimum of twenty actors is called for, but the upper limit is elastic. The futuristic style you find to make the story work is accommodating, and its only limits are those of the human imagination itself.

Bedbug was a popular and well-understood piece in Russia. It is a terrible take on the Russian Revolution for us to see 75 years later, and in some respects foreshadows such dystopias as *Animal Farm*. Mayakovsky knew that the play would cause outrage; and not long afterwards he committed suicide. It is about aspiration – the working classes wanting to be middle-class, although the Revolution was supposed to be about everyone being working-class. Connections can be made to globalisation and the fears it invokes.

Snoo is not in favour of giving anyone a free hand with the text. It's as finished as he can make it, and it's there because it's an imagined correlative of the original. He's an intermediary for Mayakovsky and it is important to honour his voice.

Half of the play is set in the future. In the 1920s Mayakovsky was looking towards a Utopia and seeing its darker side before Huxley and Orwell, his final trick being to bring in the audience through the fourth wall. The play is full of Aristotelian terror. It has a strong narrative drive, conflicting interests and strong characters.

The initial outing of *Bedbug* was for the first cycle of *Connections*, after which Snoo's then-agent put him in touch with Gary Kemp and Guy Pratt, as he wanted to do something more with it. The Russian composer Shostakovich wrote brief slices of music for the original play, and Mayakovsky said of the music that it should sound like a provincial firemen's band. Gary and Guy have respectfully ignored this. The music consciously contains different themes, such as the character's love themes and a theme for the street. It has a somewhat Brechtian feel, making this a play with music rather than a piece of conventional musical theatre. And there are folk elements to the way the music is written – Varlet carries his guitar with him, and so has the ability to sing when he wants. Guy was daunted by the Shostakovich involvement, and sought a style closer to vaudeville (not least because of the amount of drunkenness portrayed). Then we discovered that Shostakovich based his whole score on circus music . . .

Snoo has now made Mayakovsky a character who introduces the action, and this had a peculiar genesis. Mayakovsky was relatively unknown in the West. His reputation was eclipsed following his suicide, but Stalin rehabilitated him 1935, announcing that speaking against Mayakovsky was a crime, thus securing his reputation inside Russia. This is why Snoo introduced the figure of the writer into the play – it is a fractal drama of Mayakovsky, who had already put himself into the play, as Varlet. He had a large ego and a theatrical manner, and when he shot himself in the head at the age of thirty-six declared in his suicide note: 'The love boat has crashed.' As with much of Mayakovsky, the translation is not exact, but the title has now become a song. So Mayakovsky himself can be the 'way in' to the weird and wonderful world of this play, also allowing it to be done with as much or as little staging as you wish. Snoo didn't consider it an option to bring Mayakovsky back at the end. The play is a kind of apologia for his suicide, so by this time the contradictions have become clear, and Varlet's 'articulate wail of grief' speaks for Mayakovsky.

The evolution from the 'straight' version involved Snoo working with an accomplished Russian actress, who had played at the Moscow Art Theatre. She talked him through the two extant translations, but she would correct these, saying: 'Mayakovsky's making a joke here – you must put something in in English.' Snoo thinks of the play not as written in scenes but in a series of 'panels', each having room for a scene or a song, then moving on to the next.

The play contains so much – the history of theatre, of oppression, dance, music, movement, science fiction, stylisation. People are even making up a new ritual for a wedding. This is a complete behaviour envelope, written at a time when Marx and Lenin were considered the engineers of men's souls. It is a real Russian tragedy, of the loss of innocence, in 'a revolution that devoured its children'. The play is in a heightened style, so it's not strange when the characters start to sing. It is in the Meyerhold tradition. Try and find your own variant on a physical, rough-theatre style.

Snoo likes the idea of having Mayakovsky speak in a Russian accent, and this is how he's written him – missing out the definite articles. There is a tension between how the characters of the play speak and what they want to say – they're struggling to maintain a balance in a bureau-cratic nightmare of verbiage. The actors must understand the struggle going on in the language between the text and the hidden subtext of bureaucratic literature and nonsense. There is an obligation to be garrulous and to entertain, but there is a lot of plain speaking too. If it's clear that the characters are totally out for themselves, then the actors can start playing with the possibilities of the language. They're intoxicated with their own verbiage.

MUSIC

The guitar is symbolic. It could be fiddled with, it could be a stratocaster, but it is the lyre of Orpheus. It can't be dramatically changed.

Snoo imagines the 'Fireman's Song' to be in a similar style to Eliza Dolittle's father in *My Fair Lady*. You should be able to 'turn on' the Firemen, and the Chorus is in on the joke in a Gilbert and Sullivan kind of way. You can have separate musicians or musicians on stage as part of the action. The latter would be perfect for the first half of the play, but probably wouldn't work so well in the futuristic section. The machine could be quite musical. The first two lines of the 'Cellar Song' are sung solemnly by the girls, in reference to Zoya: these are Zoya's friends.

The 'Love Boat Song' is central to one of the most challenging 'panels' in the piece. There are many layers which must co-exist in the playing of the scene and the song. It's a mistake to play the emotion of the scene. Gary believes this song is about the failure of the Utopia, while for Zoya it's a love song. It becomes a love song for Varlet later.

CHARACTERS

The play benefits from MAYAKOVSKY's authorisation of the bubble of spectacle and music. He's essentially reading stage directions so the audience can have more fun. There's a real tension between him and the Russian revolutionary ideas, a tension he resolved by shooting himself. Varlet is asking for this at the end, too. The conundrums of Mayakovsky's life are all in the play. A world awash with revolutions would rewire you on a permanent basis, and this play reflects what artists face in revolutionary times. Mayakovsky was terrified of being bored, so everything had to be bigger, brighter, fancier. The play is slapstick, but it is also tragic – it goes straight to the heart of the human condition. Mayakovsky was an extravagant dresser and a dashing, handsome womaniser. His is an imposing presence, properly distinctive, but not to be overemphasised – he shouldn't intrude on the action, except when he moves people around. He is in control when he chooses to set the scene, but the energy of the scene must then take over. Mayakovsky is making fun of the Russian bid to stop being Darwinian – the belief that if you were a weight-lifter, your children would be too. Modern connections might be with genetic modifications, organ transplants, etc.

Like Mayakovsky, VARLET weaves through the piece. He is an aspiring prole, an example of how the State was trying to dignify labour, and Mayakovsky shows the paradoxes inherent in that. This is well explored in the boarding-house scene – is it alright to better yourself? This is a universal theme, not limited to the Russian Revolution. There is an innocence to Varlet, and experience doesn't change him – he doesn't apologise to Zoya. The past shreds itself before a bright and shiny future, so characters have to have short memories, and to be forgiven for it. In the end, the play is about Varlet's humanity: he's a lout and a bore, a comic oaf who in the first half is the villain; but in the second half he's a hero. Varlet personifies the hyperbole of Soviet propaganda. His mistake is that he thinks it applies exclusively to himself.

Where Varlet thinks he's 'upwardly mobile' in joining the bourgeoisie, the HAIRDRESSERS are a minor capitalist class trying to retrieve their status by having a prole in the family. The ambitions of both are base and greedy. Everyone is involved in hideous social engineering and manoeuvering.

OLEG is a fixer, and can invent a style for new thing to happen. This was originally a part for a man. She might be compared with a contemporary celebrity such as Ruby Wax – or Whoopi Goldberg ten years ago. The Russian state imposed atheism as a 'state religion', so a civil wedding had to be invented, and Mayakovsky is making fun of this. Even today, though, couples look for new ways to get married. Oleg needs to pitch this marriage as the ultimate desirable smooch, the most delectable thing imaginable. But it's like an American menu – nothing will live up to its description.

ZOYA's aging mustn't be a distraction. This will be a challenge. She is the hero of the whole play – the only human character in the future it portrays. The audience must recognise her and love her. She has compassion and a big heart, and knows it's difficult for Varlet. Zoya is an ideal. She's oddly classless, despite being a card-carrying member of the working class. It's worth reading about Mayakovsky and seeing how he treated the women in his life.

STAGING

The action should be continuous, without blackouts: dissolve as opposed to breaking. After the fight, you can have a blackout with fight sounds, superimposing fire sounds, then into the firemen. Or you could show time passing. There are many ways of doing this through physical theatre, but it's essential that the action keeps moving forwards. Mayakovsky is always in charge of the story. The original point of his entering through the screen was to show Russia then and now – a deliberate destabilising of the great unconscious out of which he pops. There may be other ways of showing this, so long as he remains a showman, a show-off.

In the first half of the play the design should indicate urban Russia in the 1920s, perhaps with selected icons of that period. Once the play has moved into the future, it's up to you – anything's possible. You might consider the first half of the play as being red – not only because red was the colour of the Revolution, but because temperaments are hot. People are hungry for things. The second half is ice-blue – cryogenic white, doctors' coats, the coldness of defrosting. It is more reflective once the defrosting has taken place: the characters have cold hearts.

Don't get into knots trying to make things like the stove too literal. A smoke machine would be good. Work up to a choreographed fight during the song. The reason for the fight is class conflict. The mechanics are honest scruffs; the hairdressers are pretentious. The hairdressers take the stage, the mechanics don't have a voice. It's like trying to groom a savage dog: the only way the mechanics can resist the hairdressers is to fight: it would be good to mix the genders, as you don't want this play to become a 'battle of the sexes'. It is a battle about class.

'Blossomy' was how the French Revolutionary Council renamed April. The renaming needs to be emphasised, and must be significant to the actors.

CREATE A HUMAN MACHINE

1 Have the actors stretch and walk around the space. Encourage them to get a feel for the entire space, and to be aware through their feet.
2 Slow the pace down. Have the actors follow their own individual journey, and listen to instructions as they go. Encourage them to show their emotional journey.
3 Get them to speed up, slow down, freeze, etc. See their individual journeys, but make them a coherent group.

4 Take the same journey, but now in a kingdom in which the ceiling is five inches lower than their own height. This will change their shapes and spark their imaginations.

5 Count down from ten to one, then ask them to freeze. On the 'freeze' instruction, have them change into a statue of their character on this journey. Get them to be a vision that helps the audience understand where they are. Ask them to increase the emotional volume as you count from five down to one. Then get them to freeze again.

6 Have them imagine they are in an art gallery, and get them to look at an exhibit, a piece of 3D art. What does the piece of art say about their world?

7 Walk and stretch again.

8 Have them imagine they are in a phone box, pushing outwards and against it . . .

9 After stretching and relaxing again, ask them to lie on the floor. In a repeated one-to-four count, on the first count of four get them to make themselves into a part of a futuristic machine, then repeat, with the actors changing themselves into different components of the machine, gradually coming up from the floor.

10 As standing components, get them to interact with each other on the same one-to-four beat. Then ask them to freeze.

11 The frozen position should be the one they always return to on the fourth beat of the one-to-four count. Speed the count up and down, and get the actors to work together as a physical, futuristic machine.

12 Combine sound and movement. Increase and decrease the tempo with the one-to-four count.

RECOMMENDED READING

Theatre in the Revolution: Russian Avant-Garde Stage Design 1913–1935. Thames and Hudson. ISBN: 0500276463.

Mayakovsky, Russian Poet: a Memoir by Elsa Triolet. Hearing Eye. ISBN: 187084182. (About Mayakovsky's women.)

Making Scenes 2. Methuen. (This has an interesting introduction about *Bedbug*.)

Futurists, a play by Dusty Hughes. Faber and Faber. ISBN: 0571137784.

The Bedbug and Selected Poetry by Mayakovsky. Indiana University Press. ISBN: 0253201896.

Also see the website www.Mayakovsky.com

based on a workshop led by Anthony Banks
transcribed by Sheri Granbert

BOAT MEMORY

Laline Paull

Characters

Hannah Bridges
Walthamstow parish girl, fourteen

Matthew Wilson
public schoolboy, son of the Rector, sixteen

Fuegia Basket
Tierra del Fuegian aboriginal Indian girl,
twelve or thirteen

Jemmy Button
Tierra del Fuegian aboriginal Indian boy, fourteen

York Minster
Tierra del Fuegian aboriginal Indian youth,
seventeen or eighteen

Reverend Wilson
Rector of Walthamstow

Captain Fitzroy
aristocratic young naval officer

Professor Donovan
an eminent phrenologist

Young Man

**School children, poor of the parish,
villagers, Londoners**

Place and time
The village of Walthamstow, England,
1830–1831

Locations
The parish schoolroom, the Rectory,
the village marketplace, a London salon,
Epping Forest, the deck of a ship

The symbol / preceding dialogue
means dialogue is simultaneous or overlaps.

SCENE ONE

St Mary's schoolroom, Walthamstow. December 1830.
There are hand-made signs from the Scriptures on the
walls – 'Love One Another', 'Christ Died for Our Sins',
'Fear God', etc.
　　Led by Hannah Bridges, the ragged little class marches
round two by two, chanting the two times table. Behind
her, some of the boys bare their teeth at the girls, who get
upset. Hannah stops the march.

Hannah (*to the culprits*) Would you rather be out in the
　　fields, or burnt up a flue every day, or pulling a barge
　　in your bare bleeding feet with an empty belly? For
　　you surely don't care to better yourself here at school,
　　do you?
Boy Like you,. miss?

　　The class titters. Hannah points her ruler at one of the
　　scriptural signs.

Hannah What does that say?
Boy Dunno, miss . . .
Hannah 'Obey them that have rule over you.' Hebrews
　　thirteen, seventeen. Will I tell the Reverend that you
　　defy the Bible's authority as well as mine?
Boy No, miss . . .
Hannah Well then. Now again, this time in threes.
Girl But miss, miss, the cannibals are coming!
Another Boy Chew your shanks and gristly ears, yum
　　yum.
Girl My ears are not gristly –
Boy Slurp the marrow from your bones –

Another Boy Blood running everywhere –

The boys turn on the girls, who get frightened.

Hannah You will all be quite safe, anyone could see
you'd taste horrid. (*The class laughs.*) Do you really
think the Reverend who loves us all would endanger
us by bringing bloodthirsty cannibals to school here?
Even if they come from . . . (*carefully*) Tierra del
Fuego, which is in South America, which is –

Girl Which is where they should stay, miss, my ma says.

Boy And my da says school's a waste on girls and
savages anyway.

Girl Miss, miss, but is it true they come all the way from
London in a jarvey? How many shillings is that, on
savages!

Hannah I do not know and I am not likely to.

Boy They'll eat all our food.

Girl And smother us in our beds while we sleep!

Hannah raps her ruler for order.

Hannah Reverend says they are God's children in need of
His Light, and we are lucky enough to be chosen to
help them find it. It's a privilege!

Girl But miss, miss, I'm frightened, don't make me sit
next to them –

Boy Black devils with yellow eyes –

The girls start crying again.

Girl I'm not scared of them –

Boy Me neither, I'm going to bring in the pig knife and
when they try to eat me I'll – and I'll – (*Mimes
stabbing a girl, who starts crying.*) – oh, be a cannibal
properly – (*He thumps her in annoyance.*)

Hannah You will do no such thing! (*as chaos breaks out*)
Sit down at once, all of you!

But the game sweeps the class, the boys attacking the girls, some of whom fight back as cannibals, some cowering.

(*completely ignored*) Sit down!

Behind her, Matthew Wilson enters, elegant in his public-school uniform. Seeing him, the class quickly take their places.

I should think so too – when I give you an instruction I expect you to take it at once – Reverend Wilson has given me authority in this classroom and you will obey it. For though I be but young and a female, I can read and write as well as a man, and that is a fact.

Matthew But how is your trigonometry?

Hannah Oh! Good day to you . . . Mr Wilson.

Matthew Good day to you, Hannah. Miss Bridges.

An awkward little pause.

Boy The cannibals are coming, sir!

Matthew Captain Fitzroy has assured my father that they are quite docile. And compared to what I saw when I came in –

Hannah They are normally very well behaved. (*to the class*) Turn to your primers and read silently from the second chapter.

The class groan, but do as she bids. She is silent a moment.

Hannah I thought your term did not end for another week.

Matthew But then I'd miss the great arrival! I made a bargain with my housemaster, a good fellow – I will write a paper on 'The Noble Savage', and deliver it next term before the whole school. I shall be famous sooner than I thought. (*A beat.*) My father did tell you I would be helping with them, did he not?

Hannah Yes. He did.

Matthew If that does not displease you?

Hannah I will do what the Reverend asks.

Matthew But you would rather I was not here?

Hannah (*to the class*) Is there something of fascination here? Attend to your primers, please. (*A beat.*) I am happy for you to be here or not, as is your preference, Mr Wilson.

Matthew Hannah, will you talk to me normally, please?

Boy I can hear the jarvey! The cannibals are here!

The class rushes to the windows, Hannah and Matthew with them.

SCENE TWO

Rectory parlour, day. Tense and silent, the three Tierra del Fuegian teenagers sit close together, Fuegia Basket between large and powerful-looking York Minster and younger, sharper-looking Jemmy Button. They wear light and raggedy sailor clothes.

Opposite, in winter wear, are Matthew, his father Reverend Wilson, and Captain Fitzroy of the British Admiralty. Hannah stands at the back. Silence. Reverend Wilson leans forward to the Fuegians.

Rev Wilson We must all look as strange to you as you do to us. And I know I am no oil painting, so if the urge takes you to laugh at me, I will take it in good part. All the children find me comical enough, do they not, Hannah? I strike no fear, call down no fire and brimstone . . . I am your friend, children.

The Fuegians just stare at him.

Are they not chilled to the marrow?

Fitzroy In their native state they would be naked but for a couple of greasy pelts, if that. They do not feel the cold like us, do you, Fuegia? That, at least, is no peril for them.

Rev Wilson Most unfortunate about the other boy, indeed. Unbaptised as well. To think of that lost soul, wandering in perpetuity . . . Well, it must be done directly, they shall find the icy font no discomfort at least.

Fitzroy Without delay. But I vaccinated them twice, first in Montevideo, and then again immediately on arrival in Plymouth. I believe it was the second one that did for poor Boat Memory . . . he had the best disposition of all.

Rev Wilson You must not blame yourself.

Fitzroy There is none other.

Silence.

Matthew Montevideo is the capital of Uruguay, whose principal export is . . . is . . . cattle and livestock?

Fitzroy Indeed it is. You apply yourself to your geography lessons then?

Matthew Captain Fitzroy, sir, I long above all things to be an explorer like you, and see the world, and I wish to join the navy when I have finished my schooling. Father, may I ask him? (*on his approval*) Captain, sir, when you are taking them back to Tierra del Fuego, might you be able to use my services in some way, on your ship? I am quick and willing, and of course I shall know them, for I am committed to helping with their needs – in fact I am writing a paper on 'The Noble Savage' for my oration class next term.

Fitzroy What say you, Reverend, to all this enthusiasm?

Rev Wilson (*kindly*) I say, Captain, that we shall see. It is of course my own wish that Matthew shall follow me into the Cloth, but let us see.

Fuegia Basket (*suddenly*) Not cold, Capen.

Everyone looks at her in surprise. Fitzroy smiles.

Fitzroy Good girl, Fuegia. She has picked up a smattering of English – Spanish also – with some ease, Jemmy Button likewise – as good a fellow as may be found – but the poor brute York Minster is ill-favoured in any tongue.

York gazes into the middle distance, oblivious, or perhaps defiant, of their attention.

Rev Wilson Their spirits must be dampened by the loss of their compatriot. I forget, was it the cholera, or the smallpox?

The Fuegians look up at Fitzroy in alarm.

Fitzroy The latter. I entreat you, sir, make no more reference to it if you would have them quiet.

Rev Wilson Certainly, certainly. No mentioning you-know-what, do you hear me, Matthew and Hannah?

Matthew / Of course, Father.

Hannah / Yes, sir.

Fitzroy Likewise, let them not be permitted to roam together unsupervised . . .

Rev Wilson Aha. Oh yes indeed. 'Catch the foxes, the little foxes, before they ruin our vineyard in bloom.' Song of Songs, Captain, a racy little number.

Fitzroy I have skimmed it.

Rev Wilson Worth a second look, sir, it refers to the love between God and Man, there is no shame in its enjoyment. Well, well, have no fear, these heathen children have found safe harbour here. Matthew here has even given up the field this season, to assist with their care. And Hannah here will help, she is as good and diligent a girl as ever lived, despite she is an orphan of the parish. Since my dear wife went to the

Lord, she has been an excellent housekeeper to us, in addition to her schoolroom duties.

Fitzroy Shall you care for this, Miss Hannah?

Hannah I think it will prove most interesting, although calming the fears of the other pupils will prove the most challenging.

Rev Wilson Hannah, answer simply, do not boldly initiate conversation! Excuse her, Captain.

Fitzroy She will be good for Fuegia, at any rate; she chatters away when she is at ease. Now, the matter of the purse –

Rev Wilson It is privilege enough to bring the light of God to shine on the dark souls of this world. That is payment enough, I do not ask for coins. (*Pause.*) However, when I have occasion to be in London, it would be most convenient to have membership of a club . . .

Fitzroy I see. Quite. Then perhaps, as we discussed . . . without a more protracted farewell . . . (*Kneels in front of the Fuegians.*) Capen say safe. Capen come back. Fuegia be good. Jemmy be good. York Minster . . . be good.

Jemmy mutely takes hold of his clothing.

Fitzroy (*disengaging gently*) Capen promise come back soon.

Fuegia (*quietly*) If he says he's coming back, he's coming back.

York You'll believe anything.

Rev Wilson What do they say?

Fitzroy I began an attempt at a dictionary on our return voyage, but I must confess to complete ignorance. (*to the Fuegians*) You must speak English now, only English. (*to Rev Wilson*) Surprisingly, the female is the most linguistically advanced.

81

Hannah shoots a look at Matthew, who is relieved at this contact, and makes a face back. Observing it, Jemmy smiles. Matthew smiles back.

York Up on your hindlegs for the white faces.
Fuegia English . . .
Jemmy Jemmybuttonwhatafellow.

Fitzroy smiles, exits with Rev Wilson. Hannah and Matthew remain with the Fuegians. Silence.

Hannah Hello.
Matthew Hello. I am Matthew Wilson. This is Hannah Bridges.

The Fuegians simply stare.

SCENE THREE

Rectory, side-by-side attic bedrooms, night.
   On one side of the space, Hannah's room: two beds, one with an old cover, one snowy white.
   On the other side, cramped quarters housing Jemmy and York, each huddled on their grey-covered beds. A bad silence between them.

Jemmy I like it when you just shut that big fat face of yours, and no sound comes out. If only your arse could do the same. (*Silence.*) But you have to talk to *them*, you're their prisoner too, as much as me. (*Still nothing.*) You were staring at the girl, I saw you. Don't tell me you weren't because you got that funny look, that big blubbery lip started twitching.
York You don't even have hair on your balls, so shut up.
Jemmy (*checking*) I do now. Soon I'll have more than you've got on your head. Look –
York Child.

Jemmy All quiet when Capen's here, then the big ugly booby again when he goes.

York Filthy food too.

Jemmy I like it.

York You'd eat seal shit. Because you're an Acaluf.

Jemmy They don't care here. It doesn't matter.

York That's why you like it. That's why you hid the boat. To get away.

Jemmy (*stung*) I never took it, I never hid it! You did it, you should just admit it, you took it and that's why they took us and brought us here and Kagora –

York springs up, grabs Jemmy by the throat.

York None of this is my fault. (*shoving him back*) Acaluf.

Jemmy curls up in his bed, pulls the covers over himself. York lies down on his own bed, turns away. On the other side of the space, Hannah and Fuegia enter.

Hannah Is everything still very strange, or have you been away from . . . Tierra del Fuego . . . for so long now that strange is normal? (*on her silence*) I've decided to talk to you as if you could understand everything and then gradually you will – you'll be here three years, after all. And when you go back you'll build a little church and show everyone how to be a civilised Christian lady . . . hopefully. Am I talking too much? People always say so. You can too, if you want – we could have some sort of signal, look, like this:

Hannah puts her finger to her lips, shakes her head. Fuegia copies her. Hannah smiles.

You're a clever girl, Captain Fitzroy said, and you look so to me. But a clever girl is a waste, they say.

Hannah sighs, pulls a white nightgown out from the white bedclothes. Fuegia shrinks away.

Miss Fuegia Basket, you cannot sleep in those funny clothes you wear. Come now, it is I who should be more frightened of you, with all this talk of cannibals. I have read *Robinson Crusoe* you know, from cover to cover. Reverend disapproves of Mr Defoe, but Matthew lent it to me, when we were . . . younger. Mr Matthew Wilson Esquire. (*Holds up nightgown again.*) Come, Miss Basket, please do not oblige me to change you myself, you are a large grown girl – and look at it, a missionary society sent it for you: it is absolutely new!

But Fuegia shrinks away miserably, lies down on the ground and curls up.

I know that you have slept in beds since you arrived, even though you were used to hovels before. Reverend will be very displeased with me if I cannot get you even to sleep, so come now –

Holding out the nightdress, Hannah gets up purposefully. Fuegia cringes from her. Hannah loses patience, gets into her own bed.

Then be a savage and sleep on the ground like a dog, if that is what you want. (*A beat.*) Fuegia, that floor is very cold, I'm telling you, you will get sick if you lie there like that uncovered. Is that what you want, to get sick? I don't want to nurse you either, I've got enough to do.

Fuegia gets up, comes over to the foot of Hannah's bed, giving the white one as wide a berth as she can. She shakes her head, points at it.

Fuegia Kagora sick . . . die. Fuegia Basket not sick.
Hannah Kagora?

Fuegia Fuegia Basket not die.

Hannah stares at the white bed. It dawns on her.

Hannah The one who died in Plymouth? In a hospital bed that looked like that? (*She gets into the white bed.*) I'm very happy to sleep here, you get into mine, Fuegia, that is a splendid arrangement. Go on, into mine, I've only got a few hours before I do the breakfast.

Fuegia hesitantly obeys. Hannah smiles to herself.

Hannah I understood . . . I understood her. Goodnight, Fuegia Basket.

Hannah turns out the light. Silence.

Fuegia (*sweetly, in the darkness*) Goodnight, me briny bastards.

SCENE FOUR

Schoolroom, Christmas, day. Reverend Wilson stands on a raised platform, marking the rhythm as Hannah leads the class round in a big circle, clapping in time and singing the alphabet. They make sure to keep a good distance from the Fuegians, who stick close together as they also go round. Jemmy and Fuegia making a good effort to join in, but York remains resolutely mute.

Seated to the side, Matthew Wilson observes it all, making notes in a small book. His eyes go as often to Hannah as the Fuegians, which is not lost on his father.

Rev Wilson Splendid, children, splendid! Now, shall you be good kind souls to your new brothers and sisters in Jesus Christ, and help them learn the Christian way?

Class Yes, Reverend.

Rev Wilson Good, children. Continue, Hannah. (*checking his fob watch*) Matthew, I must choose a new gundog from the Baines litter, will you come?

Matthew Thank you, Father, but I think I will stay here and observe the class. (*A beat.*) For the paper for my housemaster, you know.

Rev Wilson Ah yes. Then good day, children, good day.

Class/Hannah Good day, Reverend.

Rev Wilson exits. Hannah claps her hands together.

Hannah Very good, class, take your places, we shall do some spelling now.

As the class take their places:

Boys Black monkeys –

There is a sudden bundling crush near the Fuegians, and Jemmy cries out, holding his ear in pain. York grabs one of the boys, who cries out and tries to punch him, but York is too strong. He prises a stick out of the boy's fist, holds it up to his neck.

Boy Don't hurt me it, wasn't me –

Hannah Let go of him at once, York Minster!

Matthew York, there's a good chap –

Matthew tries to break York's grip, but it's too strong. York bares his teeth at the boy.

Fuegia / Let him go, he's nearly dead of fright anyway.

Girl / She wants to eat him too!

Matthew I shall get my father –

Hannah I will handle this – let him go, York!

York releases the boy, who drops coughing to the floor. He throws the stick down in front of Hannah. Jemmy and Fuegia quickly join him. Fuegia looks at Jemmy's ear, holds up a hand with blood on it.

Who did this? (*to Jemmy*) Did you see who did this to you?

Jemmy shakes his head miserably. She picks the stick off the floor, holds it up.

Whose is this?

Silence. She turns to the boy York held.

Jemmy Button, York Minster and Fuegia Basket have just been baptised. They are as Christian as you or I in the eyes of God and the world now, and you will treat them as you would be treated yourself. Is that clear?

Boy (*mutinously*) Yes, miss.

Hannah (*throws the stick in the bin*) Then apologise, please.

Boy To that dirty savage? Never.

The class burst out laughing. Matthew stands.

Matthew Then my father will turn you out of this school for disrespecting your teacher Miss Bridges and for defying his order that you love each other.

Boy (*bitterly, to Jemmy*) Sorry.

Fuegia (*softly*) Quick, say thank you.

Jemmy Thank you.

Hannah And we will have no more of that.

She picks up the handbell, rings it hard. The class file out.

(*to the Fuegians*) Are you alright? It will get easier as you learn English, and how we do things here. I'm sorry that happened.

Jemmy It wasn't my fault. (*to York*) None of it.

York Don't start.

Fuegia (*whispering*) It's obvious she's hardly got any control; we're going to have to be very careful.

Hannah What are you all saying? English please, Fuegia.

Fuegia We all happy.
Hannah Is that true?
Fuegia God is love.
Matthew She learns fast.
Hannah For survival.
Fuegia (*to York and Jemmy*) Say it, they like it.
Jemmy Godislove.

York yawns insolently.

(*to Fuegia*) See how she makes the big manatee eyes at
   him.
Fuegia And his face gets all red.
Hannah English, please.
York That's because he wants to take her by the poom-
   poom –
Fuegia So do you.
York And the father too.
Fuegia If I was her I'd take the father, he's the big man
   here.
Matthew Do you think they might be talking about us?
Fuegia Stop. He knows.
Hannah / Probably.
York / Always trying to be in charge.
Jemmy On the boat, the whole way, and she's worse now
   we're here.
Matthew What do you think they're saying?
Fuegia / That's because I'm cleverer than both of you,
   Capen said so.
Hannah / I have no idea.
Jemmy No, he didn't –
York He would never say that –
Jemmy See him staring at her breasts, he can't stop.
York They're very nice,
Fuegia (*sticking her chest out*) So are mine,

Matthew stares – looks away, embarrassed. The
Fuegians burst out laughing.

Told you.

Hannah Outside for some fresh air, go on!

They go, giggling. Hannah and Matthew are left alone.
A fertile silence.

SCENE FIVE

London, lecture hall, spring. More smartly dressed than
we have yet seen them, Jemmy, Fuegia and York sit on
three stools at the front, Captain Fitzroy, accompanied by
Matthew Wilson, sit near them on stage. Professor
Cornelius Donovan, of the London Phrenological
Institute, addresses us.

Prof Donovan It gives me great pleasure to see you all
here, in support of the growing science of phrenology
– the reliable and amazing indicator of character,
temperament, and both physical and emotional
aptitudes. I am delighted to introduce to you Captain
Robert Fitzroy of the British Admiralty, and his three
specimens here, brought from a far and barbarous
land for the salvation of their souls. As you know, they
are being educated in seclusion in Walthamstow, far
from the hurly burly of London, and to aid their tutors
and carers, I will now disclose the secrets of their
skulls. Who shall go first?

Fitzroy Miss Fuegia Basket.

Professor Donovan ceremonially walks round Fuegia,
staring at her, pulling her ears forward, tipping her
chin up, nodding to himself. She looks straight ahead.

Prof Donovan Were it not for her swarthy aspect, she
would not be unattractive. Her features are regular
and symmetrical, her eyes level and well spaced – a
biddable, sociable tendency is indicated, but the
cranium will confirm – or refute.

*He goes behind her, and begins to feel her head. York
starts up, displeased at the sight. The crowd murmur
in excitement.*

Fitzroy Steady now, York, all is well, be seated.

*York sits down again, but he does not take his eyes off
Fuegia and Donovan.*

Prof Donovan Yes . . . yes . . . the cranial characteristics
of the Brazil Indian and even the Negro . . . in the
lateral parts of the forehead . . . the propensity for
Cautiousness is smaller than I expected . . . a tendency
towards Amativeness, yes, yes, and here . . . the bump
of Benevolence . . . a kind nature, perhaps . . . I find no
organ of Causality . . . nor Ideality . . . but what is
this: a pronounced bump of Secretiveness, and a
depression where one would expect the mound of
Inhabitaveness.

*He moves on to Jemmy, tipping up his chin, knocking
lightly on his shoulders, positioning his head. Jemmy
screws up his face, trying not to laugh. Fuegia
splutters.*

Fitzroy Fuegia Basket!

*Fuegia looks down at her feet, desperately suppressing
her own laughter.*

Prof Donovan Ah yes, yes indeed. Captain Fitzroy, I am
impressed to draw a parallel here with the skull of the
Hindoo, you will remember from my last lecture? A
race, ladies and gentlemen, whose skulls are so generally

deficient in the bumps of Combativeness and Destruc-
tiveness that it takes a mere handful of superior
Europeans to bring a nation of hundreds of thousands,
nay, millions, under complete subjugation. The Negro
and Carib races similarly, whose skulls demonstrate a
marked propensity to play, at the expense of the
constructive organs. (*dismissively, of Jemmy*) An
inoffensive specimen, no marked characteristics, I
would class him with the Hindoo or the Negro.

He moves on to York, who meets his eyes in challenge.

Now now, my fine aboriginal fellow, I shall not take long
with you – Captain Fitzroy, may I make a request for
the future, that I should be able to receive this skull
when it is no longer useful to its present owner? It is
already a marvel, to the trained eye.

Fitzroy You will need to travel to Patagonia and wait
patiently, good Professor, he is in as rude good health
as you will ever see.

Prof Donovan You never know, our climate, and what
not – come now, my good fellow:

*He goes to touch York, who moves back. Fitzroy gets
up and goes to him, puts his hands on York's
shoulders, holding him down. York does not move, but
he is furious and humiliated.*

Fitzroy Begin, Professor, but do not linger on Mr
Minster, we try his patience already, I think.

*Professor Donovan feels York's head, steps back out of
harm's way.*

Prof Donovan On a very cursory examination, Captain,
that specimen there is disposed to cunning and
caution. I would say he is self-willed to an
extraordinary degree, he will be difficult to instruct
and will require an exhaustive amount of energy to

persuade into the simplest tasks. Beware, in short, Captain. Perhaps you would like me to read the head of your assistant also?

Matthew Very well, I thank you, sir.

Matthew sits beside Fuegia. Professor Donovan feels his skull, frowning.

Fitzroy What is it?

Professor Donovan shakes his head, concentrating. Concludes, bows to Matthew.

Prof Donovan A fine and unexceptional Anglo-Saxon skull, with all attendant virtues of superiority.

Matthew Unexceptional.

Prof Donovan Yes yes, that is an excellent reading. I could detect a pronounced mound of Love of Approbation, and one of Ideality. But you are still young, and they may well subside.

Matthew Thank you, Professor. (*He returns to his place, rather dampened by the reading.*)

Jemmy Jemmybutton, whatafellow.

Prof Donovan Indeed you are, young sir. And how do you like England?

Jemmy Very fine. Godislove. Butter pig chicken linen.

Fitzroy They are making good progress in Walthamstow, I am vastly pleased with them. They are all baptised, they are learning Scriptures, gardening, young Fuegia is beginning to make her letters, Jemmy also.

Prof Donovan If they are to go into service then surely that is not necessary?

Fitzroy Oh no, sir, they are not to be servants: they are to found a mission station and trading post on their return; I would not spend this time and effort on training them for service.

Prof Donovan I should say not, Captain, they are ten a penny from the colonies in any case. (*eyeing York*) And

properly broken in before they come here. Never get a
half-breed, though, that is my advice to you, for I see
a great many through this science, you may be sure.
I could tell you some stories – but of course, with the
recent situation in Antigua, that will not be necessary.

Fitzroy All suppressed, sir, you will be pleased to know,
Jamaica also. (*to the audience*) You may help
yourselves liberally to sugar once more, it is all under
control again.

SCENE SIX

*On one side of the space, York works intently on a piece
of wood with a small whittling knife.*

*On the other, Walthamstow's small outdoor market,
early spring. Jemmy, Fuegia and Hannah are shopping
amongst other villagers. Jemmy is now extremely well
turned out, Fuegia dressed like Hannah. Hannah watches
Fuegia buying vegetables.*

Fuegia Carrots. Thank you.

Hannah Very good, Fuegie! Oh look, there's the chicken
man – you keep going, I'll be back directly.

*Hannah exits. Jemmy picks up a small hand-mirror
from a stall. He gazes at himself in it, feels his head
where Professor Donovan did. He looks concerned.
Fuegia comes over to see.*

Jemmy He knew I was an Acaluf.

Fuegia No he didn't. He was just rude to all of us.

Man in Crowd What are they talking about?

Woman in Crowd Dirty beasts, dressed up like monkeys.

Jemmy He said nice things about you.

Fuegia That I could be a good servant.

Jemmy Hannah is a servant,

Fuegia But she doesn't like it, does she?
Woman in Crowd Walking around like they own the place, look at them.
Jemmy How do you know?
Fuegia Her face, when she's giving out the food to Matthew.

Jemmy looks at himself in the glass again.

Jemmy Is he handsome?
Fuegia Maybe.
Woman in Crowd My one says them boys stare at her in school.
Man in Crowd They want their heads broke open is what they want.

Jemmy smiles at his reflection. Shows Fuegia hers. She smiles at herself.

Jemmy You're pretty.
Fuegia Am I?

Behind them, the stallholders leave their posts, begin to encircle them. The ringleaders from the schoolroom move to the front. A low murmur begins. Fuegia passes the mirror back to Jemmy, who gazes into it again. Then they realise what's happening.

Across the space, York feels some internal alarm, stops working and looks up.

Fuegia and Jemmy, back together, look around urgently for Hannah. The crowd advances closer, the hum now threatening.

Across the space, York raises the wooden mask to his face.

The noise stops, the crowd quickly resume their places in the market. Hannah enters with a brimming basket – Fuegia and Jemmy are frozen together in fear. She runs to them.

94

Hannah What? Whatever is the matter?

Jemmy and Fuegia look around them. Everything is normal again. A bell begins to toll. The crowd and the market become the congregation and pews of –

SCENE SEVEN

A church service. The Fuegians sit with Hannah, Rev Wilson in the pulpit, Matthew sitting at the front. While his father speaks, he looks back occasionally at them.
    Captain Fitzroy is revealed on the other side of the space.

Rev Wilson The good Lord himself came into our midst as an outsider, he was derided and mocked – a few would listen, but the rest were quicker to scourge him if they could –

Fuegia Scourge . . .

Fitzroy My dear Reverend Wilson, I write to you with I hope pardonable pride –

Rev Wilson – yet still He carried His message of love and fellowship to every man and woman and child he met.

Jemmy What is scourge?

Congregation Shh.

Fitzroy – to inform you that due in no little part to my dear sister's enthusiastic report of our Fuegian project –

Rev Wilson The halt and the lame and the leper and the fallen woman, as well as the little children, all were welcome at His Father's table.

Fuegia (*whispering*) Cat-o'-nine-tails, like Capen did to those sailors.

Fitzroy – the pleasure of their company is requested –

Jemmy (*frightened*) They do that in here?

95

Rev Wilson And every one of us within these walls as I speak to you now, has a home in Jesus Christ and a place at that table, and a feast for the spirit if we will only bow down in our hearts.

Jemmy Not to us!

Fuegia I don't know.

Others Shhh!

Fitzroy – by none other than King William and Queen Adelaide, at St James's Palace!

Rev Wilson O let us pray without ceasing, in all that we do and with every breath we take –

York Let them try.

Fitzroy Needless to say, I will bear the expense of this presentation, though the honour in name must be shared with you, too.

Rev Wilson – to open our hearts to God, and our arms to our neighbours, be they ever so strange and new to us, for this little school, and church, and village –

Fitzroy And the people of Walthamstow who support this dear endeavour.

Fuegia Hannah, not to us?

Rev Wilson – and this whole Christian nation, must pray to live as an example to the rest of the world, and bring the light and love of God to those brothers and sisters still living in the darkness of ignorance.

Hannah (*whispering*) Of course not . . .

Fitzroy Salutations, good Reverend.

Rev Wilson The gates of heaven are open to us all.

Fitzroy Post cript . . . I have recommended you to my club.

Rev Wilson Let us rise and sing in joyful praise our newest hymn, 'All Things Bright and Beautiful'.

SCENE EIGHT

The Rectory, day. Summer. Matthew helps Jemmy put the finishing touches to his formal wear. Jemmy preens in front of the mirror. York lies back on his bed in his rough day clothes. A formal suit like Jemmy wears is laid out beside him.

Matthew York, old fellow, even if you do not care about meeting the King and Queen of England, then at least look forward to the feast you will surely be given there? Beef, and pickles, and sauces –

Jemmy Jemmy Button shoes dirty! Find cloth –

Jemmy finds a pocket handkerchief, begins shining his shoes. Matthew picks up York's suit.

Matthew Come, York, you must be dressed with more respect.

York does not respond. Matthew does not know what to do. Jemmy basks in the contrast.
Across the space, Hannah dresses Fuegia. They look at her reflection. Fuegia shakes her head.

Hannah Fuegia Basket, you look most presentable indeed, anyone would imagine you had come from the ends of the earth loaded with trunks of the latest fashion, the way you are carrying on today. Do you not recall the smelly shirt and ragged old sailor pants you arrived in? And were so loath to relinquish?

Fuegia Relinquish?

Hannah Give up.

Fuegia Relinquish . . . (*Points to Hannah's skirt.*) Relinquish me that one.

Hannah Mine? But it's cheap stuff compared to these that Capen sissa sent.

Fuegia Hannah best. Hannah's clothes best.
Hannah Fuegia . . . if I let you wear this, that is it, alright? This is what you wear, no more changing.
Fuegia Relinquish changing.

Hannah gets out of her skirt, gives it to Fuegia. She admires herself.

Fuegia Basket beautiful now. Go to King and Queen.

On the other side of the space, in the boys' bedroom, Matthew demonstrates the court bow to Jemmy. York watches cynically.

Matthew And it's very important to keep your eyes low as you go, like this –

Jemmy copies him perfectly. Looks triumphantly at York.

York Pathetic.
Matthew York, I don't understand your words but of your tone I am in no doubt – but still I try my best to be your friend while I am here. My father has long been of the opinion you should be removed for the good of the other two – were it not for their affection for you Capen would have agreed –
Jemmy Oh he berry berry bad fellow Matthewwilson.

York smiles.

Matthew You probably are a thoroughly bad fellow, York Minster, and not to be trusted in any way, but perhaps you were brought here against your will, and who is to say that you did not have a family perhaps, or were of some importance in your . . . well you did not have villages, Captain Fitzroy says, only wretched hovels . . . but in any case . . . you are here now, and you are going to Court, and I for one care greatly you are so honoured. The King is second only to God . . .

(*putting some clothes in Jemmy's arms*) Shall Jemmy
be as a nurse with a naughty child, York, and dress
you like an infant?

York Try it and I'll club you like a seal.

Jemmy He say no thank you very much, Matthewwilson,
go like him is.

*Opposite, Hannah dresses Fuegia's hair. Fuegia is
happy.*

Fuegia Hannah come Court too?

Hannah I don't think so, Fuegia.

Jemmy Come on, he's trying to be nice to you, you big
hairy lump.

York You can dress like a dancing monkey but not me.
And if Capen wants to leave me again while you go
visiting fat pale faces with stinking breath then I'll stay
here with Hannah. (*A beat.*) She can dress me if she
likes.

Matthew What's that about Hannah?

Fuegia Please?

Jemmy Fat-head yourself, she doesn't like you, she likes
him. (*to Matthew*) Hannah very nice lady.

Hannah You have to be asked, you know. You have to
be wanted.

York He's just a child like you. She needs a man. She's
ready.

Fuegia Fuegia asking! Fuegia want, please?

Jemmy Don't be stupid, we can't have white girls.

York / I know that, idiot.

Jemmy / But we could share Fuegia . . .

Matthew Speak English, the pair of you. I know you can.

Hannah Fuegia . . . you have to be somebody first.

Jemmy Hannah very nice lady. Fuegia little girl, godislove.

Hannah Of noble birth, or very rich, or even a precious
savage . . .

Matthew Are you telling the truth, Jemmy?

Jemmy Yamana, berry fast language. (*A beat.*) He say he go in him clothes.
Hannah Never an ugly orphan parish girl.
Matthew I suppose that's something.

York smiles, shrugs.

Hannah I'm nothing.

Silence.

Fuegia Hannah Fuegia friend?
Hannah What? Yes . . . I am that, anyway. I'm your friend.
Fuegia (*kissing Hannah's hand*) Fuegia Basket Hannah friend.
Hannah Are you? Thank you . . .

She smiles, suddenly near to tears.

SCENE NINE

Rectory garden, later that day. Hannah sits on the step, peeling potatoes. Matthew enters. She continues her work without looking up.

Matthew Hello, Hannah.
Hannah Hello.

He sits down nearby.

Matthew What do you suppose our friends are doing now?
Hannah Learning to bow and scrape, I expect.
Matthew (*laughing*) Now I think I start to recognise you again. (*A beat.*) Hannah, have I given you cause for offence?
Hannah What makes you think that?
Matthew You're so cold with me. We're old friends.

Hannah We were. Before you were sent away to become a gentleman, Mr Wilson. And now you may not play with your old friends, nor expect them to be at their ease with you, as I have been most sharply told.

Matthew My father –

Hannah It was not just your father, suddenly you were as happy for me to fetch and carry for you as if I were just a –

She throws a potato into the pail of water, splashing him.

Matthew A servant.

Hannah takes it out on the next potato.

Hannah There shall be no liberties again, no free discourse, and certainly no borrowing of the newest books by me.

Matthew I still feel free to talk to you –

Hannah Yes, well, that freedom is not general.

Matthew But why must we –

Hannah Because we are not children any more!

Matthew Now you are being foolish, / it is not to do with our age.

Hannah / Do not call me foolish. You may come and go and plan your voyage for when you finish your studies. Despite what your father might say you are a man and you may choose your course – you may even offer me wine at table, as a jest –

Matthew Must I apologise for treating you as an equal?

Hannah Yes! Because although I am one, in every manner but birth, and your better on certain matters of good sense and understanding –

Matthew Name one.

Hannah When I warned you not to swim from that jetty because of the current –

Matthew Oh. I was all but clambering out –

Hannah When I pulled you in with that branch.

Matthew Bring that up again, have your point.

Hannah Every time I beat you at hangman, at cards –
I play with no one now.

Matthew I am glad.

Hannah Oh, you would have me friendless.

Matthew That is not what I meant.

Hannah Then say what you did.

Silence.

Matthew Hannah . . . I would not have you lonely.
Maybe it would be good for you to marry a good
honest fellow, and be mistress of your own home.
There must be plenty in the village . . .

Hannah Oh, the ignorance . . .

Matthew You have chosen already, have you? Well then,
tell me who it is: John Baines? He will be taking over
his father's building firm, he can build you a little
cottage. Or maybe George Reid, who stares at you in
the street. Or perhaps . . . no, you would have to wait
too long for Tom Bowyer to grow up, but then you
would have as many looking-glasses and fine linen –

Hannah How dare you speak to me as if I were for sale?
You may strut about in your fine uniform as much as
you like and drink wine and coffee and throw your
chest out in the schoolroom because they are all in awe
of you, but you will not impress me with it one jot.

Matthew How may I impress you then, Hannah? What
must I do?

Hannah Respect me.

Matthew I do. But I cannot change the world.

Hannah (*returning to her peeling*) I am not asking you
to. I am not asking you for anything, ever again. Not
friendship, not books, nothing.

Matthew stands.

Matthew It is as my father said, Hannah. You have grown so . . . hard. (*on her silence*) But I shall not force my company on you any longer.
Hannah As you wish.

Matthew bows to her, exits. Hannah does not move for a long time.

SCENE TEN

High summer. Walthamstow, ready for a street party, three days later. Villagers and schoolchildren crowd excitedly, waving little Union Jack flags. Reverend Wilson leads the cheer:

Rev Wilson God Save The King, God Save Captain Fitzroy, God Save Jemmy Button, Fuegia Basket, and York Minster, pride of Walthamstow and presented at Court. Hip-hip –
Crowd Hooray!
Rev Wilson Hip-hip –
Crowd Hooray!
Rev Wilson Hip-hip –
Crowd Hooray!

Captain Fitzroy ushers in the newly confident Fuegians, who smile broadly, even York Minster. Fuegia wears a pretty bonnet, and is clearly very proud of it. She also admires a little ring on her finger. Spotting Hannah, she runs to her and embraces her.

Fuegia Hannah! (*showing ring and bonnet*) Look what Queen give Fuegia! For Fuegia Basket!
Fitzroy It was indeed an act of the greatest kindness.
Rev Wilson (*going to see*) Queen Adelaide herself? Or one of her ladies in waiting?

Fitzroy Queen Adelaide, Reverend. We spent quite two hours with their royal personages.

Jemmy Drinking tea! Even York not spill one drop.

York almost smiles.

Matthew Good man.

Fitzroy Never have I been asked more pertinent questions of the maritime life, than by His Majesty – he commiserated with me about the pettifogging candle-counters at the Admiralty, he understood the limitations of the Cherokee class of ship, so it –

Jemmy Jemmy eat sandwich!

Fuegia Fuegia eat sandwich!

York Sandwich good.

Fitzroy – so it was a pleasure to discuss –

Rev Wilson (*to Fuegia*) Was there cake also? I must confess I have a hunger for every detail of the event, Captain.

Jemmy King like Jemmy shiny shoes!

Fitzroy – to discuss seafaring with –

York Many meat, many fish.

Fitzroy – so knowledgeable a man! (*A beat.*) They were very well turned out, Hannah, it was noted.

Rev Wilson Good girl, Hannah, well done.

Jemmy King William whatafellow!

Fuegia Fuegia Basket Fuegia Bonnet Fuegia Ring!

York York eat sandwich one two three four five six seven eight.

Fitzroy Indeed you did, York, every sandwich within sight, and it was fortunate for us Their Royal Highnesses took it in such good part – (*to Rev Wilson*) The Queen declared to her ladies that they should always serve them as they were so popular with guests. (*to Hannah*) You could make them quite easily, my dear.

Rev Wilson I have had them myself, with both potted meats and cucumber, at the Reynolds', of Banbury, do you know them?

Fitzroy I confess I have not had the pleasure. York, my good fellow – (*Puts a friendly hand on his shoulder.*) Now that was not so bad, my boy, was it? I spoke highly of your good work here, Reverend, you may be sure. Their Majesties were greatly taken with their guests, it was most gratifying.

Rev Wilson Were they indeed? Well, I appreciate it mightily, Captain. Did you mention the good air of Walthamstow? Perhaps Their Majesties might desire a tour on some future occasion? King William likes his fishing, it is well known, and we have –

Fitzroy I spoke highly of all aspects of the Parish, Reverend. Jemmy and Fuegia were quite voluble on the subject.

Rev Wilson Splendid! And what did you say?

Jemmy Hannahbridges bery nice England bery nice.

Fuegia (*glancing at him*) Reverend Wilson very nice, church very nice. (*Shows her gold ring to the crowd.*) Queen Fuegia friend, Fuegia Queen friend.

Rev Wilson Ah, the privileges of the savage.

Jemmy turns to him very seriously.

Jemmy Not savage now, gentleman. Jemmy Button English gentleman.

Everyone laughs, Jemmy too, not understanding. Fuegia slips her arm through Hannah's.

Fuegia Fuegia lady. Hannah lady.

More laughter.

Matthew (*quickly*) Yes, you are. Both of you.

Fitzroy The excitement will die down presently, Reverend, but I must leave you with them, with my greatest thanks for all your good offices.

Rev Wilson The honour is all mine, the credit to the good Lord. To think Walthamstow the subject of praise at Court – shall we declare today a holiday, in celebration of our honour?

The crowd cheers.

Fitzroy Perhaps some exercise for our new ladies and gentlemen, Reverend? They have been exemplary, but have been cooped up for near three days now.

Matthew Oh, Father, may I take them to the forest? It is such a beautiful day, we could take a picnic.

Jemmy With sandwiches!

Fuegia Sandwiches and bonnets!

Rev Wilson Then Hannah must accompany you if Fuegia is also to go.

Matthew and Hannah don't look at each other.

Matthew I would not give Miss Bridges extra labour.

Hannah I am quite happy to take care of Fuegia, Reverend.

SCENE ELEVEN

Rectory kitchen, day. Fuegia packs a hamper. Reverend Wilson enters.

Rev Wilson Fuegia dear, where is Hannah? I cannot find my spectacles in my study, she can always put her hand upon them.

Fuegia looks at him evenly. She walks up to him, stands in front of him. Rev Wilson smiles, but he is discomfited by her closeness.

Fuegia Hannah pretty . . . Fuegia pretty . . .

She smiles at him. He turns away, suddenly alarmed. Hannah enters behind him, blocking his path.

Hannah A picnic, Reverend! Will you come with us?
Rev Wilson Indeed no, the children may play in peace.
Hannah Oh. Then did you want for something,
  Reverend?

Behind her, Fuegia smiles at him again.

Rev Wilson It has slipped my mind . . . (*He exits hastily.*)

SCENE TWELVE

*Epping Forest, late afternoon. Hannah, Matthew and the
Fuegians lie by the remnants of a picnic, York still idly
picking it over. It is hot. They are all barefoot, the
Fuegians in the greatest undress. Hannah rearranges
Fuegia's skirt to be more modest. She still wears her
bonnet.*

Jemmy Fuegia Basket pretty lady . . .

*York looks up from his grazing. Fuegia smiles at
Jemmy. York gives her some fruit. She takes it, smiles
at him too. She gets up, feels his head, pretending to be
a phrenologist.*

Fuegia Big bump of clever, big bump of good.
Jemmy He big bump all over, Matthewwilson.
Matthew Hannah, I know you are still not talking to me,
  but I wish you had been there to see it. I know Captain
  Fitzroy gives all credence to it, but Professor Donovan
  told me I was an unexceptional Anglo-Saxon
  specimen, and that hopefully, I would grow out of
  anything interesting!

Hannah almost smiles.

What was it he said I had . . . bumps of ideality . . . and
love of approbation – apparently those are bad things.

I'm sure he would have found much of interest in your head, were you there . . .

Hannah shrugs, determined not to take the bait.

Hannah Why? What about my head?

Matthew jumps up, goes behind her, pretending to be Professor Donovan. Enjoying it, Jemmy, Fuegia and York form an audience.

Matthew Yes yes, a splendid cranium before me, well-balanced features, a docile and pliable disposition – pardon me, ladies and gentlemen, that is purely wishful thinking, she is a strident mare –

Despite herself, Hannah laughs.

– mm, yes indeed, now let us see . . .

He puts his hands on her head. Hannah starts – but does not protest. Matthew slowly feels her skull, and the sides of her face.

Matthew Here we find the bump of ideality, this subject is highly intelligent, with a great inborn desire of excellence . . . and strong poetic feeling. She is a good reader, of people as well as books.

Hannah It doesn't say that . . .

Matthew Shh, this is important science. And here . . . the ridge of mirth, which gives feeling to the ludicrous, ah yes, and here, the rigid mound of firmness, which creates in the subject the determination never to forgive a friend for past injury, despite his utter sorrow at ever having hurt her feelings –

Hannah You're just saying what you want.

Matthew Yes.

She pulls away, embarrassed, but pleased. Silence.

York (*aside*) There's two other bumps he wants to read.

Jemmy and Fuegia burst out laughing.

Matthew (*to Hannah*) I'm used to them now, it doesn't worry me when they speak of us like this.
Hannah They have affection for us, though. I am convinced.
Matthew I feel it too. Strange, isn't it? That you, and I, and these three, should be together like old friends, feeling no differences . . .

Hanah looks away first.

York (*politely*) More beer, Matthewwilson?
Matthew All gone, Mr Minster, sir. And more would not be wise, in this heat.

York produces two large bottles of it, passes one to Matthew.

Matthew Where did you get this!
Jemmy King give us money, Jemmy buy beer.
Hannah Did Captain Fitzroy know this?
Fuegia Capen not worry, we all good children all day.
Matthew Where did you buy it?
Jemmy (*stupid question*) Tavern, Matthewwilson.

Fuegia takes the bottle from Jemmy, politely passes it to Hannah – who really wants to.

Matthew It is a holiday, after all.

Hannah drinks.

Matthew Oh, what a glorious day . . . on a day like this the rest of the world does not exist, it's like that poem we were learning at school, 'Ode to a Nightingale'. How does it go . . . 'My heart is pained –'
Hannah Aches. 'My heart / aches –'
Matthew / 'My heart aches, and a something something coldness –'

Hannah 'My heart aches, and a drowsy numbness pains
my sense . . .' You care now for poetry.

Matthew Perhaps I have changed without you realising.
Perhaps I am an altogether different person from the
one you so disliked. (*A beat.*) Tell it, Hannah.

*Hannah turns away a little, so he cannot see her face.
Fuegia takes the opportunity to surreptitiously hoik up
her skirt, allowing Jemmy and York a better view.*

Hannah
'My heart aches, and a drowsy numbness pains
My sense, as though of hemlock I had drunk
Or emptied some dull opiate to the drains
One minute past, and Lethe-wards had sunk:
'Tis not through envy of thy happy lot
But being too happy in thine happiness –'

She continues, as Matthew joins her.

Matthew
'That thou, light-winged Dryad of the trees,
In some melodious plot of beechen green, and
    shadows numberless,
Singest of summer in full-throated ease.'

Hannah You knew it.

Matthew Once you began it. Do you know more?

Hannah I forget.

*Aware of the current between them, the Fuegians
watch with interest.*

Matthew I think you'll remember.

Hannah I doubt it.

*Silence. Fuegia gets up, takes off the bonnet and gives
it to Hannah.*

Fuegia Hannah pretend be Queen.

Jemmy jumps up too, clapping.

Jemmy Give bonnet to Hannah, meet Jemmy Button, Jemmy bow – Matthewwilson be King, Hannahbridges Queen. Please?

Hannah takes the bonnet.

Hannah Um . . . I am Queen Adelaide . . . um . . . it is uncommon fine today.

Matthew And I am King Billy, not a-whoring in Brighton for once –

Hannah How excessively charming to see you, husband: I trust your gout does not plague you today?

Matthew Excessively, madam, I am quite riddled with it, but I have dragged myself away from the doxies and nags, to welcome our guests all the way from Walthamstow.

Hannah Walthamstow? Where is that?

Matthew Up and right a bit from Tierra del Fuego.

The Fuegians clap.

Hannah What are your names, my dears?

Jemmy steps forward, bows deeply.

Jemmy Jemmy Button whatafellow!

York Up on hindlegs, always skylark.

Hannah Oh! We are excessively fond of skylarking at the palace, he will fit in perfectly.

Matthew Pleased to meet you, my fine fellow, and who is that handsome brute behind you?

Hannah Ladies first, I entreat you, husband – though you need no encouragement on that score, I hear.

Matthew Beg pardon, good madam – you look monstrous fine in that get up, m'dear.

Hannah (*giggling*) Let us meet this charming child, what is your name, my dear?

Fuegia (*dropping a perfect curtsey*) Fuegia Basket, thank you, ma'am.

Hannah And who taught you such pretty manners, my dear?

Fuegia My teacher, Miss Hannah Bridges.

Matthew I hear she is a prodigious clever girl, and good at climbing trees. I should like to make her acquaintance.

Hannah (*quickly*) Now, my dear, let me give you a royal bonnet to wear.

She puts it on Fuegia's head. Jemmy bows again.

Matthew Pleasure to meet you, m'boy. Fine fellow, Jemmy Button.

Jemmy turns triumphantly to York.

Jemmy Jemmy Button gentleman.

Fuegia slips her arm through Jemmy's.

Fuegia Jemmy Button good gentleman. Come. (*thinking*) 'Will you take a turn about the room, sir?'

Jemmy Charmed, ma'am.

She and Jemmy giggle, walk away, arm in arm.

Hannah She must have seen them do that at Court.

York spits on the ground, mutters something.

Matthew What's that, York?

York points at Jemmy.

York (*loudly*) Acaluf!

Jemmy and Fuegia stop walking, turn.

(*smiling the challenge*) Ongaia, Acaluf.

Jemmy shakes his head. York nods emphatically. Both look at Fuegia. She looks from one to the other, nods. Jemmy slowly walks back to York, eyes locked with him.

Jemmy Ongaia.

Fuegia (*sweetly*) Fight for Fuegia.

Hannah What!

Matthew Oh they've been boiling up to it for a long time, better they do it here than at home. Let them sort it out.

Fuegia (*patiently*) Fight good.

Matthew I'll take the winner.

Hannah No!

Fuegia (*to the waiting York and Jemmy*) Tagum!

They lunge at each other, wrestle hard.

Fuegia (*politely*) Matthew fight for Fuegia Basket too?

Hannah No! (*to Jemmy and York*) Love your brother! Stop fighting!

Jemmy and York come crashing towards them – York has the advantage. This is no playful test any more. Jemmy is losing badly. Fuegia stops Hannah intervening.

York releases Jemmy, who lies panting on the ground. Matthew goes to help him up, but Jemmy angrily shakes off his hand, staggers away.

York goes up to Fuegia, grabs her to him. She looks pleased. Hannah is shocked.

We should go back. Come on.

York (*to Matthew*) Ongaia?

Matthew (*laughing*) Ongaia indeed, York, good fellow, now let us sort out this business once and for all, like gentlemen.

Hannah Matthew, you cannot! Do not be so foolish – this is for Fuegia!

Matthew Hannah, you don't understand boys, it's quite alright. This is for sport alone, York, I do not seek Miss Basket's favours.

York nods gravely. They square up to each other.

Fuegia (*to Hannah, prompting quietly*) Tagum.
Hannah I don't want them to fight.
Fuegia Then Fuegia say?
Hannah Tagum!

*Matthew and York circle each other. Recovered,
Jemmy joins Hannah and Fuegia to watch. York goes
for Matthew – who slips out, more agile. He smiles at
York, teasing. Jemmy laughs. Matthew attacks. They
grapple. Matthew disappears under York's bulk.*

Come on, Matthew! Come on!

*But York is stronger by far, and Matthew is soon
suffering like Jemmy before him. He slams the ground
in surrender. York releases him, satisfied. Fuegia goes
to him. Hannah goes to Matthew, who gets up,
brushing off her concern.*

*He offers York his hand. York is puzzled, then
understands, shakes and smiles. Jemmy comes
forward, not smiling.*

Jemmy Why you fight York?
Matthew (*still panting*) For sport.
Jemmy Jemmy want sport.
Hannah No.
Jemmy (*ignoring her, to Matthew*) Matthew fight York,
Matthew fight Jemmy. (*A beat.*) Fair.
Matthew Very well, Jemmy Button whatafellow, if it will
make you happy to be thrashed twice, then I must
oblige you. But you must take it like the gentleman you
want to be, and not hold it against me, do you hear?

Jemmy bows, takes his position.

Just quickly, Hannah. Then we'll go back. It won't take
me long. (*He bows to Jemmy, takes his position
opposite him.*)

Hannah/Fuegia Tagum!

The boys fly at each other. A faster, harder contest than either of them anticipated. York watches, arms behind his head, his own job done.

Hannah and Fuegia move with the tumbling mass of Matthew and Jemmy – Jemmy is viciously determined to win – after a desperate struggle he twists Matthew back to the ground –

Matthew Enough!

Jemmy forces him a little further, then jumps up, honour vindicated. Matthew lies convulsed on the ground, gasping in pain.

Hannah – my back –

Hannah (*to the Fuegians*) Quickly! Run back to the village, get the doctor, something's broken – quick!

But York keeps hold of Fuegia, and Jemmy just stands there, staring in horror.

Did you not hear me? Go to the village, fetch help!

Jemmy Jemmy not want to hurt Matthewwilson. Jemmy not hurt him.

Hannah Run, Jemmy! Do it! Fuegia, go, do you hear me?

York If you go back and tell them, they might . . . scourge you.

Hannah What? Fuegia, what's he saying?

Fuegia Not go. (*shaking her head*) We frightened.

Hannah But he's hurt! (*to York, pleading*) York, you have to let them go, I beg of you, please!

York kneels down, examines Matthew, who has his eyes closed tight in pain. He takes him by the shoulders, pulls him sharply towards him. Matthew screams, faints.

York Him good now.

He takes Fuegia by the arm and leads her off. She turns and smiles at Hannah.

Fuegia He good, York make him good now.

They move into the shadows, lie down together. Hannah takes Jemmy by the arm.

Hannah Go, Jemmy, do you hear me? Fetch the doctor!

But Jemmy backs away from her, terrified.

Then I'll go.
Matthew Don't leave me.
Hannah We can't stay here, you're hurt, it's getting dark –
Matthew Jemmy, you devil – what did you do to me –

Jemmy sits down at the side, his face buried in his arms. He shakes his head.

Jemmy Not devil. Gentleman.
Hannah What should I do?
Matthew Stay with me.
Hannah But you need help –
Matthew I cannot move from here yet, though. Stay with me, Hannah –
Hannah I will . . .

He reaches for her hand. She lets him take it. Slowly, strokes his hair.

'I cannot see what flowers are at my feet.
Nor what soft incense hangs upon the boughs.'
Matthew You remember . . .
Hannah
'But, in embalmed darkness, guess each sweet
Wherewith the seasonable month endows
The grass, the thicket –'

Behind them, York and Fuegia are having sex. Jemmy stares at them. Aware of it without looking round, Hannah falters in her recitation.

'– and the fruit tree wild . . .'

Matthew Don't stop.

Hannah I . . . I can't remember any more.

Matthew

'The purple-stained mouth . . .'

Silence . . . They kiss.
As darkness covers them all, alone in his limbo between the two couples, Jemmy Button puts his hand down his pants, rocking himself.

Jemmy Jemmy Button gentleman. Jemmy Button gentleman.

Silence. Then torches in the darkness –

Voices Here! Over here!

SCENE THIRTEEN

A few days later. Hannah and Fuegia, and Jemmy and York, silent and separate in the Rectory bedrooms. Captain Fitzroy in London. Rev Wilson in his study. Matthew Wilson back at school.

Rev Wilson Dear Captain Fitzroy, I am sensible of the esteem in which you hold the primitive character, though I am forever unable to share in that happy delusion, given the shocking events of the last week.

Fitzroy If what you say be true, I am most grievously concerned for the well-being of my Fuegians –

Jemmy What will they do to us?

York Nothing. He's gone back to school. He wasn't hurt.

Matthew Of course it wasn't my fault, Father! I couldn't drag them back if they didn't want to come.

Fitzroy I deplore that Admiralty business keeps me in London at this most sensitive time.

Rev Wilson So of course it falls to me to contain events –

Matthew I do not want to get Hannah into trouble, but . . .

Rev Wilson 'However, I have no doubt that you will join with me in believing the swift removal of these –'
These bloody and treacherous savages –

Matthew I did try to bring everyone back, please do not punish me for it, Father.

Jemmy If I had gone back for help –

York It would be the same now.

Matthew All I want is to be back at school and at my studies.

Rev Wilson '– these . . . three young people . . .' – dirty monkeys – 'will be in the best interests of all concerned.'

Jemmy No, you would not have taken Fuegia!

Matthew gets up, hits himself on the chest.

Matthew You are no gentleman.

Fitzroy But I earnestly entreat you to keep me informed as to their well-being, which as you know, is paramount.

Rev Wilson Forget my son, the parish, my very reputation –

Fuegia How Matthew Wilson now?

Hannah Never speak to me of him again.

Fitzroy I must however ask you, Reverend, to account to me and to the missionary board.

Rev Wilson I, should account, to you?

Fuegia Hannah not cry more.

Hannah I will never shed one tear on him, do you understand? He is not worth one tear.

Jemmy Matthewwilson whatafellow . . .

Fitzroy How it came that the young people were
permitted to venture so far from supervision, that their
absence was not noted until the damage was done.

Rev Wilson My very dear Captain Fitzroy.

Hannah And you, Fuegia, you say oh, Fuegia Basket
Hannah friend, but when I needed you, when I
thought he was dying, or paralysed, you stayed with
York, didn't you? You don't know the meaning of
friendship.

Rev Wilson You visited, you squired them to Court and
took the laurels, but from day to day, the burden was
mine.

Fuegia Fuegia sorry.

York You're a boy. I'm a man. I make decisions. You
obey them.

Hannah Oh, you have no idea. (*bitterly hurt*) You
savage . . .

Rev Wilson I will not be scapegoated in this matter.

*Rev Wilson gets up angrily, casts the letter aside. He
goes to the bedrooms, bursts in on Jemmy and York.
They look up in alarm.*

You have brought the devil to this place, do you know
that? All that good work, Jemmy, going to Court,
shining your shoes – and what do you do? Shame,
shame on you. And as for you . . .

*He goes up to York, who does not blink. Rev Wilson
stares at him – York holds his eyes, ready.*

Matthew Dear Hannah . . . I feel bad about . . . Dear
Hannah, I owe you an . . .

*Reverend Wilson turns away, goes to the girls' door.
Within, they hear him and freeze. He curbs his
impulse, exits. Matthew screws up the paper, throws it
away. He is disgusted with himself.*

SCENE FOURTEEN

Church, day. A hymn finishes. The Fuegians and Hannah keep their eyes downcast. Rev Wilson stares at them.

Rev Wilson Let those who have sinned look into their hearts, strip themselves of pride and deceit, and beg forgiveness. (*looking at Hannah*) Let those who seduce, be repaid for their vice with justice. (*at York*) Let those who are wicked and obstinate, who refuse Your love dear Lord, learn through suffering and be saved. (*at Jemmy*) Let those who are weak, and vain, and foolish, be reminded of Your great sacrifice on the cross, and renounce the counsel of the Devil for ever.

Jemmy suddenly rises, points up at the Cross.

Jemmy Jesus Yamana! Jesus Kagora – (*distress rising*) Jesus Kagora!

Rev Wilson Quiet!

Jemmy Jesus say Jemmy go home, or Jemmy die here, Jemmy die – Kagora on cross.

York Shut up, you fool, you'll only make it worse for us.

Hannah You're not going to die, Jemmy.

Jemmy Jesus look me now, he up there, on cross, he hands he feet he bleed, he cry to Jemmy: Go Home.

Fuegia (*seeing it too*) Kagora Jesus – He look at Fuegia, he cry!

Rev Wilson Hush them –

As Rev Wilson comes down to deal with Jemmy, he cries out:

Jemmy Boat Memory, Jesus! Jesus Kagora want Yamana go home, want Acaluf go home –

Fuegia Yamana go home! Jesus say go home!

Staring at them, the congregation begin to murmur together:

Congregation Go home . . . go home . . .

York grabs Jemmy and Fuegia, drags them out. Hannah is about to follow.

Rev Wilson Stay where you are. (*turning to the congregation*) We will now sing –

SCENE FIFTEEN

Rectory. Rev Wilson's study, where he stands waiting. At the sound of the knock, he smooths his hair, turns.

Rev Wilson Come.

Hannah enters. He looks at her coldly, holds up an envelope.

Now that Captain Fitzroy has finally managed to arrange a ship to remove the Fuegians back to their country, I have written to the Reverend Wigram at Rochester, desiring to know if there are any situations that you might do for.

Hannah I am to be sent away as well.

Rev Wilson Do you expect less? I trusted you, Hannah. Completely.

Hannah But Matthew asked me not to leave him, he was in pain, I thought it might be dangerous to move him, and Fuegia, Jemmy and York were so frightened to come back without –

Rev Wilson I left those children in your care –

Hannah Children, sir? They came with every adult faculty and sense –

Rev Wilson And you are expertly familiar with those, as you have shown the entire parish.

Hannah It is my disgrace alone, then. My part in their progress counts for nothing.

Rev Wilson You set your cap at Matthew, you have nursed most passionate feelings in secret –

Hannah I am most deeply sorry!

Silence.

Rev Wilson For what? Speak its name.

Hannah For staying in the forest. For my lack of judgement . . . (*A beat.*) For going further than was wise . . . for losing the way. (*A beat.*) With what complexion sir, did Matthew paint the event? For if I am already cast out for boldness, it matters not to deepen the offence.

Rev Wilson I blame myself. It was I who instructed your education, who fostered this wretched unseemly facility of confidence – a canker on the gentle sex. Better you had never thought of yourself as equal to him, Hannah. Now the folly of your pride must bite deep.

In an overcoat, Matthew Wilson enters.

What is this? What has happened! You have not been sent down –

Matthew No, Father, but I have come without permission, so I might yet be. Father, I was wrong to let her take all the blame, it was dishonourable, you must not punish her for what happened.

Rev Wilson You dare speak to me of what I must and must not do? Indeed I have been too liberal with you, I have been blind –

Matthew It is I who should bear all your displeasure, Father – and yours too, Hannah, I was cowardly and despicable to go back to school and leave you as the guilty party.

Rev Wilson Hannah, I forgot to make mention of your spelling abilities, in my recommendation of you to Mr Wigram. For you have certainly cast one on my son.

Matthew Father, I have thought about it, and the only decent thing to do is to marry Hannah.

Rev Wilson You did this thinking in a tavern then, I take it.

Matthew You cannot send her away. We were lost, I was injured, she stayed at my entreaty. (*A beat.*) Then we were found. That is the point of fact, Father, that is why we stayed.

Silence.

Rev Wilson You were lost. In the forest. And injured.

Matthew Yes.

Rev Wilson You stayed only to assuage my son's pain and distress.

Hannah . . . Yes.

Rev Wilson You were all fatigued . . . and frightened . . .

Matthew . . . Yes.

Silence.

Rev Wilson The Fuegians could not find their way back, knowing nothing of the forest.

Matthew No, Father.

Silence.

Rev Wilson There is room, perhaps, for some leniency. But soon enough, Hannah, you will know the consequence of your . . . comforts . . . to my son. And you will inform me at once, and we will deal with any . . . consequences as I see fit, and in a Christian manner. Is that clear?

Hannah Yes, sir.

Rev Wilson Leave us.

Hannah Yes, sir. (*to Matthew*) Thank you.

She exits. Silence.

Rev Wilson You would protect Hannah.

Matthew Yes, Father.

Rev Wilson You have risked my displeasure, and the punishment that will surely await you back at school, for your absence, to do what you consider the honourable thing.

Matthew Yes, Father.

Rev Wilson But I must have something more from you.

Matthew Ask it and I shall do it.

Rev Wilson Look not to the other side of the world, but to the continents of hearts and minds in this country, in a living which I have already secured for you, in Oxfordshire.

Matthew But Father, you know my dream.

Rev Wilson Then you should not come to bargain like a man. Perhaps your honour is not so important as your voyages with Captain Fitzroy. (*A beat.*) You will forget her soon enough, when she is gone to Rochester.

Matthew I choose honour.

Rev Wilson Above your dream?

Matthew nods. Rev Wilson slowly and deliberately tears up the letter.

Then you may accompany them as far as Plymouth.

SCENE SIXTEEN

Walthamstow, outside the Rectory, day. Autumn. Hannah stands by as the villagers and schoolchildren carry on various household articles, piling them up in the centre. She writes in a small notebook.

Hannah One dozen wine glasses . . . one large looking-glass . . . Jemmy will have to be careful with that . . . one fine-worked wooden case . . . one brocade chair . . . one canteen of cutlery . . . three quantities of white table linen . . .

Matthew enters. He seems older.

Matthew You may add one quantity of pencils, some dull algebraic equipment, a gold-tooled dictionary courtesy Dr Keat himself, a good fellow though he looks more like a pike each term . . . I am glad to see you well again, Hannah. (*A beat.*) You are fully recovered?

Hannah Yes. Thank you. (*A beat.*) Everyone has told me it was best I lost it . . . God's will, in any event. But let us not speak of it . . . please.

Matthew Forgive me.

Silence.

Hannah Thank you for your offer, in any case. Of . . . marriage.

Matthew I meant it.

Hannah But now of course you do not need to. And you are to take orders, it does not do to be married before.

Matthew No . . .

She is cut. He knows.

I go as far as Plymouth with them. Then on to the seminary. And later, a fine living near Banbury awaits me. Perhaps you will visit me there one day.

Hannah Matthew, I listened outside the door. I know of your promise.

Matthew I do not regret it, Hannah.

Hannah I do.

They become aware that Jemmy has appeared, very smartly dressed, and is watching them.

Come, Jemmy, chaperone us.

Matthew Jemmybutton, whatafellow! (*But Jemmy only smiles thinly.*)

Hannah Be cheerful, Jemmy, you wanted to go home, and now you are. Kagora said to, didn't he?

Jemmy smiles, shrugs.

Matthew But the vision –

Jemmy looks at them enigmatically, shakes his head.

Jemmy Jemmy no have woman. Jemmy no want stay, be called devil.

Hannah But you saw Kagora. So did Fuegia . . . Didn't you?

Jemmy (*shaking his head*) Jemmy Button, what a fellow . . . what a skylark . . .

Hannah You made it up?

Jemmy Hannah come with Jemmy? (*quickly*) More bad skylark . . .

Hannah Hannah Bridges no good for wife, Jemmy, only teacher.

Jemmy Hannah change mind, Hannah find Jemmy. (*Pats Matthew on the back.*) Sorry, for hurting.

Matthew I'm hale and hearty Jemmy, you have nothing to worry about.

Jemmy (*sadly*) Godislove. (*examining his shoes, frowning*) Need polish.

Hannah I saw they have given some. You will have plenty of time on the voyage.

York and Fuegia enter, also dressed smartly and warmly. Reverend Wilson with them. Hannah gives him the notebook.

The full inventory, sir.

Rev Wilson Thank you, my dear. (*Turns to the Fuegians.*)
I hope you will remember the lessons you have learned
here, and live in love of the Lord.

Fuegia/Jemmy Thank you, sir.

Rev Wilson One word, York? To let me feel I have not
failed completely? (*smiling*) My little school a laughing
stock, when I had such vanity for it . . . such hopes of
change, and doing good . . .

York Thank you.

Fuegia suddenly takes Hannah's hand, distressed.
Hannah puts her arm round her.

Fuegia Fuegia Basket take canoe, Fuegia Basket family
hide boat, Capen take us because Fuegia Basket not
tell about boat . . . Fuegia Basket kill Kagora. Fuegia
Basket bad –

Rev Wilson No no . . . Good girl, Fuegia. Jesus is proud
of you, for speaking your sin. (*A beat.*) Let us say a
prayer, before you go, Jemmy, and Fuegia, and York.
Join with us, Matthew and Hannah. (*They form a*
circle around the pile of goods.) Let us pray for the
soul of Boat Memory, your dearly departed friend and
compatriot, whose bones are committed to this land,
but whose spirit we commend to our Lord, despite his
lack of Christian baptism. Let us pray for Fuegia
Basket, who had the courage to speak of the burden
of sin on her heart, free her from pain and sin. Let us
pray for Jemmy, in his loneliness, and for York, in his
pain and anger at this time of imprisonment here with
us. Let us pray for Hannah Bridges . . . and let us pray
for my son Matthew, in his courage and honour. Let
them be rewarded with Your Love, O Lord, and walk
in your ways all their days. Send these young people
out into the world, in the glory of your name, and into
life everlasting. Amen.

All Amen.

SCENE SEVENTEEN

Plymouth docks, winter, day. The Fuegians stand shivering on the quay. With them are Matthew Wilson and Captain Fitzroy, who looks impatiently at his fob watch.

Fitzroy If he is not here by noon we will miss the tide – but we shall sail without him in that case. Ah – is that him? Come along, sir, let not this timekeeping be a fixed trait, we shall not do well if so.

A young man loaded with boxes, a suitcase and a gun case, hurries up to them. He shakes hands vigorously with Captain Fitzroy.

Young Man A merry Christmas to you, sir! I am heartily sorry for my timekeeping, Captain, but oh what a fine shoot it has been since Boxing Day, and the suppers stretching on into the night, what wines and brandies and talk – of course, all were agog to hear of your plans and we quite wore through the atlas, tracing the route! Are you fond of pheasant, sir, let us hope so, for I have brought us two brace to see us on our way. I have all the equipment I need and books for our entertainments, I have pencils, watercolours, paper and suchlike – but no cards, do not fear, for I have been told –

Fitzroy Enough, sir! Let me introduce to you our three returning specimens, Miss Fuegia Basket . . .

Fuegia (*curtseying, smiling*) Good day to you, sir.

Fitzroy Master Jemmy Button . . .

Jemmy (*elegant bow*) Charmed.

Fitzroy And Mr York Minster.

York inclines his head, very much as Fitzroy does.

Oh, and of course, my young friend here, Mr Matthew
   Wilson, who has most ably assisted in their care during
   their time here. Mr Matthew Wilson – Mr Charles
   Darwin, sportsman and gentleman, just down from
   Cambridge.
Matthew Pleased to meet you.
Darwin (*not really interested in him*) The pleasure is
   mine.
Matthew Of that I have no doubt.

Fitzroy pats him awkwardly.

Fitzroy Matthew wished to come in your stead, Mr
   Darwin, but is now to be a man of the cloth.
Darwin Why then, become a missionary and see the
   world! (*turning away*) Captain, I am most anxious to
   meet our vessel's artist, Mr Augustus Earle, I hear he is
   the most particular colourist, perhaps he may be
   prevailed upon to sketch some creatures for me?
   (*going up the gangplank*) It came to me that a dragnet
   would be the very thing, with your permission,
   Captain, and of course space permitting – I have
   brought with me a prodigious array of bottles but of
   course – (*He disappears into the ship.*) – space being
   what it is –

Fitzroy turns to the Fuegians.

Fitzroy It is time.

*The Fuegians turn to Matthew. They embrace him in
turn, Jemmy last. From his jacket, York produces the
mask he has carved. Matthew takes it.*

Matthew Thank you.

*York takes him by the shoulders, claps him hard in
salute. Matthew copies him. Bows. Then York leads
Fuegia and Jemmy up the gangplank. Matthew holds*

*the mask to his face as they disappear into the depths
of the ship. They do not look back.*

SCENE EIGHTEEN

Aboard the Beagle, *mid-ocean, day. Brilliant sunshine.
Fitzroy looks through a telescope, Darwin sketches.
Nearby, the Fuegians, in elegant formal summer clothes.*

Fitzroy What strange cloud is this? Mr Darwin, here is
something different for you.

> *Darwin jumps up, takes the telescope from him.
> Behind him, the Fuegians quietly take his crayons, turn
> their backs to all.*

Darwin It seems to be shimmering . . . it is coming
towards us, is it not, but it is so low . . . could it be
butterflies?

Fitzroy Have you been drinking, sir? It must be nearly a
mile wide. There are not so many butterflies in all
creation.

Darwin And yet it looks like nothing so much as that.

Fitzroy (*taking the telescope back*) We shall know soon
enough, for we are on a collision course with it.

> *Matthew and Hannah appear, on either side of the
> space, in separate worlds.*

Matthew Dear Hannah, all excuse for interchange
between us is now lost, so I will write but once, to tell
you that our friends have got under way, and have
vanished over the horizon. I met the fellow who takes
the berth I so wanted, most bumptious in his good
fortune, as no doubt I should have been. He claims he
is a naturalist. (*A beat.*) I have discovered I can be
bitter. I must be close to manhood.

Hannah Dear Matthew, a visitor from the Missionary
Society informed me of a need for Christian teachers in
New Zealand . . . I have been invited to London for an
interview, and have given your father my notice in any
event.

Darwin Sir, it *is* a cloud of butterflies!

Matthew I will amuse myself imagining York and Fuegia
setting up home in some exquisite wilderness, and our
good Jemmy setting up example of how to be a
London dandy . . .

Hannah There is an emptiness here now. / I think
perhaps I grew to love them.

Matthew / They gave me a wonderful mask. One day
I would like you to see it.

Fitzroy Call for Augustus Earle! He must capture this in
ink at once!

Darwin I see the markings – a gold cross on the white of
the upper quadrant, they are heraldic!

Matthew Take care where you recite your poetry . . .

Hannah I shall write to you again, if I get to New
Zealand.

Fitzroy They are almost upon us . . .

*Behind them, the Fuegians begin tearing off their
clothes. Underneath, their bodies are painted with
tribal markings.*

Matthew Your affectionate friend always, Matthew
Wilson.

Hannah Yours most truly, Hannah Bridges.

The Fuegians mark their faces with dirt.

Darwin Here they come –

Fitzroy We shall be consumed by Nature!

*As the butterflies swarm the ship, the Fuegians walk
forward, strike themselves on the chest:*

York Not York Minster: El'leparu.
Jemmy Not Jemmy Button: O-rundelico.
Fuegia Not Fuegia Basket: Yok-cushly.

They hold up their arms.

Fuegians *Yamana!*

Lights slowly down, leaving the Fuegians, and then only Mr Darwin, his telescope still to his eye, illuminated to the last.

Darwin And now . . . they melt away like snow.

End.

An Alien Abduction as a Footnote to History

Laline Paull interviewed by Jim Mulligan

Some years ago a footnote to Charles Darwin's *The Voyage of the Beagle* caught Laline Paull's eye. Three young people were being returned from England to Tierra del Fuego. Why? Why were they in England? What happened to them? Research could answer some of the questions, Laline Paull's imagination did the rest.

In 1830 Captain Fitzroy sailed to chart the shores of South America. He had four skiffs on board – essential equipment for him, but also priceless to the tribes, who were completely dependent on the sea for survival. When one of these boats was stolen the success of the expedition was threatened, and Fitzroy kidnapped four young people, in the belief that the tribe would exchange the boat for the prisoners. Sadly, the boat appears to have been more valuable to the tribe than the children, so Captain Fitzroy had no option but to bring them back to England.

> These four kids were abducted onto a ship that was to them what a spaceship would be to us. They were taken to a culture where there were vehicles and animals they'd never seen before, and statues made of stone that looked as if they could leap out and eat them. I thought: this is science fiction set in the past.

Captain Fitzroy was committed to the young people and was devastated when one of them, Boat Memory, died. He entrusted the three survivors to one of the most progressive priests of the period, Reverend Wilson – by contemporary standards a bigoted snob, but enlightened for his time, and eager to educate the Fuegians in his school at Walthamstow, the first-ever Church of England school.

The Church of St Mary and the school are still there in
Walthamstow. You can go there and walk in the foot-
steps of the characters in the play. You can sit in the
same pews, and when I went there to research the play
I saw the baptism of an Indian child. The congregation
was completely multiracial, and I thought how
incredible: it's less than two hundred years after the
events in the play, and now the Fuegians would fit into
this community without any difficulty.

The play starts as the Walthamstow children are waiting
to 'greet' the strangers in the language familiar to asylum-
seekers today. They abuse the visitors and are only
stopped when the Fuegians are baptised. There is, it
appears, something to be said for enforced baptism.

It's probably relevant to the story that I'm Indian and
grew up in London, where my family and I experienced
racism. Growing up was a struggle and I identified
with these kids. But I also see it from the other side,
and I can see that people can be very frightened by
people and cultures they don't understand. But things
are changing. The more I travel, the more I realise
what a compassionate country this is.

Hannah, Laline Paull's invention, is an orphan of the
parish who, as an intelligent girl, is making the best of
herself in the only way available to her. At the age of
fifteen, she has become the governess and housekeeper in
the Reverend Wilson's household. His wife is dead and
he is probably unaware of his feelings for Hannah and
his jealousy that he may be usurped in Hannah's regard
by his son. The Fuegians do not need to be told of the
undercurrents. They are aware. They have no sexual guilt
or sexual manners. The Reverend is the most powerful
member of the tribe, so why should Hannah not want him?
In one scene, Fuegia turns all the power of her young

female sexuality on the Reverend and, uncomfortable and alarmed, he exits hurriedly.

This is the point when the experiment fails spectacularly. York Minster fights Jemmy Button for possession of Fuegia Basket, and Matthew and Hannah sleep together in the forest. The consequence of these relationships is that Hannah is banished by Reverend Wilson, and the Fuegians become dangerous influences.

> Jemmy is intelligent enough to know he has been left without a woman. He has been cut out. He cannot have Fuegia Basket and he cannot have an English woman. His only hope is to return home, and so he has a vision in which Jesus tells him that he must go home. Whether or not he sees a real vision is up to each production.

The return voyage is hastily arranged, with Matthew's place taken by Charles Darwin (the scientist who wrote *The Voyage of the Beagle* and *The Origin of Species*, books which transformed the way people think about the Bible's account of creation). Once on board, the Fuegians can reject what they have used only in order to survive, and they cast off their English names and their clothes.

> At the end I wanted to empower them. Clothes are like chains to them, and by rejecting clothes they are rejecting everything that has been imposed on them. And they reclaim their true Yamana names. I feel glad that these dead children at a distance of a hundred and seventy years can say their true names and we can remember them.

So how did the young people fare? As far as we know, their return led indirectly to the destruction of the tribe. There are now no longer any full-blooded Yamana people left and the language is dead. We know nothing about

York Minster, but Fuegia went on to become a fat, toothless old woman who liked to show off about her time in England. Jemmy Basket was a celebrity, and later notorious when ten years later he was implicated in the murder of a missionary.

I'd be proud to see young people put this play on. It could be interesting to do it with reverse casting – the Fuegians white and everyone else black or mixed race. That would say everything. All the issues would be so much clearer. And it could be very empowering for kids who have experienced racism or alienation or rejection to see they are standing at the front of a long line of people who have endured something similar, despite the years between them.

Production Notes

Boat Memory has five main teenage characters (the three Fuegians: two older boys and a younger girl; and the two Walthamstow lovers); two principal male adults; a supporting male adult; and assorted schoolchildren and villagers who can double if required. It's unnecessary to cast the Fuegians with actors of a different nationality from the others: the differences in culture will be evident in the playing of the piece.

Laline Paull was intrigued by the question of whether or not the Fuegians survived psychologically. Why they went back to Tierra Del Fuego was a mystery, but the knowledge that Walthamstow was then little more than a pretty village, disconnected from London, led her to speculate about how such a community might have been offended by their behaviour.

While evolution, gender and race are certainly themes in the play, Laline Paull has approached the story without the intention of tackling 'issues'. She describes *Boat Memory* as 'an alien abduction story set in the past' – an interesting way of viewing the play to bring out its visual possibilities, and a good overall key to unlocking the problems of its staging.

Less is more when it comes to staging. Lighting and sound are far more important than scenery. The more versatile the set the better. Use floor space and different levels of rostra, as well as exits which will allow a large number of the to enter as speedily as possible. It's important that the changing status of the Fuegians is shown in their costumes, also for them to be body-painted at the end when they discard their western clothing. Costume is a good way of signalling the progress of a character's status, and for illustrating shifts not specifically pointed out in the story. In Scene Eight, there is a potentially dramatic contrast between Hannah's dowdy clothes and the dazzling ones worn by Fuegia Basket, which reinforces our sense of her growth.

York Minster is an outsider trying to resist the 'neck-upwards' model pre-Victorian society wants to force him into. He's not influenced by verbal reasoning, and wears a mask as an animal act of defiance – it's consciously meant as a symbol of power. The markings associated with the concluding butterflies, with their evolutionary overtones, might be a design influence.

NOTES ON THE CHARACTERS

- The FUEGIANS have been traumatised by their experiences, but there is a strong bond between them. They probably haven't been brutalised on the ship, but they have been confined on it for three whole months. They may not be immediately aggressive, but there are frustrations beneath the surface.

- The English characters should not be judged by a too modern standard. In particular, the success of the play depends to an extent on whether REV WILSON is seen as being sympathetic. Though his actions might seem unreasonable, Wilson's view of Hannah as his 'surrogate wife' after being widowed was gradual and inevitable, and his consequent anger understandable. His hopes to advance his own 'missionary' status are ruined when the Fuegians gain notoriety. Added to this is his sense of being inferior to FITZROY, whose formality seems to be the result of higher status and natural superiority. There is a minor power struggle going on in the dialogue between Wilson and Fitzroy, stemming from Wilson's desire to better the other. Fitzroy's paying for the Fuegians is a mark of his higher status, something felt by Wilson.

- The English characters' sexuality exists 'from the neck upwards', and the Fuegians 'from the neck down'. Yet the realisation of their own feelings is just as unexpected and violent for the English characters. Wilson has assumed that Hannah is his, but in his head he hasn't really considered his feelings towards her. There is a moment in Scene Eleven when Fuegia Basket's sexuality dawns on Wilson. He is then confronted by Hannah, and there is a sense that his own repressed feelings (of which Hannah is unaware) are confusedly rising to the surface. The primitive jealousy he feels when he gains knowledge of Hannah and Matthew's attraction is behind his decision to dismiss Hannah unless Matthew takes holy orders.

- HANNAH and MATTHEW's 'professional' relationship, replacing a probable former friendliness, influences their attitudes towards each other in Scene One. Added to this is the possibility that the gap between them has widened, following Matthew's time at public school while Hannah has remained a servant – a position in which she might face disrespect from the others. With regard to the later scenes, especially Scene Nine, the conflict is between Hannah and Matthew's need for one another, on the one hand, and Hannah's intense pride and Matthew's youthful thoughtlessness on the other. Matthew's decision in Scene Sixteen to take holy orders and prevent Hannah's dismissal is an important shift towards maturity for his character. By this time, the sense of romance felt by Hannah has gone, and she too matures as the play progresses.

- There is a bond quite early on (Scenes Three–Four), between FUEGIA BASKET and Hannah, and a sense that Fuegia is usurping Hannah in Scene Eight – though not consciously, as she still views Hannah with a sense of wonder. In Scene Four, Fuegia's linguistic advance begins to create an uneasy tension between the three Fuegians.

- JEMMY's growing need to claw back respect within the tribe is based on a sense that his manhood will be decided by the fight. This is why its effects on him are so devastating. His vision in Scene Fourteen is real – a result of seeing the cross (which he may well feel to be a sign of oppression) so soon after his distress. There might well be an element of manipulation – part of a desperate idea to get them sent home.

- The Fuegians are probably playing up to the English linguistically in Scene Eight. In Scene Eleven, Hannah's dismissal of the Fuegians suggests that they are aware of the sexual tension between her and Matthew, and that Hannah is aware of their knowledge.

- The Fuegians are attempting to inhabit the language with lines such as 'me briny bastards'. Private talk between the Fuegians might be more stylised. Collectively, the Fuegians function on a more visual, intensely observant level, especially at the beginning.

- FUEGIA feels both anxiety and arousal at the level of attention paid to her by York Minster. In Scene Eleven there is a sense that she is increasingly confident, and ready to become a viable partner for the head of the tribe. This might be emphasised by putting her in the dominant position in her coupling with York Minster.

- YORK MINSTER's behaviour is one of simmering aggression, particularly in Scene Five – but it is only at the end that he assumes dominance. His growing stature should be built with subtlety

- The citizens of Walthamstow become gradually more mob-like, or Fuegian-seeming.

- The atmosphere of the piece changes in the final third of the action. This is because very little time has elapsed – perhaps two months. This partly explains why Hannah and Matthew have difficulty resolving their feelings for each other – they are swept away by uncontrollable emotions and events. There is no set moment where the romance between them dies, or when sex between them becomes inevitable.

EXERCISES

Here's a warm-up exercise which Phyllida Lloyd led at the Keswick retreat that developed into a practical exploration of the script. It was originated by Jacques LeCoq, based on the idea that all energy in theatre and life can be divided into seven levels – namely:

1   POND LIFE Imagine yourself as amoeba or frog-spawn. Explore the sound of how you feel as these things.

2   COOL COWBOY Coming out of the amoeba stage, this stage involves a spacy feeling without tension – no resistance to anyone who might push you. Some words might rise to the surface.

3   STAGE MANAGEMENT This stage involves direct, assertive actions, meeting people in the eye and generally maximising body potential.

4   TODDLER This level should have a '*Teletubby* dimension'. The feeling is of being a toddler in a playground in which it's hard to sustain any level of concentration

for long. This level is full of brightness, an atmosphere of surprise, and of staccato, fractured movement.

5 This level is linked to the last, but here the stakes are much higher, and there is a strong objective of alerting someone to something. However, the music of this level is very off-centre – it's as if everyone has had the idea of organising a surprise party, but knows that there isn't enough time to organise it.

6 EMERGENCY Actions in this level should create complete pandemonium, and it should feel as if there is a house on fire.

7 MELTDOWN This, the climactic level, is basically a gargantuan intake of breath. Everybody needs to focus an immense thought and breath which then leads to 'meltdown'.

This process led to a staging of an early scene, with the three Fuegians staying at Level Three throughout. Around them the crowd enters at Level Four, reverts to a zombie-like Level Two, and then to Level Three when Rev Wilson enters. This gave a sense of how the different levels of action in the piece might be brought out, as well as of its fluctuating rhythms and dream-like moments; it also created a sense of the potential tension within the scene and a consideration of when this tension should be broken. There was also much experimenting with how the action would appear when performed in-the-round.

Look at the staging of Scene Two: sit the Fuegians in a circle with their backs to one another. Performing the piece this way might help the audience to feel implicated, and prevent the scene from being too private, enabling the other characters to talk over the children's heads. The actors playing the Fuegians in Keswick felt genuinely unnerved, as they couldn't tell from which direction speech was coming, enhancing the feeling that the Fuegians were 'under glass'.

Try a similar approach in staging Scene Seven in order to make the audience feel its 'three realities' – of Wilson, Fitzroy and the Fuegians. Wilson's words are the bedrock of this scene – but while his words are an anchor for the shifts within, it's not necessary to see his face. After experimenting with having him turn his face away from the audience, bring it to the back of the auditorium in order to play with the idea of turning the audience into the congregation. From this position, Wilson's lines should feel more energetic and involving. The individual stories should seem more pronounced, and the links between them – such as Wilson's words about Jesus coinciding with Fitzroy's words about the 'club' – should be given a clearer importance.

In staging Scene Five, focus on how Professor Donovan's actions make an audience feel. He might move from child to child to emphasise the arrogance he embodies. Bringing the actors into the audience will intensify both the feeling that they are specimens on display and that the audience are implicated in their predicament.

Experiment with having the audience in-the-round here. This could create a circus atmosphere, with Fitzroy parading Fuegia Basket and Jeremy Button round as if they were horses being trained.

Explore the audience's fear of York Minster, with the Professor treating him as a 'tiger in a chair'. There is a suggestion in the text that Donovan is too scared to approach York Minster.

When staging Scene Thirteen, emphasis should be placed on Matthew: the events are his immediate reality, while for others they not presently occurring. Place Matthew in a strong position on stage so that it's clear he's at the heart of the scene.

The other characters might be isolated or clustered in groups – York Minster and Jeremy Button perhaps mirrored by Hannah and Fuegia Basket in different couplings (though without quite making eye-contact). The protagonists' reactions to being verbally attacked in this scene might be defensive and guilty. Matthew's 'no gentleman' comment was originally meant to refer to himself, but might equally include his father. The space should always be balanced, and the scene might run effectively with different characters moving off when attacked. Hannah and Mathew might be left alone on stage.

In Scene Fourteen explore how the congregation might feel contaminated by the Fuegians. When Jeremy Button experiences his vision, the congregation's intensity level should move from Level Three to the pandemonium of Level Six. While in actual staging his action wouldn't be realistic, it could help as a way into seeing how a sense of hysteria is released without actually resorting to the literal enactment of the feeling.

Explore the escalating tensions, passions and unspoken power struggles of the characters in as bold a way as possible – especially in the moments where the protagonists' repressed passions are most obvious. Don't be put off by the 'alien' qualities of the Fuegians or the less easily sympathetic English protagonists, but find a way into the complications of all the characters in order to express what is both conflicting and universal about their personalities and cultures.

HISTORICAL AND PRONUNCIATION NOTES

Events Darwin mentioning the return of the Fuegians, and the knowledge that Fitzroy was forced to take the children home, is where the story began. It is known that the children visited a phrenologist at the time depicted, and that they visited royalty and became celebrities. Why they returned to Tierra del Fuego is unknown, but since the visit to the Royal Family was in July and the departure probably in September, there is a sense that something dramatic happened in the meantime to give offence in Walthamstow.

The Beagle Fitzroy's ship. For the return voyage, Fitzroy, because of a history of mental instability in his family, wanted a a gentleman of his own class to accompany him. Charles Darwin was a late recommendation.

King William and Queen Adelaide The reigning British monarchs, who are visited by the Fuegians. The action takes place in a decade which is post-Georgian and pre-Victorian (without its own label).

Kagora Means 'sacrifice' in Yamana language.

Yamana Dominant tribe.

Acaluf 'Lesser' branch of Yamana tribe.

Ongaia Fight.

Tagum Signal to begin fighting.

York Minster So named because of his impressive build.

Jemmy Button Named after his early interest in clothes on the voyage.

Fuegia Basket Connotations of tribal women's interest in basket-weaving.

Fuegia Pronounced 'Fway-jeer'.

Boat Memory Fitzroy's favourite Fuegian: the fourth of the group, who died on arrival in Plymouth.

Song of Songs Book of the Old Testament which celebrates the pleasures of the flesh.

Manatee Acquatic mammal..

Jarvey Hansom carriage.

based on a workshop led by Phyllida Lloyd
transcribed by Paul Williams

DEAD END

Letizia Russo

translated by Luca Scarlini
in collaboration with Aleks Sierz and Lia Ghilardi

Para o Pedro Miguel
A Gianluigi

Characters

Sirius, eighteen, boy

Spyrus, eighteen, boy

Kent, eighteen, boy

Kris, seventeen, boy

Reiko, seventeen, girl

Nimar, sixteen, boy

Laura, sixteen, girl

Audrey, sixteen, girl

Doris, fifteen, girl

Kim, seventeen, girl

Sirius, Spyrus, Kent
aged eleven

*The actor who plays Spyrus aged eleven
also plays Kent aged eleven.*

ONE

Spyrus and Sirius, aged eleven. Sirius is standing in the middle of the stage. He's lost. After a minute, Spyrus arrives. In one hand, he holds a ball. With the other, he steadies a black sack, which looks rather heavy and is carried on his shoulder.

Spyrus What are you doing?
Sirius Don't know.
Spyrus Want to play?
Sirius Play?
Spyrus With the ball.

Silence.

What are you doing here?
Sirius Don't know.
Spyrus Don't you want to play?

Silence.

Bye, huh.

He turns to go.

Sirius What's this?
Spyrus What?
Sirius This, where we are now.
Spyrus It's a hill.
Sirius We could live on a hill.
Spyrus If you like, yes.
Sirius Why don't you kneel?
Spyrus Where?
Sirius In front of me.

Spyrus Why should I, who are you?
Sirius (*slight pause*) Don't know.
Spyrus Then why should I kneel?
Sirius I was hoping you'd recognise me.
Spyrus Well, I don't.
Sirius I remember somebody told me that people must
kneel before me.
Spyrus Who said that?
Sirius Don't know.
Spyrus What's your name?

Silence.

Sirius What does play actually mean?
Spyrus I throw the ball to you and you throw it back.

*He throws the ball and it falls at Sirius's feet. Sirius
sees the ball and kneels down. Grabs it. Looks at it.*

Now you have to throw it back.

Sirius walks to Spyrus and gives it to him.

Spyrus No, not like that . . .
Sirius (*disappointed*) Playing is stupid. (*He sits down.*)
Where are we now?
Spyrus On a hill.
Sirius I'll come and live on this hill. (*Slight pause.*) What
have you got in your bag?
Spyrus My dog.
Sirius Is that where he lives?
Spyrus He's dead. I'm going to bury him. And, after that,
I'm going to play.
Sirius What do you mean: he's dead?
Spyrus You have to put him in the ground – and don't
call him any more. That's what they told me. (*Pause.*)
Sirius What's your name?
Spyrus Spyrus.
Sirius And the dog. What's his name?

Spyrus Sirius. (*Pause.*)
Sirius Give me a name as well.
Spyrus A name?
Sirius Yes. Want to live on this hill? Give me a name and teach me to do things. So that I will be able to remember.

Pause.

Spyrus If it's okay by you, I'll call you Sirius.
Sirius Good. Now teach me.

As the lights fade, Spyrus puts the ball on the ground and kicks it lightly. The ball rolls up to Sirius's feet but he doesn't move. Spyrus teaches him. Sirius is very awkward.

Black.

TWO

Kris and Kent. They have arranged to meet.

Kris You made it.
Kent Sorry.
Kris Three-quarters of an hour late.
Kent Sorry.
Kris We've missed the bus.
Kent (*touches his pockets*) Sure you gave me my ticket?

Kris stares at him. Silence.

Kris The next bus is due in a month's time.
Kent Never mind. A joint, and the time will soon pass.
Kris We'll have to walk.
Kent To walk? But it's far.
Kris How far?
Kent Don't know.

Kris Listen, how did you get here?

Kent Don't know. I just followed the road.

Kris Which road?

Kent (*looks around and points*) That one.

Kris Are you sure?

Kent Yes, I think so. (*Pause.*)

Kris How did it go?

Kent What?

Kris At school.

Kent Oh. I failed.

Kris You too?

Kent You too?

Kris Yes, but I knew I would.

Kent Don't you like school?

Kris The teachers are bitches.

Kent Yours too? Mine are real slags.

Kris I think they fail you at the end of the term if you break one rule.

Kent A rule?

Kris Huh?

Kent Like?

Kris Like if your breath doesn't stink of fish, chips and onion, and your spots don't ooze plutonium and you don't play with yourself while reading *Pickwick Papers*, they fail you.

Kent In that case, I should have passed.

Kris Your breath stinks?

Kent No. I play with myself while reading *Pickwick Papers*.

Silence.

Kris Oh, I've seen those comics. Japanese comics – nurses with big tits.

Kent No, not those. That book, by what's-his-name – Dickens. I got bored of my dad's porno mags; the girls in them, they had pointed tits.

Kris Maybe they're all dead by now.

Kent Exactly. So I get the first book on the shelf. By what's-his-name. Dickens. I go to the toilet. So I'm there, quietly working, without any hurry. Then, suddenly, crash: the door opens.

Kris Your mum.

Kent My mum. I get such a fright, I finish immediately. Mum screams. She grabs the book from my hands. Then she goes all quiet. She looks at it, and just goes out again.

Kris And then?

Kent Then she goes to my dad and says: 'I knew he was more my son than yours. Look – he's an intellectual.'

Kris Cool.

Pause.

Anyway, my name's Kris.

Kent And I'm Kent.

Kris Mmmh.

Kent What do you think? Shall we walk?

Kris Okay. I'm not going back to school.

Kent I have to go back. Because of Dickens and all that. I don't want to admit I'm not an intellectual.

Kris It's just that you don't want to upset them.

Kent That's right, but in any case we have two months off.

Kris Okay.

Kent So – (*Looks around.*) That way.

They leave. Black.

THREE

Sirius and Spyrus, aged eleven, on the hill. Not much time has passed since Scene One. On the ground, there's a large package, which clearly contains a chair.

Sirius I don't remember.

Spyrus Come on. I told you loads of times.

Sirius Arm.

Spyrus (*corrects him*) Lover. What's the opposite of lover?

Sirius Cat.

Spyrus Lover! Lover! Mum is the opposite of lover! Cat is the opposite of dog.

Sirius What's the opposite of arm?

Spyrus Leg.

Sirius How many things have I now learnt?

Spyrus Very few.

Sirius But I'm good at kicking babies.

Spyrus Ball. I told you: the word is ball.

Sirius I keep making mistakes with mustard!

Spyrus Words! They're called words.

Sirius Here, where I live, it's a hill.

Spyrus Good.

Sirius At least I remember that.

Spyrus (*gets something to eat from the bag and gives it to him*) Here.

Sirius What's this?

Spyrus Something to eat. I told you the name.

Sirius Yes, it's true. (*Pause.*) I like willy.

Spyrus What?

Sirius I said: I like willy.

Spyrus Bread, it's called bread. Willy is what you've got between your legs.

Sirius (*drops a crumb between his legs*) Got it. When it's big, it's bread, and when it's little, it's a willy.

Spyrus You haven't understood a thing.
Sirius (*becomes sad*) Tell me, who am I?
Spyrus Don't know.
Sirius Because I don't remember.
Spyrus Don't know.
Sirius I feel good on this hill, but I'd like to know who I am.
Spyrus I can only teach you the things I know. You'll have to remember the rest yourself.
Sirius Why can't I remember who I am?
Spyrus Don't know.

Slight pause.

Sirius How did I get here?
Spyrus Don't know.
Sirius Sure you can't help me?
Spyrus No.

Slight pause.

Sirius I think I'll have to find another moron.
Spyrus Teacher.
Sirius No, I really mean moron.
Spyrus Thanks a lot.

Slight pause.

Sirius How's your dog?
Spyrus My dog is dead.
Sirius And you won't see him any more?
Spyrus No.
Sirius And where's he gone?
Spyrus Deep in the ground.
Sirius You don't want to make love with him any more; that's why you put him in the ground.
Spyrus To play, to play with him – to make love is something else. But it's not that. One day, he lay on his side, closed his eyes and my parents told me he was

dead. But I don't know the difference between a dead dog and one that just closes his eyes and sleeps.

Sirius What do you think? Will I remember who I am one day?

Spyrus Why do you want to? As soon as you say your real name, they'll send you back to school. Better not. Better to live like this. Or, if you like, we can swap – I'll go instead of you.

Sirius Thing is, I remember. Somebody once told me that people must kneel before me. (*Slight pause. He turns to the chair.*) What's this?

Spyrus Something for you.

Sirius For me?

Spyrus Yes.

Sirius What is it?

Spyrus Open it.

Sirius goes to the chair, unwraps it, holding the wrapping paper in his hands. He doesn't look at the chair; he's only interested in the paper.

Sirius Beautiful; what's it for?

Spyrus Look, that's just the wrapping paper; the thing is inside.

Sirius Ah. (*Looks at it.*) What is it?

Spyrus A chair.

Sirius What for?

Spyrus To sit on.

Sirius (*embarrassed because he doesn't like it*) Beautiful . . . (*Shows him the paper.*) But can I keep this?

Black.

FOUR

*The same hill. Years later. The chair is still there and
Sirius is still sitting on it. But now he's a leader: he's
different from the forgetful kid he was; sometimes he's
positively domineering. He mistreats even Spyrus, who
has never left him and is always near his side. The rest
of the group are Nimar, a boy of sixteen; Reiko, a girl of
seventeen; Laura, a girl of sixteen, who is devoted to
building a pile or heap of discarded things; and Audrey
and Doris, sixteen and fifteen, who are alter egos of each
other. The group has rituals, during which Sirius
officiates. They are many types of rite and now it's time
for the 'party rite'. At one side of the stage is a switched-
off TV and on the other a little heap of rubbish created
by Laura. They are all in a row and sleepy, except Sirius.*

Sirius Come on!

*Spyrus takes several silly party toys from a sack and
gives them to the others: little hats, toy trumpets and
other things. Laura hurries over to see if something is
left in the sack. She shakes out dust and receipts.*

Now, is everybody happy?
Kim Absolutely.
Sirius I've come up with another surprise party and you
just sit there as if it was a funeral.
Kim It's five in the morning.
Sirius So?
Nimar Yesterday we took turns to lick your shoes until
three . . .
Sirius Exactly: You behaved well and that's why I've
organised a party. Anything wrong?
All No, no . . .
Nimar I was happy just licking your shoes. It was enough.

Sirius (*stops distributing gifts*) Two tits to him.

Spyrus Not tits, trumpets!

Sirius It's the same. Give him two.

Nimar Thank you; you're so kind. (*Slight pause.*) I love you.

Sirius Are you happy?

Nimar I'm always happy. (*Pause.*) I love you.

Sirius (*looking at him intently*) Me too.

Reiko Doris, Audrey: what happened to you?

Doris *and* **Audrey** What?

Reiko I'm watching you so . . .

Doris So?

Reiko So.

Doris So?

Reiko I never realised you had so many split ends and so much cellulite! I'm sorry, but I can see it through your trousers.

Kim Some people have it on their bums and some people on their heads.

Reiko On the head? Is that serious?

Nimar No, it just means you have an extra bum. That way, you can fart from two places – and you don't have to think either.

Reiko Isn't that bad for your health?

Nimar How are you? Are you feeling alright?

Laura goes on looking for objects.

Reiko Yes.

Nimar So, everything's alright then.

Reiko (*doubtful*) Are you taking the piss?

Nimar From which hole?

Everybody laughs, including Reiko. Their jokes are never nasty.

Come here.

He hugs her. They laugh.

Reiko Would you like to have two bums?
Nimar Yes, I would – and I bet you'd love to have one as firm as mine.
Sirius (*interrupts them*) So, where's the music?

> *Spyrus goes to switch on the TV. They sit down in a circle with hats and trumpets – only Sirius sitting down where he is; the others presenting their backs to him. But the TV programme is boring.*

Reiko (*in a low voice*) Who's got the dope?
Kim (*in a low voice*) I have. (*She produces hash, rolling papers, filters, cocaine bags, carefully making sure that Sirius can't see.*) I found them near my house.
Reiko (*in a low voice*) Who do you think leaves this stuff there?

> *Laura arrives; she sees the things on the ground and tries to pick them up. The two friends send her away, making sure that Sirius can't hear them.*

Kim (*in a low voice*) Don't know; and don't care.
Sirius Is everybody happy?
All (*tired*) Yeeesss!
Sirius I don't hear the trumpets.

> *They all play the trumpets.*

I don't see you waving your hats.

> *They all play the trumpets and wave their little hats. Pause.*

Laura Can we watch something else?
Sirius What?
Laura Something else, on the telly.
Sirius What do you want to watch?
Laura Something in colour. Something nobody watches – you know.

Sirius goes up to the TV. Kim and Reiko hide all the dope. Sirius changes channels, chooses a very well-known music television programme.

All Ooohhh . . .

They start enjoying themselves. Somebody dances, somebody talks, Laura collects things. Spyrus, who has been silent until now, approaches Sirius.

Sirius Everyone's having fun, aren't they?
Spyrus We started early.
Sirius What's the problem – you sleepy?
Spyrus No.
Sirius So?
Spyrus Nothing.

Nimar approaches.

Nimar (*to Sirius*) May I lick your shoes?
Sirius You did that yesterday.
Nimar Only once.
Sirius I . . .
Nimar Please.
Sirius Fine. (*Offers him the toe of a shoe.*)
Nimar No.
Sirius Changed your mind?
Nimar No.
Spyrus Well?
Nimar I want the sole.
Sirius I stood in pit the other day . . .
Spyrus You mean you trod in shit.
Sirius (*corrects himself*) I trod in shit and don't know if it's still on my shoe.
Nimar If it's yours, I don't mind.
Sirius It was dog shit.
Nimar Give me the other shoe, that'll do.

Sirius lifts the other foot. Nimar licks. Sirius withdraws the foot.

Sirius Happy?
Nimar Only once?
Sirius Only once.
Nimar Another time.
Sirius No.
Nimar Please.
Sirius I'm only letting you do it because it's party time.
Nimar (*licks slowly, enjoying all of it*) Thanks . . .
Sirius Now go. (*He pats him on the head.*) Go . . .
Nimar (*almost crying*) Thanks . . . (*Goes away.*)
Spyrus He loves you.
Sirius Everybody loves me.
Spyrus Yes, but with him . . .
Sirius You know, she's (*meaning Reiko*) the chosen virgin.
Spyrus Virgin . . .
Sirius She's a virgin. I know for sure.
Spyrus No, you don't.
Sirius I know all, I see all.
Spyrus I know.
Sirius I'm omnivorous.
Spyrus Omniscient . . .
Sirius Same thing. In any case she's the chosen virgin – so explain that to Nimar. It's not possible . . .
Spyrus Maybe it's better if you tell him.

Laura comes.

Laura Don't you have anything for me today?
Sirius What have you done for me?
Laura (*gets something like a Buddhist rosary out of her pocket*) Yesterday I said five prayers.
Sirius Five, really?
Laura I couldn't sleep.

Sirius You pray so you can fall sleep?

Laura No . . . I was scared.

Sirius Of what?

Laura Don't know.

Sirius And when you pray, you feel better?

Laura Yes, because I know you know all and see all –

Sirius I'm omnivorous –

Spyrus Omniscient –

Laura – and if we get into trouble, you'll rescue us.

Sirius Of course.

Laura So, do you have something for me?

Sirius (*puts a hand in his pocket and takes out a handkerchief*) Have this.

Laura Is it yours?

Sirius Yes.

Laura Have you used it?

Sirius Yes.

Laura Thank you. I don't need much more stuff to finish the heap. (*Slight pause.*) If one day I say ten prayers, will you give me something pointed? All the tallest things are pointed. I need something pointed.

Sirius But you have to say ten prayers without stopping.

Laura Yes.

Sirius Fine, now go. (*He pats her head.*) Go . . .

Laura leaves.

She loves me too.

Spyrus Everybody loves you.

Sirius I am all-knowing, all-powerful. Though I didn't think I could do it. I thought nobody would pay me any attention. But when I told them who I am, they didn't laugh, not even for a second.

Spyrus Why should they laugh?

Sirius Don't know. I thought things were different.

Spyrus It's not so bad.

Sirius See you.

Spyrus Bye.

Sirius exits. Spyrus goes to the others, who are innocently enjoying themselves. As soon as Sirius has left, the kids get the dope out and start frantically misbehaving.

Black.

FIVE

Kris and Kent have obviously been travelling for a while. They're tired; they're having a rest. Kris is exhausted.

Kris Trust me: if I was born an animal I'd kill myself.

Kent Why?

Kris All this effort. For a rat – (*He has a rat in his hand and lifts it up.*) – and four berries. Listen: hooray for vivisection!

Kent But we aren't trained.

Kris No, rats ain't what they used to be. And why a rat?

Kent Apparently it's nutritious.

Kris Right, with all the shit it eats in the sewer; we'll get E-coli.

Kent You told me it's nutritious.

Kris You'd better learn for yourself: don't listen to me.

Kent Ah.

Kris And how do we eat it?

Kent We have to light a fire.

Kris I can't.

Kent Me neither.

Pause.

Kris (*looks at his hand*) It's bitten me.

Kent You're lucky it wasn't a woman.

Kris Why?

Kent They trap you like that. A bite and you're gone. My dad has a theory.

Kris Eh?

Kent There's a female being for each man. Like a punishment. The first time it happens, it's with your mum, who, when you're a baby, bites you and gives you the curse of the female spirit, and this female spirit stays with you, and is then part of all the women you have. First love. The first you have. Then your wife. You think there are many, but there's only one – and she was born to suck your brain from your ears.

Kris Really?

Kent My dad's theory.

Kris Just one bite?

Kent When you're too little to protect yourself.

Kris And you believe it?

Kent Yes, and I don't let them trap me. Never enter the 'wife' zone. The most important thing is to avoid the last zone.

Kris And?

Kent And you stay free; my dad only got it when it was too late.

Kris Poor man.

Kent But I can tell you, he always puts up a fight.

Kris How come?

Kent Porno. (*Makes a gesture to indicate masturbation.*) The last rampart of freedom.

Kris You know – you're really wise. But sometimes I think about love. (*Pause.*) You scare me, but I like your dad.

Kent I'm just waiting for him to die.

Kris Mine is always so quiet, too quiet.

Kent Sometimes that's a blessing.

Kris Sometimes, yes. Many times, even. (*Long pause.*)

Kent How long have we been travelling?

Kris Three weeks; how much is there still to go?

Kent Not much. I remember the road.

Kris Really? I've never travelled before.

Kent Me neither.

Kris But you came to town.

Kent But I was alone.

Kris Why did you come here?

Kent I simply went forward.

Kris While you were alone?

Kent I don't want to talk about it.

Kris Please tell me: why are we going there?

Kent I told you: to see a friend.

Kris Couldn't he meet us halfway?

Kent He doesn't know I'm coming.

Kris What's his name?

Kent Dunno.

Pause. They look at each other.

Kris Where are we going?

Kent To the place I was born.

Kris And why do I have to come with you?

Kent So I have somebody to talk to.

Kris Listen: I'm tired.

Kent Me too.

Kris Do you have a mock driver's licence?

Kent I've got this; a policeman gave it to me when I was in primary school. (*He shows his wallet.*) Look, the picture; I was chubby then . . .

Kris Listen.

Kent Eh?

Kris You a junkie?

Kent No, why?

Kris I was thinking . . .

Kent No, no. (*Pause.*) Something wrong?

Kris It's just that you're strange.

Kent Me?

Kris Yes.

Kent Sorry.

Kris I think you can't help it.

Kent No, I'm really sorry.

Kris No worries; what are you going to do when you get there?

Kent Meet a friend of mine.

Kris Don't you want to tell me?

Kent No.

Kris Don't you trust me?

Kent It's not that.

Kris What's the reason then?

Kent It's a long story.

Kris We have time.

Kent It's a long story and I don't want to tell you.

Kris Okay, but if I find out there's some trick, you'll pay dearly.

Kent No trick.

Kris No problem.

Kent Some day, maybe I'll tell you.

Kris All the same to me. Sorry, I shouldn't have asked.

Kent No worries.

Kris Now I'm a bit tired.

Kent Me too.

Kris I'm not even hungry. I'm a bit tired.

Kent takes the rat and throws it away. Gets the berries from Kris's hands and does the same. He covers him with the care of a true friend and starts to sleep.

Black.

SIX

The next scene should be played on two separate parts of the stage. Nimar is alone and speaks as if Sirius is in front of him. Meanwhile, Reiko and Spyrus are in bed, having just finished making love.

Nimar I always tell you I like you. But I don't know if
you understand me. Sure, you're omniscient and so
you know it all, though I like it more when you say
you're omnivorous, and I don't like Spyrus always
correcting you. I must say: that guy's a yes-man.
Yesterday you made me lick your shoe. How
wonderful: you don't let everybody do that. But I'm
not sure whether it's because you love me or because
you pity me. But then again, you being perfect, maybe
you pity all of us. I don't know if I like you pitying me
more than anybody else.

Spyrus There's nothing I can do. That right?

Reiko I never said I wanted to stay with you.

Spyrus I thought we didn't need to say anything.

Reiko You were wrong.

Spyrus I hope you're happy now.

Reiko I'm always happy. I don't need you.

Spyrus I knew it.

Reiko If you're so intuitive, why are you talking so much
bollocks?

Spyrus You were chasing me.

Reiko What's that got to do with anything?

Spyrus I thought you liked me.

Reiko I do.

Spyrus Before, when we were shagging, you yawned.

Reiko (*laughs*) I'm sorry . . .

Nimar I accept that you pity me. I accept everything. But
when I think of you, I'd like to stay with you. I can
take it or leave it. I can do it or I can do something to
annoy you. Because, till now, when I thought of that,
I held back the thought and then I was able to silence
it. But now it's like I can't help it any more. When I see
you, I feel as if I've got a serious illness. And at that
point I don't know any more if I can do it or not. I
don't know if you even see me. They say you see all

and know all. They say you're everywhere. So, you're also here. But if you're here, why do I miss you?

Reiko (*enthusiastically*) Really?

Spyrus He told me.

Reiko When?

Spyrus Yesterday.

Reiko So I'm –

Spyrus Shut up! He mustn't know, you know.

Reiko (*laughs*) I can't believe it . . .

Spyrus He told me.

Reiko And when's he going to tell *me*?

Spyrus Don't know. I didn't ask.

Reiko I knew it!

Spyrus You knew it.

Reiko Do you remember the story?

Spyrus Which one?

Reiko Don't you remember? The king comes home, and there are ten virgins: five with their lamps lit and five with their lamps out. The king arrives, and he has the five virgins with the lamps lit.

Spyrus What does that mean?

Reiko Destiny: I always sleep with the light switched on.

Nimar The thing is: I can't forget you. I can't. I look around, but, you know, perfect people like you are very few. Maybe I'm sick because I'm in love with somebody who's perfect. Because I'm in love with somebody we know will never betray us. That's sickness. Because the other times I was in love, I always knew it was going to end. First a time for love and then I'd be back even more alone than before. But with you everything seems endless and I don't like it. I let you pity me, I let you pity me more than the others. I dream about your skin when you let me lick the sole of your shoe. But when I think there's no escape, I feel sick.

Reiko When did he tell you?

Spyrus Yesterday, after the party. That's the fourth time you've asked.

Reiko And how did he tell you?

Spyrus (*loses his temper*) He told me: 'That girl, she has a lovely bum, maybe I'll have her.'

Reiko I knew he always loved me, always.

Spyrus Oh yeah?

Reiko In any case, don't start.

Spyrus I'm not.

Reiko Did I lie to you?

Spyrus No.

Reiko Did I ever say I wanted to be with you?

Spyrus No.

Reiko Did I say I loved you?

Spyrus No.

Reiko Did I ever say I'm sick when you're not around?

Spyrus No.

Reiko Did I ever say I think of you?

Spyrus No.

Reiko We shag and I yawn – what did you expect?

Spyrus I thought maybe you could change.

Reiko You were wrong.

Nimar Maybe the next time, during confession, I'll tell you. I'll explain to you without letting on that I'm talking about you; so I can find out what you think.

Spyrus You were chasing me.

Reiko You know why? I was dumped by my other boyfriend.

Spyrus So what?

Reiko It's a law of nature. If they cheat on you, you need to cheat twice on somebody else.

Spyrus Very nice.

Reiko At least I didn't lie.

Spyrus You could've stayed on your own. You didn't have to chase me.

Reiko Whatever. Who cares? I'm the chosen woman.

Spyrus So they say.

Reiko Moron!

Spyrus Thanks.

Reiko Why did you tell me?

Spyrus Because I knew it would make you happy.

Reiko You really are a moron! (*Pause.*) You know?

Spyrus What?

Reiko Next time, during confession, I'll ask him.

Spyrus Are you crazy?

Reiko I'll ask him if it's me, but I won't let on that I'm talking about me.

Nimar I'll ask you and you'll give me a yes or a no. You tell me if I can or can't. If I can at least think of you and me together. And tell me if you really know everything or not.

Spyrus And when you marry, what do you want to be: the housewife on the hill?

Reiko I don't . . .

Nimar If you're God, you have to answer me.

Reiko If he's really God, he'll make me happy.

Black.

SEVEN

Sirius, aged eleven, is sitting on the hillside, but not on the chair. Around him is a hecatomb of small dead animals. He is cutting off the heads of living animals. Spyrus comes; he looks at him for a while. He begins to go away, but then stops. He bends down, collecting the small dead animals.

Spyrus What are you doing here?

Sirius I've understood.

Spyrus Why aren't you on your hill?

Sirius I escaped, but I'll be back very soon. I've remembered.
Spyrus What?
Sirius Who I am. (*He's happy, laughs.*)
Spyrus And who are you?
Sirius I am God.
Spyrus Who told you that?
Sirius I remembered it.
Spyrus How did you do that?
Sirius It was Death. I learnt it from Death.
Spyrus You can resurrect the dead?
Sirius No, the dead are dead for ever. I can't help it.
Spyrus But you said you're God.
Sirius I'm God because I'm Death's master. I can call Death whenever I like. (*He indicates around him.*) As you can see.
Spyrus Is that what it means to be God?
Sirius That and no more. And when you believe in me, you can't escape. Do you believe in me?

Spyrus is silent.

Do you believe in *me*?
Spyrus Yes. (*He kneels down.*)

Black.

EIGHT

The group is together again. Everybody is there, except Sirius, who hasn't arrived yet. Spyrus is far from the group. He lies on the ground, hand under his head, smoking a cigarette. The TV is switched on: a music channel. All of them are doing different drugs. Laura goes around collecting things that she thinks are there, but are not. Her heap has really grown: it looks almost finished.

Reiko I see elves.

Kim Where?

Reiko Here. In front of me; I see elves.

Kim It's true, with red hoods.

Reiko No, they're green.

Laura (*more bewildered than the others*) All these things . . . (*She collects and puts them on her heap.*)

Doris *and* **Audrey** He'll be here soon.

Laura All these things. Something pointed, I need something pointed.

Kim Who's coming?

Doris *and* **Audrey** Him.

Kim Sirius.

Reiko I don't care.

Kim You know he doesn't approve.

Reiko Of what?

Nimar The dope. He doesn't like it.

Reiko Okay, we won't give him any.

Nimar You know he gets angry.

Reiko By the time he comes, we'll be fine.

Kim I don't understand why he's so bothered.

Nimar Don't know.

Doris *and* **Audrey** It's simply because he loves us.

Kim Do you think he really sees us?

Reiko In what sense?

Kim I mean, when we are here doing this.

Nimar I always ask myself the same question, not only about this, but also about other things.

Reiko In the end, it's not important.

Kim Apparently, he loves us anyway.

Doris *and* **Audrey** He's nice.

Kim And if you ask him in the right way, he'll always gives you things.

Reiko He never says no.

Nimar And then those caresses.

Reiko I feel guilty.

Nimar Me too.

Kim I feel guilty, but I don't want to stop.

Doris *and* **Audrey** If he sees us when we're like this . . .

They look at Reiko's face. They laugh.

Look at her face . . .

Reiko What's wrong with my face?

Nimar Please, don't look, it's awful!

Kim Shut up.

Reiko Thanks – at least you stand up for me.

Kim Simply because you're unable to.

Reiko I'm a wise virgin.

Slight pause. They all laugh.

Spyrus . . . don't laugh, don't say anything.

Spyrus turns onto his other side.

Kim What's the matter with him?

Reiko I know. (*She laughs.*)

Spyrus You bitch.

Reiko So? What's the matter with you?

Spyrus I don't care. I'll find another girl.

At that moment Laura arrives. Spyrus looks at her.

Or maybe I'll stay by myself; maybe that's better. (*He lights another cigarette.*)

Reiko Didn't think you'd take it so badly.

Spyrus Your problem is simple: you can't think and move at the same time. And because you're always moving . . .

Reiko Taking the piss?

Spyrus No, it's true.

Reiko I thought you were just being a moron. Come on, I know we're friends anyway.

Spyrus If you say so . . . (*He turns onto his other side, completely withdrawn.*)

Kim They have red hoods.
Nimar Who?
Kim The elves.

Sirius enters. Everybody suddenly gathers round.

Sirius What are you all doing? Fine. Never mind. Now come here. Get in line.

They are all in a row, including Spyrus, who is completely absentminded. Nimar is the last. Sirius takes off his belt.

Last night I couldn't sleep. I have to take it out on somebody. (*He whips them.*)
Reiko Good start this is! But if he thinks he's going to carry on like this after the wedding, he's very much mistaken.
Kim He barely touched me.
Laura That whipping was for me.
Kim Aren't you glad I saved you?
Doris *and* **Audrey** It's not fair.
Kim What?
Doris *and* **Audrey** Him whipping us.
Reiko Pretty soon, he won't be whipping me again.
Laura Are you about to die?
Reiko Shut up! (*Crosses her fingers.*)
Doris *and* **Audrey** Not fair.
Kim Shut up, he might hear you.
Reiko He beats us for ages.
Doris *and* **Audrey** Exactly.
Laura It hurts.
Reiko Come on!
Laura Yes, it really hurts.
Kim Do you think things are better in other places?
Doris *and* **Audrey** What places?
Kim Dunno. I've never been.

Doris *and* **Audrey** It's not fair and that's all. He can't whip us like this.

They don't realise they are in front of Sirius. Sirius stops them and looks at them.

Sirius Come here.
Doris *and* **Audrey** I . . .
Sirius Here.
Doris *and* **Audrey** I . . . (*Pause.*)
Sirius Don't you dare say that again.
Doris *and* **Audrey** Please whip us harder.
Sirius (*laughs*) I'm no savage. (*always laughing*) To insult God is a crime.

He whips them many times.

I'm no savage.

He stops whipping them. The two girls are going away.

You ought to thank me for not punishing you for what you've said. Instead, I forgive you. Next.

While Nimar talks, Sirius whips the others, who then get back in line quietly.

Nimar If you like, you can whip only me.
Sirius Why?
Nimar Because I like it.
Sirius For me you're all the same, I can't do you any favours. It's too much.
Nimar For you, there's no difference.
Sirius You said it.
Nimar Please.
Sirius No.
Nimar Please.
Sirius No.
Nimar At least whip me twice.

Sirius And what do I tell the others?
Nimar Tell them you really hate me.
Sirius I'll whip you how I like. In any case, you have to join the queue again. It's your turn.

Nimar comes in front of Sirius. Sirius whips him firmly. Nimar behaves as if he is experiencing a rapid climax.

Nimar Ah, ah, aahh . . .

Pause. Everybody stares at him. He feels embarrassed.

Ehm . . . Aahh . . . It really hurts . . .

Pause. The queue starts again. Sirius whips everybody until he has no more energy. Nimar continues to feel pleasure, but doesn't make any more noise.

Sirius (*exhausted*) Fine. I feel better now. How do you say it?
All What?
Sirius How do you say it?

Silence.

I'll start again.
All (*except Nimar*) No . . .
Nimar (*at the same time*) Yes . . .
Sirius So, how do you say it? Spyrus, tell them.
Spyrus What? If I don't know what you want to say, how can I tell you the word?
Sirius What's the matter with you?
Spyrus Nothing.
Sirius Did I hurt you?
Spyrus Not with the belt.
Sirius So what's up? You coot?
Spyrus The word is depressed.
Sirius So what?
Spyrus Nothing.

Sirius (*slight pause*) Fine. It wasn't that difficult; you
  only had to say thanks.
All (*as schoolchildren*) Thank you.
Sirius I have decided that today is self-abuse day.
Nimar (*happy*) Yippee!

  Everybody looks at him. Silence.

Spyrus He means confession day.
Sirius Exactly, that's it.
Nimar I want to come first.
Sirius Fine.

  The others leave.

  Black.

NINE

Kris and Kent. Even more exhausted.

Kent Very quiet.
Kris What?
Kent I remember this place.
Kris You remember it?
Kent Yes.
Kris Obviously. It's the third time we've been here.
Kent You reckon?
Kris I think so.
Kent I didn't think we'd been here that often.
Kris (*turns his back to Kent*) Please!
Kent What?
Kris Scratch my back!
Kent Where?
Kris There. More to the right. Put your hand inside.

  Kent puts his hand inside.

More to the right. More to the middle. Up there. Yeess.
   Good. Aahhh. Thank you.

Kent No problem (*Between his fingers is a big insect he's
   removed from Kris's back. He throws it away.*)

Kris What was that?

Kent An antibody.

Kris Good for you. You know, you're brilliant at
   scratching.

Kent My dad taught me. You know, the girls and all
   that.

Kris Yes, I thought so. (*Pause.*) I'm stopping here.

Kent Today, we didn't even have a rat.

Kris The fourth time we pass here, we'll get a prize doll.

Kent Really?

Kris (*looks at him, falls to the ground*) I'm stopping here.

Kent When did we start this trip?

Kris Almost a month ago. (*Slight pause.*) Oh.

Kent (*softly*) Eh.

Kris (*more loudly*) Oh.

Kent (*even more loudly*) Eh.

Kris (*loudly*) Know what?

Kent What?

Kris You stink.

Kent I stink.

Kris You stink.

Kent I 'stink'.

Kris You. Stink. (*Slight pause.*)

Kent You too.

Kris But you stink more.

Kent Really?

Kris Really. (*Slight pause.*) Know what?

Kent What?

Kris Your bum and your breath smell the same.

Kent I'll have a bath at the next river. (*Slight pause.*)

Kris Oh.

Kent Eh.

Kris (*louder*) Oh.
Kent Eh.
Kris Know what?
Kent What?

He gets a cigarette end and lights it. From now on they smoke in turn.

Kris I don't know why you asked me to come with you.
Kent Because the other guy I asked said no.
Kris Ah. (*Silence.*) Oh.
Kent Eh.
Kris Oh. Know what?
Kent What?
Kris I didn't know you'd asked somebody else.
Kent Nothing to be ashamed of.
Kris No, no. (*Pause.*) Oh.
Kent Eh.
Kris Oh.
Kent Eh.
Kris Know what?
Kent What?
Kris Don't know which class you're in at school.
Kent A.
Kris Oh. (*Pause as before.*) Oh.
Kent Eh.
Kris A. Oh.
Kent Eh.
Kris Know what?
Kent What?
Kris I don't know how old your sister is.
Kent Twenty-four.
Kris Ah. (*Pause.*) Now I know you better. (*Pause.*) Oh.
Kent (*this time he shouts immediately*) EH?!
Kris Who is this guy we're looking for?
Kent Friend of mine, I told you.
Kris What's his name?

Kent Don't know.

Kris And why do you want to meet him again?

Kent No particular reason. (*Slight pause.*)

Kris If you don't want to tell me . . .

Kent No. Now I can tell you. I was eleven. I was born in the place where we're going to and I stayed there eleven years. But one day, when I was eleven, something happened. I forgot who I was. I couldn't remember any more. I stayed outside the town. I stayed on a hill. With a railway nearby. It wasn't used any more when I was there. I wasn't alone on the hill, there was him, my friend, the one we're going to meet. We played. We had a lot of laughs. And then I don't remember anything at all. I know I fell down. I always kept my eyes open. I never closed them. But I don't remember. The only thing I remember is him looking at me, with blood on him. He was looking at me as if I was dead. I had my eyes open, but I couldn't speak. I was half-dead, but I felt better than him. I wanted to say something, but I couldn't. I don't know how long we stared at each other. Then he escaped. He shouted. He shouted so loudly and he was so scary, he looked almost happy. I stayed there for a while, then I left.

Kris And then you remembered who you were?

Kent Yes.

Kris And you came to this place?

Kent Yes.

Kris And why do you want to meet him again?

Kent (*sarcastically*) Because he might've killed himself out of sorrow.

Kris But was it him who harmed you?

Kent No, we were friends.

Kris Is it far?

Kent No, we'll get there tomorrow.

Black.

TEN

As the lights of the previous scene fade, Sirius, aged eleven, appears – he's visibly nervous.

Sirius How did you get here?
Kent I walked.
Sirius This hill is mine.
Kent Mine too.
Sirius Go away.
Kent I want to play here.
Sirius I'm the only one who can play here. Me and my mate.
Kent What are you going to do about it?
Sirius I . . .
Kent You can't do anything, you don't even know who you are. But I know who you are – and who I am.
Sirius And who are you?
Kent Some day I'll be back.
Sirius No, you won't.
Kent Yes, I will.
Sirius This hill is mine.
Kent Mine too.

> *Sirius attacks him. Kent laughs at first, but then he's overwhelmed by Sirius's fury. He falls down but doesn't close his eyes. He looks dead, but Sirius continues to attack him ferociously. Then he tires. He stops. Looks at him. Kent's eyes are wide open and observe him, but Sirius is sure Kent is dead. He puts his hands on his head: at last he remembers who he is. He runs around the stage for some moments. He's in high spirits, he shouts with joy, while Kent lies still on the ground. At last Sirius arrives in another place. He starts collecting small living creatures: flowers, plants, little animals. He sits down with open legs like a child*

*playing 'normally'. He starts tearing apart the things
he's collected. Around him is a hecatomb. On the
other side of the stage, Kent is in a pale light and starts
to wake up. Slowly he stands up. He cleans himself.
He smiles. And turns into Spyrus, aged eleven, by
changing his clothes. He approaches Sirius, who is still
killing everything.*

Spyrus What are you doing?
Sirius I've understood.
Spyrus Why aren't you on your hill?
Sirius I escaped, but I'll be back very soon. I've remembered.
Spyrus What?
Sirius Who I am.
Spyrus And who are you?
Sirius (*he's happy, he laughs*) I am God.

Black.

ELEVEN

*Starts where Scene Six ends. Sirius sits on his chair.
Nimar is kneeling in front of him.*

Sirius Fine. Repent.
Nimar Of what?
Sirius I don't know, *you* have to tell me.
Nimar Honest, I didn't do anything wrong.
Sirius So, what do you have to say?
Nimar I have a problem.
Sirius Tell me.
Nimar I love you.
Sirius Me too.
Nimar You say it in a funny way . . .
Sirius The way of him who loves you all.

Nimar Can't we stay together?

Sirius More together than now . . .

Nimar I know you're God and God isn't gay . . .

Sirius Repent.

Nimar Of what?

Sirius Repent and the rest will come.

Nimar Did you ever think of marrying?

Sirius There's a chosen virgin. She waited for me with the light switched on.

Nimar Virgin? So it's a woman.

Sirius Reiko.

Nimar (*freezes, now knowing for certain that he doesn't have any hope*) That's too bad.

Sirius For whom?

Nimar For you and for me. I thought you and me were more friends than the others.

Sirius It's true, I only listen to you. By the way, do you have something to say?

Nimar (*flies into a rage*) She's not a virgin. She's a bitch.

Sirius She's virgin where it matters.

Nimar How do you know?

Sirius I know all, I see all.

Nimar So it's all over?

Sirius Nothing started, so nothing can end.

Nimar I hate you.

Sirius God doesn't mind.

Nimar goes out.

Next.

Reiko comes in.

Hi.

Reiko Hi.

Sirius So.

Reiko I have a question for you. Who has more power: God or the telly?

Sirius God.

Reiko So, if God wants to, he could find everybody a job in TV?

Sirius If he wanted to, yes.

Reiko (*happy*) That's good enough for me.

Sirius Now, you know I only listen to you. You're the only one I trust. Is there something you can tell me about the others?

Reiko (*looks around, in a low voice*) The dope. It's Kim. That's all.

Sirius Mmmh. Very well. Anything else?

Reiko No.

Sirius Fine, you can go.

Reiko leaves. Kim arrives.

Hi.

Kim Hi.

Black.

TWELVE

Kris and Kent in front of the gates of the town of Sirius. They look astonished at the entrance to the town because it's very big. Throughout the scene they walk around while looking upwards.

Kent This thing wasn't here when I went away. It wasn't.

Kris They built it recently.

Kent Yes, but it looks ancient.

Kris It's really big.

Kent Yes. (*Pause.*)

Kris We made it.

Kent Yes, we're here. (*Without looking at him, he puts a hand on his shoulder.*) Anyway, thank you.

Kris (*embarrassed*) Don't mention it.

Kent So, shall we go in?
Kris Yes.
Kent I've come to get back what is mine.

Suddenly, Kent is very aggressive. Kris looks at him, amused and questioning. They go in.

Black.

THIRTEEN

Starts where Scene Eleven ends.

Kim Hi.
Sirius (*looks at his watch*) Now. I know you're a good girl. I bet you've got nothing to confess.
Kim That's true. How did you know?
Sirius I see all and I know all. Now, you know I only listen to you. You're the only one I trust.
Kim Doris and Audrey. They say bad things about you.
Sirius Really?
Kim Yes, they say it's not true that you see all and know all.
Sirius Really?
Kim Really.
Sirius Fine, you can go.
Kim Bye.
Sirius Bye.

Kim leaves. Audrey and Doris arrive.

Are you two always together?
Doris *and* **Audrey** Yes.
Sirius This morning, you knew you had to come here. So, why didn't you change your knickers?
Doris *and* **Audrey** (*embarrassed*) We . . . we were late.
Sirius I know all and I see all. Repent.

Doris *and* **Audrey** (*really embarrassed*) We repent . . .

Sirius Repent!

Doris *and* **Audrey** We repent.

Sirius Repent!!

Doris *and* **Audrey** We repent!

Sirius Repent!!

Doris *and* **Audrey** Okay, we got it – we repent.

Sirius Just making sure.

Doris *and* **Audrey** Okay, okay . . .

Sirius Now, you know I only listen to you. Because you're the only ones I trust, I have to be sure you repent. What do you have to say?

Doris *and* **Audrey** Spyrus.

Sirius What's the matter with him?

Doris *and* **Audrey** He had a bad dream.

Sirius What did he dream?

Doris *and* **Audrey** There was an awful wave. And we were in the middle of the beach and a big wave carried everybody away. Then, after being underwater for a while, he comes out and sees that you're the only one on the beach – and you're smiling at him. What does it mean?

Sirius Mmmmhhhh.

Doris *and* **Audrey** It's a bad thing.

Sirius Very seductive.

Doris *and* **Audrey** Very worrying.

Sirius No problem. (*Slight pause.*) Fine, off you go. Who still hasn't come?

Doris *and* **Audrey** Laura and Spyrus.

Sirius Tell Laura to come.

As Doris and Audrey go off they nod to Laura, who goes to Sirius.

Sirius Laura, this is for you. (*From the back of the chair he picks up a Christmas tree star.*) You can go, darling. Do you have anything to say?

Laura No . . .

Sirius Good girl. We'll talk another time. Anyway, you know you're the only one I trust. You're the only one, I only listen to you.

Laura Yes. Yes.

Sirius gives her the star.

Thanks . . . With this I can finish my heap . . . Thank you! Thank you!!

She's touched and goes to the heap and finishes it off with the star. It's a rather sad scene. Sirius nods to Spyrus, and Spyrus comes nearer.

Sirius How are you?

Spyrus Okay.

Sirius What's the matter?

Spyrus I didn't sleep.

Sirius But you did have a dream.

Spyrus is silent.

I know all and I see all. The dream doesn't mean anything. I'm here to protect you.

Spyrus I don't give a piss about the dream.

Sirius So, what's the matter?

Spyrus You've taken her away from me, haven't you?

Sirius Who?

Spyrus The chosen virgin.

Sirius It's been decided. Today I'll make an announcement.

Spyrus Nothing else to say. (*He stands up*).

Sirius What are you doing?

Spyrus Nothing else to say.

Sirius But our talk –

Spyrus Not today.

Sirius But you know you're the only one I trust.

Spyrus I should think so. It's me who brought you up. Me who taught you things.

Sirius That's why you're the only one I trust.
Spyrus But today I have nothing to say.
Sirius Don't be angry.
Spyrus I'm not angry.
Sirius You're my best friend, even if I am God and you're not.
Spyrus (*after a pause*) You're mine too.

They embrace. Spyrus leaves. Sirius stands up.

Today I have an announcement to make. An announcement which will make everybody happy. An announcement followed by an entire week of parties.

Reiko starts to tremble.

The announcement I have to make is serious. The announcement deals with me and also deals with somebody else. The announcement is this: your God, Sirius, never born and never dead, living on this hill from the night of Creation, has decided to marry.

Reiko is almost hysterical.

Only one of the women on the hill will be my bride.
I have carefully chosen her from one hundred maidens.
My bride will be happy and I'll be happy with her.
We'll be happy – and her name is –

Kris and Kent break in. Sirius freezes. Everybody looks at them.

Reiko Bollocks! Who are they? And why now?
Kent Hi.

They are all silent.

(*sarcastically*) I see you've taught them good manners.
Sirius Say hello to him.
All Hello.
Kris He's your friend?

Kent Yes.

Spyrus (*to Sirius*) Who's he?

Sirius Don't know.

Kent Now, you that see all and know all, how are you?

Sirius Who are you?

Kent I told you that one day I would be back.

Sirius feels uneasy.

Kris But is it the custom here to say hello in this way? No kiss on the cheek? Listen, I get that girl with the dark hair, okay?

Kent (*completely indifferent*) Shut up, moron.

He pushes him and he crashes into the others.

Kris Moron yourself. What're you doing?

Kent attacks him, using a death blow which may be physical or supernatural. Kris falls down. Long pause.

Kent (*to Sirius*) I told you that one day I would be back.

Kris (*in feeble voice*) What have you done?

Kent I've killed you.

Kris Why?

Kent I had to set an example.

Kris What have you done?

Kent I've come back to get what's mine.

Kris You've killed me, but why?

Kent We travelled together, I needed someone to talk to – but now I don't need you any more.

Kris What? Just like that – suddenly?

Kent Did you want to know in advance? To be told by post?

Kris I . . .

Kent I did you a favour. You're not suffering.

Kris But why?

Kent I told you.

Kris Couldn't you have chosen somebody else?

Kent The other guy said no – I told you that already.
Kris I didn't expect it.
Kent Nobody ever expects it, but this is how it is.

Pause. Kris breathes faster. He dies.

Sirius I don't know you.
Kent Are you sure? You killed me when I was eleven. On the hill near the dead-end railway track.
Sirius So you're dead?
Kent You thought I was, but I wasn't. Afterwards, I got up and went away. Now I'm here to get back my hill.
Sirius Why?
Kent Because *I'm* God . . .

Disorder in the group.

Spyrus (*to Sirius*) Who is he?
Sirius Don't know . . .
Kent I'll tell you. Me, who knows all and sees all. Some years ago, he was on this hill. He didn't remember who he was. But I always knew. Who he was and who I was. We saw each other on the hill. We struggled for the hill. He pushed me to the ground. He was sure he'd killed me. But no, you're not the real God. The real God kills – and you failed to kill me.
Spyrus I brought him up; I taught him all the words.
Sirius Yes, he bought me to walk.
Spyrus Taught me to talk.
Sirius Same thing. In any case, you know me. You know I'm God. You know it and so does everyone here.
Spyrus (*the only one to answer*) Yes . . .
Kent (*goes to Sirius's chair, gets out a sack*) Do you know what's inside? Your souls.

He empties the sack, and all the souls fall out.

Reiko What's that?
Kim Bollocks.

Nimar Our souls.
Spyrus Sirius.
Sirius I . . .
Spyrus Sirius.
Sirius I . . .
Kent Tell him – now.
Spyrus Sirius.
Kent Tell him.
Sirius I . . . (*Pause.*) It's true.

All except Spyrus – who is petrified – go with Kent.

What did you expect? That you could decide? That I
could be God and not want anything in return? I gave
you everything you wanted. I gave it to you. Did you
think it was you who invented the world? Did you
think you could do things in secret? Well, you couldn't;
I gave you everything. I trusted each of you. I gave you
the world you wanted to have. Without surprises. But
I needed something back. I didn't steal anything from
you. I let you stay there and believe that all the decisions
were yours. But actually it was me. Now, you are
perfectly happy. You enjoy obeying orders. You like it.
It's what you like most. To obey orders and pretend
you're free and different from the others. To give your
souls in return is not too high a price. (*Pause.*)
Kent (*sees Laura's heap and goes near to it*) What's this?
Laura (*ashamed*) It's mine.
Kent And your God let you keep all this shit here? (*He
destroys Laura's heap.*)
Laura (*in despair*) No!!

*She kneels down to collect everything and especially
the star. The group understands that Kent is not joking
and that he's violent.*

Reiko (*to Kent*) You're the only one who can make me
happy.

Kent Of course.

Spyrus It can't be done.

Kim What?

Nimar He cheated us, and you most of all!

Laura What do we do now?

Doris *and* **Audrey** What do we do now?

Spyrus Fight.

Kent Me and Sirius.

Spyrus Yes.

Doris *and* **Audrey** Not bad.

Reiko I have a list of things I want, and that you have to give me. So, do what you want.

Nimar He cheated us. I thought he loved me, but look . . .

Spyrus Wait, maybe he's a con artist too.

Doris *and* **Audrey** But he's really cool. Look: he's all dressed in black.

Kim He's got beautiful eyes.

Laura He destroyed my heap . . .

Nimar Your heap was shit. He did well, we needed some order.

Spyrus It can't be done.

Kim What?

Spyrus I brought him up. I taught him words. It can't end like this.

Nimar How else?

Spyrus Make them fight.

Doris *and* **Audrey** Only if they take their clothes off. I like this kind of thing.

Kim Look, Sirius is a failed God. Look, he's sweating.

Spyrus Let them fight, and if the other one isn't God . . .

Nimar Can't you see how much more beautiful . . .

Laura He destroyed my heap . . .

Reiko I don't care either way. In any case, I have my list in my pocket. One or the other – it really doesn't matter.

Spyrus Start the fight.

Sirius I'm God, why do you deny me?

Kim We're not denying you . . .

Nimar It's an ordeal.

Doris *and* **Audrey** If you're God, you'll win.

Kim We believe in you.

Reiko But you must fight.

Nimar I haven't bet on anything for ages.

Reiko Who do you want to win?

Nimar You're daft. The other one, obviously.

Laura He destroyed my heap.

Kim I'd love him just for doing that.

Sirius Why are you denying me?

Kent You aren't God. They can't deny you.

Spyrus Fight!

Sirius You should have believed in me for ever. So why should we fight now?

Spyrus I taught you to talk. I taught you everything. Now trust me. Fight him.

Sirius You don't believe in me any more.

All Fight!

Laura He destroyed my heap . . .

Kent (*shouts*) Come on!

> *Sirius and Kent fight. The fight is rather hard, but it's not a struggle between gods. They are rather ridiculous. Sirius is absolutely unequal to the task. At one point, Kent gets out his secret weapon, a laser sword. As he whirls it about, it makes an electronic noise. Then he uses it simply as a baton, hitting Sirius on the head and easily knocking him down. Sirius is on the ground. Kent puts a foot on his head.*

Spyrus I brought you up. I believed you when you told me you were God. Now, what do we do?

Sirius (*his face crushed by Kent's foot*) I am God.

Kent No, now I'm God. I told you I'd be back – sooner or later.

Sirius I'm God.
Nimar You're a moron! And to think I loved you! (*He spits at him.*)

In turn, all the others, except Spyrus, spit at him. At each spit he repeats:

Sirius I'm God. I'm God. I'm God. I'm God.

He tries to get up. Shouts, manages to grab Kent's legs, but Kent hits him. Every time he's hit he looks as if he's dead.

I'm God.

Kent hits him. Pause. Is he dead? Everybody looks at him. He tries again with a very feeble voice.

I'm Go–d.

Kent hits him again. As before.

I'm Go–d.

Kent takes off a shoe and throws it at him.

I'm Go–d.

Kent gets a stone and throws it at him.

Go–d.

Kent gets the chair and hits him with it.

Go–d.

Kent uses the laser sword. As before.

Go–d.

Kent gets out a gun and shoots him.

Go–. (*This time he dies.*)
Kent At last. Good morning, everybody, I'm your new God.

Nimar What, just like that?

Kim I thought God would need more time to die – and need less time to kill a man.

Reiko Now, on my list . . .

Doris *and* **Audrey** Are your eyes really so blue, or do you wear lenses?

Reiko Let me just say, on my list. I'm the next bride . . .

Laura He destroyed my heap . . .

Kent (*to Laura*) Don't be angry. From now on, things will be different . . .

Nimar How different?

Kent Just as before. We Gods are all the same. Now I get a sackful of your souls. At least I'm honest. At least I don't pretend.

All (*whispering*) What do we have to do . . . Don't know . . . Is it true? . . . I loved him . . . The list says . . . But I could love you . . . Don't be angry . . . My heap . . . What do we do . . .

Nimar That's okay, but you have to let us do everything he let us do.

Kent We'll talk about that later.

Takes off his belt.

Now. Repent.

He whips them. Nimar has a climax.

Nimar Aah . . . I love you.

Reiko But didn't you love Sirius?

Nimar Yes, but you have to look ahead . . . Life goes on . . . He would have wanted me to be happy.

Kent goes on whipping them and leads them away. Spyrus alone, in front of Sirius's corpse, decides to hang himself with Sirius's belt. He slowly gets up on Sirius's chair. Lights fade, but not completely.

FOURTEEN

Spyrus and Sirius, aged eleven, on one side of the stage.
On the other side, the corpses of Kris, Sirius and Spyrus.
Sirius is on the hill, bewildered. Spyrus comes with a ball
and a black sack in his hands.

Spyrus What are you doing?
Sirius Don't know.
Spyrus Want to play?
Sirius Play?
Spyrus With the ball.

  Silence.

What are you doing here?
Sirius Don't know.

  Silence. Black.

  End.

The Violence of Power

Letizia Russo interviewed by Jim Mulligan

Letizia Russo, born in 1980, is the youngest writer to have been commissioned by *Connections*. She wrote her first award-winning play when she was seventeen years old, not thinking she would become a writer but for a competition and in order to add points for her final school report. She has now written four plays, won three prestigious Italian awards and been commissioned to write three novels.

Dead End is a complex, surreal allegory that involves young people aged first about eleven, then at about seventeen. It is a play of ideas, and deals with such themes as the nature of power, violence, the corrosive effect of religion on society, the nature of God, and love between young people.

> I don't think my play is so complex. I simply observe young people, write what I know of them and try to get a meaning from my observations. If the play is complex it is because young people are complex. To have a complex eye on reality means not to simplify the different aspects of reality.

The action starts with two scenes on a hill where two boys aged eleven meet. There is only the present. There is no family, no society. Sirius appears to have lost most of the naming language he had and he is trying to recall a memory that people should kneel to him. Without being aware of it, he is inventing himself as God. Spyrus tries to teach him words. Here the deep and true friendship of Sirius for Spyrus begins; and then we leap forward to the same scene when the boys are eighteen years old. Sirius has become a tyrant, worshipped by a group of people aged sixteen to eighteen. The inspiration for Sirius's Godhead is the character of Tyrell in the film *Blade Runner*, where 'Tyrell is presented to the viewer as having a God-like presence . . . the leader of science and also like a God' (see *How Science Became God in Blade Runner* by Tony Schloss).

> What interested me in this play was the idea of God being coincidental with or parallel to power. I am not so much interested in a single religion as in the idea of people coming together, assembling and believing or pretending to believe in a God. For me, the idea of God is used by those in power as a controlling device. Religion for me is not a good thing – the exact opposite. I dream of a world without God.

On the hill the young people have assembled around Sirius. They include Nimar, a slave who attains sexual climax by abasing himself and gets the same satisfaction from the new leader when Sirius is killed; Reiko, who wants to be the chosen virgin of the leader; Laura, an obsessive collector who is prepared to pray obsequiously to complete the task that can never be completed; Doris and Audrey, simple-minded, complaining alter egos who want to be acknowledged by the leader but are treated with contempt by the others; and Kim, a cynical observer who is least under the spell of Sirius.

In this totalitarian society Sirius rules through unpredictable violence, the whimsical concession of pleasure, and the manipulation of the confessional.

> I think we are swimming in totalitarianism. It is such a pervasive reality of everyday life that at some point fear stops and we delude ourselves that we are free. But it is not true. It is very obvious to me that the freedom we have is a mask. And just because I, as a

young woman living in Rome, have more freedom
than a woman in Afghanistan or Sicily does not mean
that I should keep quiet about the control that our
leaders have of the media and therefore of our minds.

Letizia Russo is interested in male friendship during
adolescence, which she sees as deeply important. So she
also gives us a picture of Kent and Kris getting to know
each other on a journey which is an allegory within an
allegory. At the end of the journey Kris has to confront
betrayal, which Russo sees as a very important step in
growing up. Kent knows what the destination is and
what his purpose is. Kris thinks they are friends, but he is
being used; and as soon as they arrive at the hill, Kent, in
an explosion of violence, kills him as an example and
turns on Sirius.

Kent You killed me eleven years ago.
Sirius So you're dead?
Kent You thought I was but I wasn't.

Here we come to the extreme form of what pervades this
play – violence, which Russo sees as an essential part of
the exercise of power.

I think there are different degrees of violence, and
violence has an important place in relationships
between people and as a tool of power. The powerful
people we have in our society now were violent when
they were young. I do not mean that they were football
hooligans. Physical violence is not necessarily the most
dangerous kind; it is just the easiest way of getting
power over other people. The violent young leaders in
this play will be the violent leaders of tomorrow, and
the real power will be with those who can make
violence their property and are willing to perpetrate
that violence on others.

Letizia Russo has constructed a play that will, she hopes, be received on two levels. Adults will understand its deeper aspects, while young people will have a different and lighter relationship, looking at the actions themselves without thinking of all their implications. She believes that *Dead End* is not pessimistic.

I don't think young people will be worried by *Dead End*. Some of them will not agree with it, but that is healthy. We should teach young people that the human being has value in himself. He needs respect not because he is a son of God, but for what he is.

Production Notes

Dead End is the first play Letizia Russo has written for young actors, and in it she uses black humour to explore the important theme of self-identity and its challenges. In this community everything is done through orders, rules and rituals, as in a sect. But the characters talk about the mundanities of everyday life as if they're in a TV programme. They live a life of deception.

The play is set on a hill which represents an escape from the city, but also replicates what happens in cities. You could have a minimalist stage with a hill in the centre, to suggest it representing the whole world; or you could have the hill in one corner of the stage, and then some kind of road leading up to it from the opposite corner.

Letizia Russo started writing the play with a different plot in mind, and yet always had the same characters. The biggest question that became apparent in her mind was why it developed into a play about God, with such a strong focus on this isolated community of young people. She was interested in creating a metaphor that worked on different levels: the first a 'readable' level, portraying the daily life of young people from a sociological point of view when, during adolescence, struggles for power within friendship groups are easily readable; the second examining the concept of faith – through which we hope to enlighten and explore our contradictory selves.

Letizia's observations of the young exposed their strong sense of friendship – a power that can overcome the many trials they are put through. Within friendship groups, however, one person always has the power, and others always obey; and it's often the case that the most powerful member of the group is the most silent. Who has this power and how quickly can this change? And what happens when people break away from the main group – do they have the potential to become something different, or will they inevitably become replicas of the social hierarchy from which they have separated? Are the teenagers in this play looking to find God, or does God finds them? There are deliberate areas of mystery in the play, and it is important that some subjects should be left unexplained.

The imaginary world of the play may demand a complex system of imagery, meanings, movements and objects on stage. However, it's just as possible to have nothing on stage, as it is really the power of what *happens* on stage that matters. Be attentive to the style of the play itself – style can help the hidden part of one's brain to reveal its evocative powers.

LANGUAGE

Letizia found that a favourite and fruitful research method was spying on her younger brother and his friends. She then concentrated specifically on the style of the language used by this age group, before simplifying this idiom in order to make it more powerful. The Italian dialect in which the play was written contains only vague hints of Letizia's urban background, and is not class-distinctive or colloquial to Rome, but was intended to come across as neutral. In translating the play Luca Scarlini and Alex Sierz made the language insistent and simple by removing complex adjectives. The translation process involved cutting away surplus language in order to make it more powerful, the aim being to make the exchanges between the characters as strong as possible. The final draft has a heavy, Anglo-Saxon feel to it, and none of the characters are given to Latinate rhetoric. Although in this way its language is not specific to Italy, the play actually reflects a trend within the Italian arts scene to focus on issues of identity within different communities. Some of the methods used might be appropriate for the play – for example, the split-screen style used by film-makers to show contemporary events side by side on screen in order to explore the relationship between them. This technique is becoming more popular because the idea of living together in groups is now changing. Communities in Italy and their behaviour are affected by the landscape that surrounds them, and as life has become more chaotic, people are beginning to see the problems and challenges that surround family life

THE TEXT

SCENE ONE   Because this is a surrealist drama, we should not question what happened prior to the opening scene. We must believe Sirius doesn't know where he has come from. This is similar to the way we view many of Pinter's characters in his plays. Again as in Pinter, the pauses and silences gave the play a powerful rhythm, and actors must have the confidence to sustain such measured rhythms and keep the pauses alive.

Until his meeting with Spyrus, Sirius does not know that such things as names exist. However, when he realises they do, he of course wants one. He believes he is God, and yet it is Spyrus who enables him to discover this. The inspiration behind this child-god theme is *The Divine Invasion* from *The Valis Trilogy* by Philip K. Dick, a twentieth-century science fiction novel which revolves around a child god who has amnesia. This led Letizia to the simple opening image of two children on a grassy hill at dusk, one with a sack on his shoulders. It was to involve the idea that one's power of memory has been buried, and must be dug out of the hill. She was keen to explore the nature and very essence of power through the relationship between these children. Spyrus is of course more powerful than Sirius, and represents the teenager who likes to 'hang out' with the strongest member of the friendship group. Although more intelligent than Sirius, by placing himself in the position of the sidekick he becomes less vulnerable and is never attacked by fellow members. They have a loyal and deep friendship, and a genuine sense of love exists between them.

SCENE TWO   Until the meeting in this scene, Kent and Kris have not known each other particularly well at school – they may only have passed in the corridor or had brief impersonal conversations.

The use of a bus stop as the meeting place is a reference to the peripheries of towns. Letizia visualises it as a remote coach stop in the middle of an empty landscape – the beginning of a road, and therefore the beginning of the future. The two boys are not in an altered state due to drugs: the drugs that feed their imaginations are their minds. The play as a whole also has a drug-induced feel to it, a dream-like quality.

SCENE THREE   When Spyrus gives Sirius the chair, he is ultimately making him powerful, since the chair is a symbol of power and is subconsciously seen by Spyrus as a throne. The unwrapping of the chair evokes childhood rituals – just like a young child, Sirius appears to be more excited about the paper than the chair.

There is a connection between Kent and the dog in this scene – as when they close their eyes and lie down they are presumed dead.

SCENE FOUR   Sirius is now eighteen years old. Laura's pile of rubbish exists because she is filling an internal void or vacuum with objects in order to create an identity. Sirius encourages her activities in the knowledge that her naivety poses no threat to his power. She is the only member of the group who finds the pile beautiful, and her preoccupation with it suggests she is suffering from obsessive-compulsive disorder.

Nimar has a perverted and slave-like mentality. He is extremely funny, and yet at the same time just as dark.

Sirius plants the dope behind Kim's house. The teenagers believe that they are rebelling against their leader, and yet in reality they are under his tight control. During the seven years prior to this scene, the relationship between Sirius and Spyrus had developed. You can invent their back history. Sirius knows the meaning of each word he uses at this point, because language equals power.

The time the characters spend together under Sirius is the most important and defining time of their lives. Whether they stay for the duration of their lives is for you to decide.

SCENE FIVE   Kent's speech about the 'female curse' is a warning that as a young man you will always look for your mother's love in another woman. Kent is suggesting that men and women are not compatible, since women punish men by making them live with this curse. There are no positive male–female relationships in the play.

The relationship between Kris and Kent is based on one-way deception, fuelled by Kris's subservience. It is as if during the process of their journey Kent has gradually relaxed into the role of God. He sees himself as a natural leader, and is very clear in his objectives. And yet the two boys are still friends, which ultimately makes the murder at the end of the play more shocking.

Throughout the play there is a constant battle between love and power. There are some characters in the play who are always going to be winners or losers.

SCENE SIX   Here two conversations are continuing on stage at the same time, each using a contrasting style of speech. Nimar for example uses 'classical' language and ideas, whereas Reiko and Spyrus converse more collo-quially. But in many ways their exchange of thoughts is similar. Nimar is talking to an omniscient character, and so could technically face any point on or off stage. His language is feminine and obsessive, as if he is jealous of someone sexually. His feelings mirror the ancient Greek sentiment that there is no greater love than the love between two men. But does Nimar want a relationship with a human being or with a god? How much of his love is spiritual and how much sexual?

Doubts over Sirius's status as God begin to emerge in this scene, which also sets up Nimar and Reiko as sexually competitive. It is an important transitional scene, marked by an apparent change in gear in the narrative.

SCENE SEVEN   A 'hecatomb' is an ancient ritual that involved killing one hundred animals. This reflects the fact that serial killers often begin by killing animals when they are children.

SCENE EIGHT   This scene shows an even greater shift in the relationship between Sirius and his subjects. There is evidently rebellion brewing in the ranks. It's up to you to decide how to stage the whipping: it could be done as a freeze-frame, or as movements without props. There is an element of bragging over what can be seen as a result of drug-taking, and Letizia is demonstrating how drug use can shape a community.

SCENE NINE   The 'oh's and 'eh's might variously come across as exclamatory, revelatory, questioning and condemnatory.

SCENE TEN   The actor playing Kent could be the same person who plays Spyrus at the age of eleven.

SCENE ELEVEN   Scene Eleven starts where Scene Six ends. There are no obvious or exact parallels between the scenes – only similarities.

'She's a virgin where it matters' refers to marital customs in Italy, where it is important for young women to protect their means of reproduction.

SCENE THIRTEEN   The surreal killing of Sirius should come across as a ritual. You might refer to *Terminator*, to Tarantino's films, or to the popular Japanese action comics known as *manga*. The rhythm of each blow from Kent is an important aspect of this scene. The audience should be detached from the action and the violence, and be ready to laugh at the absurdity of it while feeling sad and horrified at the same time.

When Kent destroys the heap of rubbish it is a metaphor for the sham of the group – we realise that Sirius was supplying Laura with the rubbish, and thereby building up his own power. As the heap tumbles to the ground so does the old order, and a new one takes its place.

You could represent the souls on stage.

There is a cyclical element to the play: the story never ends, since history repeats itself over and over again.

NOTES ON CHARACTER NAMES

Letitzia made a conscious effort to choose foreign names,
but also to select ones that hinted at each character's
destiny. She explained that Doris and Audrey are alter
egos, representing the kind of relationship that exists
between some girls of that age who become mutually
dependent in order to provide security against others.

Sirius, the Dog Star, in the constellation Canis Major, is
the brightest start in the night sky.

Spyrus means 'to die' or 'to expire' in Italian.

Kent makes reference to Superman (Clark Kent).

Nimar is an Arabic-sounding name, helping to meet
the brief for a multicultural play.

Laura, Doris and Audrey are intentionally old-fashioned-
sounding names.

based on a workshop led by Roxana Silbert
transcribed by Tanya Winch

DISCONTENTED WINTER: HOUSE REMIX

Bryony Lavery

Characters

Ronan, a major hoodlum

Slapper, a teenage whore

Pog, a minor hoodlum

Greenie, another minor hoodlum

Snoop Doggy-Dogg, a dog

Serena, a teenage Sloanie

Ed, a prince

Hal, another prince

Cheviot, a girl anorak

Top Totties, bad Sloanies

Low Streeties, homeless teenagers

Security Men, dudes in suits

Towler, bodyguard

Brotherton, another bodyguard

Society Host

Homeless-Shelter Manager

Endangered Wrinkly

ONE
NOW IS THE WINTER . . .

A dark, terrible city somewhere.
 A place of different levels.
 There are many power failures and blackouts in this city, so its denizens use searchlights, neon signs, candles, polluted suns, computer screens, stars to light the scenes.
 Members of the Flash Mob arrive suddenly. They light the scene, provide the music, the scene title (probably one of many graffiti-ridden cards).
 Someone, somewhere, samples . . .

NOW IS THE
NOW IS THE
NOW IS THE
WINTER
OF
OUR
DISCONTENT . . .

A single flash of lightning lights . . .
 Ronan, a tough, misshapen young guy, hiding, alone.
 He has got techno gear . . . a state-of-the-art mobile, a universal remote control . . .

Ronan
 Now's not a good time
 For why? For this
 Adults are arses
 Grown-ups gobshites
 Our leaders lie
 Smell the wind. Whiffo!
 Something's came to an end

Chaos kicked off
Her boots broke my head
The spinning world's been spun
Its icy ends at boiling point
near and far . . . we're frying tonight
Phew! What a scorcher
And me? . . . I'm feeling
hot hot hot
look at me
arrived too early out of a whore's fanny
she dinks my unborn foetus
with the blow the crack
then drops me, disgraceful!
one mad night
on the floor of a Soho shite house
and I grow up a spaz
Dogs bark when I crip by them
All this makes me bitter
Therefore
I am decided to be the bad boy
in this (*drips venom*) Youth Issues Play!
So where to start?

He looks about. Directs the remote, and . . .
   Someone, somewhere, samples:

TO BE TO BE TO BE TO BE TO BE
OR NOT TO BE TO BE TO BE
THAT IS THE THAT IS THE THAT IS
THE QUESTION . . .

Ronan
Why! What! Entertainment!

He points a finger of his remote hand off.

Here comes a new cable channel!

Enter from that direction Slapper, a teenage gangster's moll, heartbroken . . .

Wotcha, Slapper.

Slapper punches him in the chest.

Bit worldweary are we?
Why?
Missing 'mi boyfriend'?
Where is he? 'Mi lovely feller'?

Slapper spits in his face.

Now that's not nice.
(*to us*) Word on the street her boyf's been banged up
For dealing, whatnot, drugs, affray.

Ronan caresses her hair.

I can't believe he done it, babe, no way.

She pushes him off.

(*to us*) He didn't! How do I know? Was me!
Who fingered him? Why me, a course!
Now I'll finger her . . . it'll pass the time . . .
till something wickeder this way comes!
(*to Slapper*) never mind, love-sick wench
they'll give him counselling
make him do 'creative writing'
come out write
'I was a teenage nogoodnik but I found God'
make a reality docu of his rehab hell
get fame get a presenter's slot get it going on . . .
it's me you'll thank
Start now.

He kisses her.
    She pretends to throw up. He seizes her by the hair.

Look how dark the sky!
You need a new protector, a Durex-type
of person what! Hello!

He lets her go.

Slapper
What? You?
What? *You??*
Why?
In your dreams!
As if!

Ronan waits patiently.

Why?
What for?
What?

Ronan waits . . .

Why not?
Whatever.

*She stands next to him. He hands her his equipment
to carry. He snogs her.*

Ronan (*to us*)
Was ever pussy in this paddy pulled?
It's the lack of self-esteem
the low expectations
the parents these days!
Just don't *validate* their daughters. Shame!
But check out 'The Wider Issue' I slipped in there!
I'll use her misuse her do her dump her
and if she talks back much I'll thump her!
(*to Slapper*) Shift it, Slapper.
What's that up there?

*He looks way way up. Flash Mob wield some serious
light.*

Slapper
Tower blocks hello?
Ronan
Two tower blocks facing.
Slapper (*sees*)
Left one eighteenth floor
that's so a flash of light
who's there?

We follow the flash of light. It is . . .

TWO
WEATHERWATCH

Flash Mob card this. Prop . . .
Cheviot, a bright, brainy, nerdy girl . . . in her
eighteenth-floor bedroom/control room looks out of her
window through powerful binoculars.

Cheviot
Captain's log.
Stardate 4th July . . .
among all the horrors of climate change
a new discovery is that the atmosphere
is growing taller . . .
almost all our weather
happens in a thin cocoon of turbulent
atmosphere hugging the earth's surface . . .
this layer is *the troposphere*
and its roof is known as *the tropopause*
and lying above it . . .
there is *the stratosphere*.

She lowers the binoculars and looks at us.

You might want to make a note of that . . .
troposphere tropopause stratosphere

the stratosphere
is almost an oasis of peace and quiet.

Someone, somewhere, samples:

WE ARE SUCH STUFF
WE ARE SUCH STUFF
AS DREAMS AS DREAMS AS DREAMS
ARE MADE ON . . .

*She looks up longingly as she dons a pair of plastic
Vulcan ears.*

Beam me up, Scotty.

*Operated by Flash Mob, some stars, far off, twinkle
beckoningly.*
    Flash Mob cards . . .

THREE
THE TOWER

Ronan
    It's just some kid with *giant* ears
    go right
    tower block two
    pay attention
    for
    cleaving, lightning-like, the stormy London atmos
    a sound of furious axe-work . . .

*A sound of furious axe-work. Plus a counterpoint
melody of excited dog barking.*

Greenie (*off*)
    Get stove in ya . . . door!

*Enter Greenie and Pog, Ronan's streetie henchboys.
With axes. And the remains of a door. And Pog's
excited and excitable dog, Snoop Doggy-Dogg.*

Greenie
Yo!
Pog
Yo!
Snoop
Arfarfarfarfarfarfarf!
Pog
Shutup quiet sitdown down downdownsit!

Everybody, but particularly Pog, will spend a lot of energy trying and failing to train and subdue Snoop.
    Pog physically wrestles Snoop to 'sit' while Greenie checks the window . . .

Greenie
Panoramic! Spettacula view!
Snoop
Arfarfarfarfarfarf!
Pog
Shut it shut down down down *down*!
Greenie
What floor?

Pog leans out, starts counting . . .

Pog
Free four five six seven . . . (*etc.*)
Snoop
Arfarfarfarfarfarf!
Both
Sit!!

Greenie calls on his mobile. Ronan's goes. 'Rule Britannia' ring tone.

Greenie
Ronan? We're in!
Ronan
What floor?

Pog

Twenny-free twennny-four . . . twenny-five!

Greenie

Twenny-fifth.

Ronan

Better be an effing elevator!

(*to Slapper*) Excitement's kicking off.

Follow the bouncing ball.

Slapper

Awesome. (*not*)

Ronan heads, with difficulty and verve, followed by Slapper, towards the tower . . .

FOUR

MEANWHILE, IN ANOTHER STRATA OF SOCIETY

Flash Mob card this . . .

Serena, a debby society Sloane, stands at a lighted mirror, applying attacking make-up to her beautiful, discontented face . . .

Someone, somewhere, samples:

ITEM

TWO LIPS

INDIFFERENT

REDDDDDDDDD EEDDDDD . . .

Serena

Meanwhile

in a happily higher strata of society

Serena

wad-wise well-orf

but

deeply disappointed in her pointless parents

and bored *titless* by her empty junior years

applies a stunning maquillage . . .
that's *make-up*, sad thick proles . . .
to her beautiful discontented face
as she ticks off the details
. . . of her brilliant but simple plot
to improve her lot . . .
looks check
frocks check
rhythm.

She performs the beginning of a seductive dance.

Check.

As she sways off . . . elsewhere, a beam of golden lights. Along it comes . . .

FIVE
TWO PRINCES

Ed and Hal, two teenage princes in polo gear, sweep through long palace corridors, towards the polo field. Someone, somewhere, samples:

MY HORSE MY HORSE MY KINGDOM
FOR A POLO HORSE . . .

Ed
Need to borrow your second pony.
Hal
Because?
Ride Pa's second pony.
Ed
Can't.
Hal
Because?
Ed
Because.

Pa's second's a slow old slapper.
Be brotherly, Bro.

Hal

Dream on.

Ed

Make it worth your while.

Hal

With . . .?

Ed

The throne?

Both laugh briefly, regally and humourlessly at the irony.

Hal

Dream on.

Ed

Okay. Last offer.
I get your pony . . .
you get top totty. Tonight.

Hal

How?

Ed

The Divine Right of a future King.

Both laugh regally but humourlessly again.

Deal?

Hal

Deal.

They don their polo helmets as . . .

But don't lame my second.

Ed

As if!

They don helmets, walk out into the sunshine . . .

SIX
IN THE TROPOSPHERE

Ronan and Slapper climbing stairs. Torches . . .

Ronan
From those crested cocks crowing
top of the dung heap
to yer actual low compost
The Lord of Misrule
The Prince of Darkness
The King of Catastrophe
checks out the gro-bag plot . . .

He enters the tower block and looks around.
Henchboys report.

Greenie
Top five floors empty on account of
asbestos scare . . . all gonna be demolished soon . . .
going down . . . we've got
hard-to-house families.

Pog
Won't make trouble.

Greenie
Then Asians.

Pog
Won't dare make trouble.

Greenie
Then wrinklies.

Pog
Can't remember how to make trouble . . .

Snoop
Arf ararfarfarfarf!

All
Shut up shut it shut it sit!

Ronan
Final question is . . .
having got in by smashing the dicking door . . .
you wombats!

Greenie/Pog
Sorry, Ronan.

Ronan
You know what a wombat is?

Greenie/Pog
It's a sorta . . .
it's a sorta . . .
No, Ronan.

*Ronan takes a broken piece of door, hits Greenie,
Pog, Snoop on the head, plus, for the hell of it,
Slapper. Whack! Whack! Whack!*

Ronan
That's a wombat, ya woms!
To repeat
having got in by smashing the dicking door . . .
how do we make it sodding secure?

Some über-brilliant thinking . . . then . . .

Greenie
Guard it.

He takes out a cosh, Pog a gun.

Greenie/Pog
Tooled up.

Pog
Dog patrols.

Snoop
Arfarafrarfarfarfarf!

Snoop is particularly keen to kill Ronan . . .

Ronan
Get the canine away!

My hate list.
One. Dogs.
Two. Everybody.
(*to Pog and Greenie*) See to it.
(*to Slapper*) We go. You stay.
Make it nice. Get a sleeping bag
magazines some scoff
we went but we'll be back.

*Boys exit. Slapper looks round. Walks to window. Puts
on secret spectacles. Looks out.*
  *Two flashes of light opposite. Cheviot with her
binoculars. Two eyes look right at two eyes.*

Slapper
What are you looking at? . . . Big Ears?
Cheviot
Over the last twenty-two years . . .
the tropopause has been rising
by an average of about 650 feet globally
and more at the poles . . . you know what
that means . . . ?
It means life but not as we know it.
(*to Slapper*) What are *you* looking at?
. . . Earthling.

They both put the 'dissing' hand up.

Both
Talk to the hand!

They turn back to their own rooms.
  Sample:

O BRAVE NEW WORLD
THAT HAS SUCH PEOPLE IN IT.

Slapper (*surveying the room*)
Lilac colour notes.

Silver fixtures.
Soft tones.
Glamour.

She fervently hums the signature tune of Changing
Rooms. *Flash Mob hum the harmony. Card . . .*

SEVEN
A POSH LADIES' LOO
SOMEWHERE IN THE WEST OF OUR CITY

Serena enters in top ballgown, checks the loo cubicles.
They are empty. Takes a mobile from her cleavage.

Serena (*mobile*)
It's empty ya.
Come.

A bevy of Top Totty, all in top ballgowns, big skirts,
come in, twittering and braying. Serena holds up
a finger. All goes quiet.

Serena
Okay. Here's the plan.
Pay absolute attention.
We are going to kidnap gorgeous Prince Ed . . .
handsome heir to our country's throne . . .

Top Totty shriek and scream.
Serena lifts her quietening finger . . .

You must be utterly unsuspicious, ya?

Top Totty all give a braying laugh . . .

Repeat after me.
We are unspeakably bland.
Top Totties
We are unspeakably bland.

Serena
We are extremely empty-headed.
Top Totties
We are extremely empty-headed.
Serena
We are total top clueless totty.
Top Totties
We are total top clueless totty.
Serena
Be what they expect.
Got it?
Top Totties
Ya, Serena.
Serena
Fulfil your demographic.
Understand.
Top Totties
Absolutely, Serena.
Serena
Fingers crossed.

They all cross their fingers.

Serena
Let's be safe out there.
Trot on.

With fingers still crossed, they sweep out like a flock of beautiful geese . . . Card:

EIGHT
MEANWHILE, UP EAST, IN A
DOWNMARKET GENTS AT THE SAME TIME

Ronan (*mobile*)
It's empty, check it.
Get here.

Several Low Streeties enter, swaggering and larging it.
Ronan holds up a finger. Instant silence.

Okay. Log on.
Check it.
We are gonna snatch and hold to ransom
Our crap country's second prince, Hal.

Streeties cheer, whistle, high-five hands.
  Ronan holds up his quietening finger . . .

Repeat after me.
We're utterly grateful.
Low Streeties
We're utterly grateful.
Ronan
We're open-mouthed with awe.
Low Streeties
We're open-mouthed with awe.
Ronan
We're rocked by royalty.
Low Streeties
We're rocked by royalty.
Ronan
We're meek, loyal subjects,
In this lies our disguise, bros.
Low Streeties
Yo, Ronan.
Ronan
Seem to serve
It serves us.
With the programme?
Low Streeties
Total commitment 200 Dredd.
Ronan
Rock on, Tommies!

They swagger off as . . .

NINE
A CHANGE OF PLAN,
A CHALLENGE TO PROTOCOL

Golden beam lights the two princes, Hal and Ed.

Hal in tuxedo, Ed in suit, with their private personal detectives, Brotherton and Towler, sweep towards their chauffeured cars.

Ed
Change of plan, Brotherton.
Hal
Adjustment to schedule, Towler.
Ed
We're swapping visits, ya?
Hal
I'm going east . . .
Ed
I'm heading west . . .
Brotherton
Change of plan . . .?
Towler
But sir . . .
Hal
Pa okayed it.
Ed
St James's Palace gave it the thumbs up.
Hal
MI6 are fully positive with it . . .
Towler/Brotherton
Yes, but Sir . . .
Ed/Hal
Just *do* it, ya?
Towler/Brotherton
Yer Majesties.

Hal
We get top totty, Brotherton.
Ed
We get pond life, Towler.
Hal/Ed
Drive on.

They sweep out.
Towler and Brotherton put up their arms, talk into
their cuffs as . . .

TEN
TWO HOUSES, BOTH ALIKE IN DIGNITY

A big scary group of royal security types in black suits
and dark glasses flood the stage, stand still, suspiciously
surveying the area.

Brotherton (*into his cuff*)
Brotherton here.
Towler (*into his*)
Towler here.

All security lift their cuffs to listen.

Brotherton
My prince is doing the homeless.
Be vigilant.
Towler
My little royal sod's doing the top totty
Charity ball thing . . .
Gonna be an easy night, lads.
Security (*into their lapels*)
Got it, Sarge.

They scope the area . . .
Sample:

WHAT FRESH HELL IS THIS IS THIS IS THIS
WHAT FRESH HELL IS THIS?

*Then Flash Mob provide a lot of pompy, fanfare,
announcing-type music . . .*

    Security types withdraw to watchful positions.

    *Flash Mob traffic-control two scenes unfolding at
the same time: one scene is a state-of-the-art homeless
shelter in the east, the other the private ballroom of a
rich person's house in the west.*

    Ronan and the Low Streeties arrive east.

    Serena and Top Totties arrive west.

    *Hal appears with unctuous Shelter Manager (either
gender), Ed with equally unctuous Ball Organiser
(either gender).*

Shelter Manager
    This!
    Your Royal Highness . . .
    is our new drop-in centre
    it's youth-friendly, hoodlum-protected
    do you see the graffiti-inspired décor . . .?
    we rationalised that
    if we're going to get graffiti *anyway* we'll
    start with graffiti . . .
    and here are the . . .
    here are our . . .
    homeless destitute youth derelicts . . .
    but we make it our policy to call them *clients* . . .
Hal
    Nice to meet you all . . .
Ronan (*aside*)
    Here's a right royal cock-up!
    It's the *wrong* pigging prince!
    This is the heir to the *throbbing throne*!

    Hal starts to shake hands, as . . .

Ball Organiser
Here it is!
I am sooo blessed to have my own ballroom . . .
it means the gels and their *very* worthwhile
charity get the venue
at a peppercorn price
so *bags* of donations
and *I'm* not out of pocket!
I believe
your great-great-great-great grandmother
once danced here . . .
isn't that splendid fun?
and here are the girls who organised . . .
Serena Sally Saffron Sarah Stiffy Samantha
Sorcha Sunila Sophie Sophie and
. . . Sophie.

Ed
So nice to meet you all.

Serena (*aside*)
Oh, here's a holy howdyedo!
This is the *wrong* pogging prince!
This is the little unimportant runty *second one*!

Ed starts to shake hands . . .

Serena
What to do?
Scratch? Cancel? Postpone?
Girl interrupted?

Ronan
What the dick to do?
Break up? Go home? Pull out?
Plottus interruptus?

Serena
No way.

Ronan
As if.

Both
Don't think so!

Serena
Be in the moment.

Ronan
Go with the flow.

Both
Give it your best shot
Give it 200 per cent
Follow the dream!!

Shelter Manager
And this is . . . Kevin?

Ronan
Ronan.

Ed
Have you been coming here long?

Ronan
Since my tragic and abusive
family circumstances got
thus unbearable making it necessary
for me to take to the long and winding road . . .
that leads to your door . . .

Streeties
Show His Royal Highness yer box, Ronan.

Streeties produce various cardboard pieces . . .

Ronan
This is my box, Your Royal Highness . . .
which, until the erection of this frankly awesome
humanely funded homeless shelter . . .
was my very cardboard castle in sun, rain, blizzard
terrorist attack
it assembles in a tick.

Streeties assemble the box as . . .

It's cardboard almost strong enough

to hold off all but the harshest elements
of a British summer . . .
its dimensions . . .
roomy without being overtly spacious . . .
care to step inside
see how you like the accommodation?

Ed
Cool.

He steps into the box as meanwhile . . .

Serena
Your Majesty . . .
the gels have choreographed a little piece
we worked on it in ballet class, ya
it's Diagalev-influenced, with just a touch
of Kathakali because Sunila's folks are from
Southern India . . .

*The Totties perform a wonderful dance, some ballet,
some ballroom, some Kathakali . . . interweaving . . .*

Sunila (*to Hal*)
Do join in for this part . . .

Hal
Awesome.

*They pull him in. He is Kathakali dancing. Meanwhile,
everyone is standing round the cardboard box.*

Ed (*muffled*)
There's actually loads of space . . .

Ronan
Like a little palace . . .

*The box collapses. Ed is gone.
   Meanwhile, everyone is Kathakali dancing.*

Hal (*above music*)
Do you think I've got it going on ya?

He is interweaving . . . He is here . . . The Top Totty
throng . . . part . . . He is gone! Another miraculous,
youth-organised disappearing trick!

Shelter Manager
Where is he?
Where's the Prince?
Ball Hostess
Where is he?
Where's the Prince?
Ronan
He was here . . .
Serena
Then he was gorn!
Both
Somebody's had him away!!
(*scarpering*) We'll find him for you!
Brotherton
He's gone! Heir to the thugging throne's gone!
Towler
Mine too!
It's Al Quaeda!
It's Saddam Hussein!
It's some stand-up comedy Herbert!
It's our jerking jobs!
Ring of steel!
Security alert!
Keflar vests!

Security covers the area, talking into their lapels and
cuffs.

Security
Check the windows! Secure the doors!
Call the Palace! Get the sniffers!
Cordon off! Clamp down! (*etc.*)

Searchlights slice the darkness. Sirens, whistles syncopate.

ELEVEN
A CAR-CHASE SEQUENCE WITH NO CARS

Flash Mob provide an exciting chase sequence with dinky cars . . . as Serena and Ronan appear from different vantage points.
  Sample:

BY THE PRICKING OF MY THUMBS
SOMETHING WICKED THIS WAY
THIS WAY
NO THIS WAY
COMES.

Pog and Greenie run across stage one way, carrying a trussed-up royal prince, bound with box tape.
  Sophie, Sophie and Sophie run another way, with Hal trussed up in girlie ribbons.

Pog/Greenie
Where to?
Ronan
The tower!
Pog/Greenie
Quick quick this way move it rapido!
Top Totties
Where to, ya?
Serena
The river!
Top Totties
Jogging ya! Speed, ya! this way this way
quickly quickly ya?

Security Men run on . . .

Security Men
Which way?

(*Half point right.*) This way!
(*Other half point left.*) That way!
(*All*) Run!

Half run off after Streeties, half after Totties.
  Enter Towler and Brotherton.

Towler (*into cuff*)
Brotherton! Where are you? Copy!
Brotherton (*into cuff*)
Towler! I'm in the street! Where are you?

*They continue to talk through their cuffs, although
they are right next to one another.*

Towler
Listen . . . I don't think it's mega-serious . . .
I think this is a
Rag-type-prank-type-kid's-type thing!
Brotherton
Wake up and smell the Nescafe, Towler!
These 'kids' are toxic! Trouble! Turds!
And if, Towler, it is indeed 'a kid's thing'
a. Where the toss are they?
b. How pants are *we* gonna look?
c. Strategy-wise we can't shagging *shoot* them!
Towler
So you think complete cover-up absolute
info blackout press
crown prince/boy prince embargo
until . . .
Brotherton
Until we can figure out a way a'
getting the royal-blue-blooded bleeders back
behind the Balmoral barred gates
and stop the proverbial waste products
encountering the air-extractor mechanism . . .

Towler

Very succinct summation of the conundrum
Brotherton!

They speed off in separate directions.

TWELVE
MEANWHILE, ON A NEARBY GALAXY

*A box with the label 'Star Trek Marketing Franchise'
stands open . . . Cheviot is putting on, over the Vulcan
ears, a replica early Starship* Enterprise *uniform.*

Cheviot

The tropopause lies ten miles above the
earth's surface at the Equator . . .
five miles above the Poles . . .
and that difference gives a clue
to global warming effect . . .

Examines the open uniform.

How does this fasten . . .?

Finds . . .

Velcro. Very logical, Mr Spock.

She fastens it as . . .

In the tropics
the land and sea is baked under a scorching sun
and sends up so much hot air
it pushes up the tropopause.

*She examines herself in the mirror, touches the insignia
on the collar.*

This means quite a high-ranking
female Starship Trooper . . .
a *human.*

She takes off the Vulcan ears.

Hello, Captain.
And of course the thinning
of the ozone layer
by
chlorofluorocarbons
you might need to write that down
'chloro–fluoro–carbons'
means the stratosphere
has cooled and contracted
also pulling up the tropopause . . .

She sits in an ordinary chair, as if it is the flight deck
of the Enterprise.
  Sample:

IN ACTION
IN ACTION IN ACTION HOW LIKE AN ANGEL
IN APPREHENSION OH BOY OH BOY
OH BOY . . . HOW LIKE
A GOD . . .

Cheviot
  Set variants for the tropopause, Mr Sulu.
  Take her up, Scotty.

Her noises and actions indicate a very large starship
taking up and off.
  At the same time, Flash Mob pick her up in her chair,
take her off.

THIRTEEN
A PRINCE IN A TOWER BLOCK

Pog, Greenie, Snoop guard axed door, Slapper staring.
Ronan enters, scopes Ed, who is still tied up.

Ronan

My nan's got a biscuit tin with a
picture of your grandma on it.
Now what I wanna know
is
has *your* nan got a biscuit tin
with a picture of *my* nan on it?

Ed is silent.

Didn't think so.

*Greenie's mobile plays 'Scotland the Brave'. He
answers it.*

Snoop

Arfarfarfarfarfarfarf!

Pog

Shutup shut it get down sit sit sit!!

Ronan

Got your mother's good looks . . .

Ed

Don't talk about my mother
mothershagger.

Ronan roughs him up.

Ronan

Don't *you* talk about *my* mother!
Your father's a bit Barking and Dagenham,
in't he?

Ed

Dont assume anything about my father,
bastard.

Ronan roughs him up worse.

Ronan

Don't assume anything about *my* father!
Where d'you think you *are*, Your Maj?

You're in *the tower*!
You know what happens to princes in towers?

He points his remote.
    Sample:

GOOD NIGHT SWEET PRINCE . . .
GOOD NIGHTIE NIGHTIE NIGHT.

(*to Slapper*) Hand me that pillow . . .

Stuffs it in Ed's face . . .

(*to Ed*) You're not the prince I want,
Sunshine, so right now your future's not
secure . . .
Greenie
    Breaking news flash, Ronan . . .
    Developments.
    My mucker Morris what's been stickin his dick
    in this Sloane Square Sophie slapper
    says somebody's got royal-boy's brother on a houseboat
    past Chelsea Reach . . .
    They want the big bro
    do we wanna do a swap?
Ronan
    When?
Greenie
    Whenever.
Ronan
    Where?
Greenie
    Wandsworth.
Ronan
    Why?
Greenie
    They're wankers.
    What'll I say?

Ronan

Say we're on our way.
Snoop . . . Stay! Guard!
One move . . . kill!
Pog . . .

Pog

Ronan?

Ronan

Stay! Guard!
One move . . . kill!
Oy, Slapper . . . ?

Slapper looks at him.

Ronan

Make our guest comfortable.
Food. Drink.

He touches her proprietorially.

Whatever
Quote him happy.

*Ronan and Greenie limp-sweep off. Pog and Snoop
Doggy-Dogg on guard.*

Slapper

You're him.
God.
Should I curtsey or what?

Ed

It's not actually obligatory
but it would be mega-hilarious to see
you try . . .

Slapper

Kiss my arse.

Ed

Clean my floor.

Pog whips out waiter's pad . . .

Pog
Sunnink to eat?
McDonald's Burger King KFC
Pizza Hut Pizza Express
Yo Sushi Happy Noodle Indian Chippy?

Ed
Not hungry.

Pog
I am.

Snoop
Arfararfarfarfarf!

Slapper
Me too.

Ed
Then why don't you three dogs eat shit?

Pog
Oooh dear, bad call
Big mistake. Big. Huge. Massive.

Pog moves towards Ed, unsticking a large roll of black gaffer tape . . .

FOURTEEN
A BOAT, A BOAT . . .

Flash Mob bring on some plans.
Ronan and Greenie walk along a plank, step onto and then down into a bobbing boat. They are seized by Top Totty, wrestled to the ground, and frisked.
Serena watches.

Serena
Clean?

Sunila
Of weapons!
And they've both got . . .

She holds up her little finger.
   Top Totty scream with laughter.
   Serena lifts her quietening finger: hush.

Serena
   Which of you yobbest of yobs
   can yak?
Ronan
   I can perform that miracle, mardy moo.

They survey each other critically.

Serena
   Your mother get you in a kit from Ikea?
   She should take you back.
   Get arms and legs that fit.
Ronan
   That nose. You're 'aving a larf, incha?
   And the boobs . . . I'm guessing . . .
   Kleenex, yeah? Daddy not love ya enough
   to stand you silicones from Selfridge's?

Serena gives Ronan a serious Indian burn.
   Ronan pulls Serena's hair slowly, hard.
   Very painful but . . .
   Neither gives an inch. So . . . parley.

Serena
   You want the second prince
   that's stupid
   why?
Ronan
   I mean to murder him.
   you want the first crown prince
   that's mental
   why?
Serena
   I mean to marry him.

Arranged marriage. Royal murder.
Let's stare moodily in the river and talk.

They go to stare, scoping each other.

FIFTEEN
A HOSTAGE SITUATION

*Hal is sitting in a galley, with several Top Totties in store-
bought comedy masks – Blair, Bush, Mickey Mouse, a cat,
the Queen etc. – sit guarding him. He is still trussed up.*

Hal
Got any idea who I am?
Got any idea of the *serious* shit you're in?
Got any notion at all what *we* can do to you?

Nothing.

Got a game plan?
Got a forward strategy?
Got a voice?
Anyone?

No.

Got a Twix bar?
Got any cider?
Got a cigarette?
Skank?

No.

Skank?

No.

Got any idea how much I'd like
to snog one of you?
Or all of you?

247

No.

Show me your boobs.
Go on
Roll 'em out for the royal.

A Top Totty in a Queen Elizabeth mask gets up,
smartly clips his ear.

Sorry, Grandmother.

She sits down again.

SIXTEEN
A MEETING OF MINDS

Ronan and Serena on the deck of a boat, looking down
into the dark river.

Ronan
   We swap the bluebloodboys
   you get your bridegroom
   we get Runty and ten thousand pounds.
Serena
   We swap the blueblood boys
   I get my bridegroom
   you get Runty and kiss my beautiful behind.
Ronan
   Bridegroom
   the white dress thing
   what's that all about?
Serena
   I get people
   I get celebrity
   I get holidays
   I get designer gear
   I get paparazzi I get coverage I get attention

I get respect
I get designer, popstar, surgeon friends
I get the love of the people
I get to go round Africa holding damaged babies
I wear a simple but fantastically cut
white shirt . . .
I'm a Queen of Hearts.

Ronan
Solid plan.

Serena
One B-list prince . . . murder
what's that all about?

Ronan
somming to do
a lark a spree
somming to plan ponder execute
with brilliant precision
get the ransom murder the evidence
the respect of master criminals everywhere
the awe of operators
the stares of scammers
the hi-fives of hackers
the cheers of cheats!
the love of liars
to be the Stephen Hawking of hoodlums . . .
A Brief History of Crime!
Better to be cruel than crippled
but, because it's the *second* prince . . .
if it goes belly-up, it's not *treason*
I don't get offed!

Serena
I once fell in here.

Ronan
Pissed.

Serena
Totally

imbibed the river water dirty, deep
see the rats that're swimming there?
I drank their piss
I sometimes feel half-girl, half-rat.

Ronan
Let's see yer tail then, Roland.

Serena lifts her skirt, shows him.

(*looking*) Or we could team up,
I get into you
You open up to me . . . ?

Serena
You're a cockroach.

Ronan
You're a rat
both survivors
everything goes bad and rots
this crap-heap could be ours
to crawl about and scavenge on.

Sample:

A BRAVE VESSEL . . .
WHO HAD, NO DOUBT,
SOME NOBLE CREATURE IN HER . . .
DASHED ALL TO PIECES.

Flash Mob make a storm, wobble the planks . . .

Serena
Look, a storm's coming.

Ronan
Boat's rocking.

It is, quite alarmingly.

SEVENTEEN
WHEN THIS OLD WORLD
STARTS GETTING ME DOWN

Cheviot, in full Star Trek uniform, climbing . . .
   Flash Mob form the many stairs.

Cheviot
   When this ole world starts getting me down
   and people are just too much for me
   to face
   I climb way up to the top of the stairs
   and all my cares just drift right into space.

   Flash Mob hum quietly 'Up on the Roof' as Cheviot,
   unaware it is a song, emerges onto her tower block
   roof, says . . .

   On the roof
   it's peaceful as can be . . .
   and there the world below don't bother me . . .
   Up on the roof.

   She looks with her binoculars . . .

   How does a higher tropopause
   affect our weather?
   It leads to taller higher thunderclouds
   that's what
   look
   red sky
   green-tinged horizon
   black clouds the size of God's tower blocks.
   Fire lightning bolts, Mr Sulu!

   Flash Mob make lightning forks.

   Thunder on full . . . Scotty!

Flash Mob make thunder rumble.

Up the surge, Uhuru!
Come storm
twisters
typhoons
tidal waves
torrent
come
annihilate this crumbling life form!

*Flash Mob make a weird storm develop frighteningly
as . . .*

EIGHTEEN
A DINNER PARTY

*Pog and Snoop Doggy-Dogg sharing a Big Mac meal in
the doorway.*
*Slapper with Medium Coke and Chicken Nuggets sits
by Ed, who now has his mouth taped with black gaffer
tape. Pog and Snoop watch the storm.*

Snoop (*whimpering*)
Mny . . . mny . . . mny . . .
Slapper
Big Mac's 952 calories.
French fries . . . 435.

Pog's mobile plays 'Land of My Fathers'.
He answers it, listens.

Nuggets . . . chicken . . . 325!!
But all shit.
Obeying your command
Your Royal Highness.

She eats shit hungrily.

Pog (*to Ed*)
Ronan's coming.
He's gonna *kill* you!
Blue ink all over the floor!
Wish you was wearing *brown* trousers?
Slapper
Bet you wish it was the old days
you'd have armour
soldiers
a horse and gallop away.

She comes closer to him.

(*Whispers.*) I won't let them.
kill you.
I like you.
You're majestical.
Your rudeness rocks my world.
Be ready.

She rips his gag off.

Ed
Aaaaaargh!
Slapper (*to Pog*)
Just giving him
some MacNuggets.
Commence his suffering.

She puts her finger to his lips . . .

Patience, my prince
I am your grass-roots support.

NINETEEN
MAKE YOURSELVES READY IN YOUR CABINS

Ronan and Serena descend to the cabin to masked Totty.
Flash Mob are rocking the boat throughout . . .

Ronan
Vamoose, space-vixens.
Princey and I wanna parley . . .

Totty look at Serena.

Totty
Serena?
Serena
'S okay Sophie Sophie and Sophie.

They vamoose, but slap Ronan playfully on the way.
Ronan whips out an awesome knife. They fly like
birds.
Ronan turns to Hal.

Ronan
Well, look at you
my royal bundle!

Gets hold of Hal, plays the knife at his body . . .

I got your bro in a tower block
you in a boat
it's really hard not to gloat!
our plan is . . . I kill you
she marries your bro by force
thus the high up plummet
the low leap
the contemporary crap cut through
how d'you like it so far?
Hal
Weak

tame
lame
and very small
consider a bigger plan . . .
untie my gesturing hand . . .

Serena

Do it pronto, spazzy man.

Ronan cuts one hand free . . . Hal starts gesticulating and specifying. Flash Mob add a capella *martial music.*

Hal

Now all the youth of England are on fire
for what?
for freedom fun for something fresh
they're gasping for some game
they're gagging at the garbage grown-ups do
let us surge up
I raise my flag in street-end school job-centre club
say here's a royal prince will lead you lads
we'll make each palace into a place of youth
get all the homeless off the street in there
Buckingham . . . an all-day club
Balmoral, Sandringham
May Castle . . . Outward Bound
lay off the army, sack the church
use all their gelt upon a better buy
fast food, shooters, recreational drugs
non-stop sex the casual sort
turn this kingdom into an all-night-rave!
In the history books they'll write us
'The Dark Ages Run by Golden Youth'
Well . . . ?

Serena

Bought.
I like this prince's prose
Who'd be your queen?

Hal

Why . . . any tart whose legs
I can get between.

Serena

That sounds like me!

Hal

Well, there you go . . .
Now, about my brother . . .?

Serena

Well, we kill your brother, no?
And serve him up before a snapping
frenzied press
Like this, yes!

*Flash Mob bring on a bloodless corpse. Serena
demonstrates with it. Very bloody.*

Saying, just to show you old guys
We mean busi-ness!!

Ronan

And who am I, the cripple, in all this?

Serena

An *undercover* operative I'd say.

Hal

Who never sees the light of day.

Serena

Serving, somehow, our high-class needs.

Hal

A *servant,* but in better threads!

Serena

We need to disseminate our plan
to all the country's youthful lugs.

Hal

Lead on to broadcast decks and cans and plugs . . .

Serena

Let me untie you oh, my lord!

She does. They're off as . . .

Ronan *(aside)*
Well, look how nothing changes in the world
who turns it? Royal runt and poshy girl!
well . . . we'll see! To the mixing decks!

He points his remote . . .

My lord! My lady! Wait for me!

Sample:

ONCE MORE INTO THE BREACH
DEAR FRIENDS ONCE MORE
ONCE MORE
ONE TIME
ONE TIME.

Flash Mob make threatening ready-for-war sounds and sights . . .

TWENTY
SOLDIERS – AGINCOURT

Towler and Brotherton somewhere, listening to headphones.

Towler
We got the barge on wire
d'you hear what's going down?
Brotherton
The kids both black and blue are breaking out!
the prince and poor and totties trying it on!
look out some semtex, mate, we're going in!
I must put my head
over parapet and not duck
and remember all this
for my money-spinning tell-it-all book . . .

Towler (*thoughtfully*)
the guttersnipe's gone silent
the differently abled donut's been cut out . . .
say, Brotherton,
we were true brothers to our class . . .
we'd back that boy, against the prince and tarts.
Brotherton
And rise up, key figures in a revolution
New Model Army Generals,
and with bigger parts . . .

They role-play . . .

Towler
We're in, mob-handed, standard-issues ready
it's dark, and . . . nobody's hand is steady
a sound there . . . I shoot! You shoot . . . another here!
Lights up! Past princes! Whoops! Oh dear!!

They take out their guns.

Brotherton
Big up the crippled boy and work him from below.
Towler
Democracy! Meritocracy!
What could go wrong? Let's go!
Brotherton
Which way?
Towler
To the top!!

They head murderously off.

TWENTY-ONE
NOW ALL THE YOUTH OF ENGLAND
ARE ON FIRE

Tower block room.
   Slapper is styling Ed's hair with her nail scissors.

Slapper
   I've always thought you should
   go cutting-edge
   a sharper look
   a happening king.

   Pog listening to a mobile call, Snoop watching him.

Pog
   Yes, Ronan.
   Yep.
   Yo. (*end of message*)
   Little walk in the air for ya, posh boy . . .

   Points his gun . . .

   My dad thieved this
   I thieved it outta my dad's sock drawer.
   Thieving runs in my family.
   Let's go.

   Slapper quietly cuts Ed's bonds, one by one.

Pog
   You heard me, no?
Ed
   Not moving.
   You'll have to shoot me.
   Go.
Slapper
   He's dead.
   A MacNugget his goodbye meal.

Pog points the gun. Fires. Nothing happens.
Ed springs, knocks Pog flat, seizes the gun, cocks it.

Ed (*instructive*)
Safety catch. Off.
Cock.
Aim. Officer composure.
Fire.

He shoots a graze out of Pog's impressive hairstyle.

Ed
Knowing how to use a gun
. . . runs in *my* family.

Snoop leaps at Ed.

Snoop
Grrrrrrarf arf arfarf!
Slapper
He's dead!
At last a doggie's goodboy treat!
Ed
Stop that barking.
Stop it.
You!
Quiet!
Sit
Sit
Lie down.
Down.
Die for England.

Snoop Doggy-Dogg does.

Command also runs in my family.
(*to Snoop*) Stay.
(*to Pog*) Stay.
(*to Slapper*) Follow me.

Slapper
To the split ends of the earth,
O my prince!

They run out of the door.

TWENTY-TWO
GOVERNMENT – THE REMIX

A street somewhere . . .
One grey-haired Wrinkly stands, waiting for a bus.
Sample:

NOW EVERY I MEAN EVERY
YOUTH OF ENGLAND
IS ON FIRE
ON FIRE
OH CHECK THE FIRE.

Streeties and Totties join the bus queue with mobiles,
ghetto-blasters, personal radios.
    Switch on and listen to . . . the house remix of . . .

Roban (*voice-over*)
Hey there all you under-twenties jive
welcome to Radio Youth-Alive!!
before we get down and dirty
here's a political broadcast
by the newest freshest party . . .

Ronan stands apart listening, as . . .

Serena (*voice-over*)
Wrinklies Zimmer-drivers Old flesh
for that you have disappointed us
for that instead of wisdom
you showed us spin
for that you sheltered us not with your age

but took us to war
be it known
all citizens over twenty are now non-citizens
but are reclassified
asylum-seekers.
Go seek asylum
for that you thought education was about rules
here are your rules
no talking
be seen and not heard
no running in the corridors
no running anywhere
we offer you
tough love
short sharp shock
zero-tolerance.
We are seizing
your weapons of mass destruction
viz: greed megalomania meanness
think detention think exclusion
think the end of *your* confusion.
Give it up for the Teen-Green Government!
Come on down
Or we'll take ya down!

Serena (*voice-over*)
Give it up for the new youthful king!

Hal (*voice-over*)
Subjects
I command you to
by Divine Right
I command you to rock the world!
Like our predecessors
our army kills
our government tells you what to do
our secret service spies on you.
We're fierce and cruel, mean and petty,

the only difference?
We're young and pretty!
Old heads on old shoulders
The hip-replaced one and all
no sudden moves
no moves at all!

*Everybody switches off their listening devices. All
young look towards the Wrinkly.*
  *He/she starts to edge off. Young things swoop, carry
him/her off screaming to certain terrible discomfort.*
  Ronan having watched all this . . .

Ronan
  Well, this is a game!
  It's like I'm back at school
  Not picked for the team, a crippled fool
  Well friends, watch out, I'm not liking this
  But I'll fix this baby king and minging miss! . . .
  Every dog should have his day
  At the end of the day, Des, it's my play!

He limps off to dark deeds....

TWENTY-THREE
A COSMIC QUESTION-AND-ANSWER SESSION

Cheviot, on the roof in awesome weather . . .

Cheviot
  you may ask yourself
  as the gallant crew of the Starship *Enterprise*
  saves yet another threatened life form
  in its ten-year mission
  why do they never get earth leave?
  it might be
  that, with their fierce moral codes and

their high expectation of correct human behaviour . . .
their family let's say their dad
doesn't come up to scratch
this is the abused-child subtext
tragic modern-girl heroine check me out.

She wipes two tears away from her eyes . . .

So the crew
particularly the wonderful commander
prefer to do overtime long long hours
in outer space . . .
Eh, Mr Spock?
(*as Spock*) That would be logical, Captain.
Eh, Uhuru?
(*as Uhuru*) Yes, Captain.
Wanna go home, Chekhov?
(*as Chekhov*) Nyet, Captain.
Eh, Scotty?
(*as Scotty*) Yon *Enterprise*'s is hame tae me, Lassie.
(*as Cheviot*) So.

Binoculars . . .

What's happening in the main plot?

Looks far down to where . . .

(*as Spock*) Earthlings in trouble, Captain.

Ed and Slapper running downstairs . . .

Ed
Quick! Down! Out!
Slapper
The star-crossed lovers lose
themselves in the lowly throng!

*Hal and Serena, Streeties and Totties appear, armed
to the teeth.*

Hal
There they are!
Grab them, ya!
Serena
Rip orf his nuts
And ruin her hair!
Greenie
Streeties!
Serena
Totties!
Ed
Not in *this* lowly throng!
Back upstairs!
Climb!

They climb, pursued as . . .
Towler and Brotherton looking far up.

Towler
Two tossing tower blocks!
Which wanking *one*?

Ed and Slapper burst back in upon Pog and Snoop.

Snoop
Arfarfarfarfarfarf!
Pog (*coming round*)
Whaaaaaaaa . . . ?
Ed (*to both*)
Sit!
Stay!

They sit and stay.
Ed goes to the window, looks down, sees . . .

Towler and Brotherton.
Chaps! Here!

Looks towards . . . a shot narrowly misses him.

No! It's me!

Another shot narrowly misses him.

It's *me* you're aiming at!
Your future king!
That's your retirement package totalled!
That's your grace-and-favour apartment
out the window!

He seizes Slapper's hand . . .

Ed
Let's go upwards.
Climb!
Cheviot
We should intervene
Assemble the entire crew!

*Flash Mob rip off bits of material from their outfits,
revealing starship insignia!*

Set flash-flood co-ordinates, crew!

*Flash Mob provide a sound of tremendous, out-of-
control water.*

Freak lightning co-ordinates!

Light sabres on.

Get ready to go in!!

She looks through binoculars, where . . .
    *Ed and Slapper emerge on the opposite roof. They
run to the edge.*

Slapper
It's hopeless!
Ed
We could just *jump*.
Slapper
End it all

better than
he goes back to his palace
she goes back to her council maisonette
he goes off skiing
he goes on royal visits
he meets princesses countesses
photo shoots in *Hello, OK*
girls from the upper walks of society
but they just don't rattle his chains
because
he can't forget her
her devil-may-care attitude
her flat stomach
her intense gaze.

They look into each other's eyes.

Ed
You're really very sweet.

They kiss.

But I'd love another option . . .

Flash Mob do a magnificent rendition of the Star Trek *theme tune.*
    From the opposite tower-block roof they push and manoeuvre a fire ladder on which is . . .

Cheviot
Grab this!
That's its ten-year mission.
Every starship
to seek out new galaxies
to boldly go . . .
to spatially sort it . . .
but make it snappy . . .
I can't hold her much longer, Captain!

Ed and Slapper start to walk across the yawning chasm on the fire ladder as . . .

Slapper
Oh, the sky's so dark!

TWENTY-FOUR
RONAN MIXES IT

Ronan walks on carrying a large cardboard box with 'Argos' on the side. Watches the rescue happening as a clock strikes twelve during . . .

Ronan
The lights burn blue
it is now dead midnight
cold fearful drops
stand on my trembling flesh.
In older plays I'd start a mighty fight
and die upon the gleaming sword of right
but I was weaned on video satellite and cable
I'll end this entertainment as only I am able . . .

He opens the box, unwraps. Inside is a huge remote control. He points the remote . . . Samples: very big!

NOW IS THE WINTER OF OUR DISCONTENT . . .
NOW ALL THE YOUTH OF ENGLAND ARE ON FIRE . . .
TO BE OR NOT TO BE THAT IS THE QUESTION . . .
O BRAVE NEW WORLD
THAT HAS SUCH PEOPLE IN IT . . .
WE ARE SUCH STUFF AS DREAMS ARE MADE ON . . .
ONCE MORE INTO THE BREACH
DEAR FRIENDS ONCE MORE . . .
IN ACTION HOW LIKE AN ANGEL
IN APPREHENSION HOW LIKE A GOD . . .
A BRAVE VESSEL WHO HAD NO DOUBT

SOME NOBLE CREATURE IN HER
DASHED ALL TO PIECES.

He smiles.

Ronan
Now's not a good time
For why? For this
Nothing goes forward
All's 'repeats'
Observe.

*He points the remote . . . other characters all wind
back . . . then, in their different places, all repeat . . .*

Slapper
Oh, the sky's so dark!
Ed
I'd like another option.
Streeties
Streeties!
Totties
Totties!
Hal
There they are!
Grab them, ya!
Serena
Rip orf his nuts
And ruin her hair!
Snoop
Arfararf!
Cheviot
Make it snappy
I can't hold her much longer, Captain!
Ronan
Everything's mixed, on replay . . .
Looping round
Regard . . .

Presses remote . . . they repeat themselves.

Slapper
Oh, the sky's so dark!
Ed
I'd like another option!
Ronan
All on 'hold'.

He points the remote. Everybody freezes.

O brave new world
that has such tech toys in it!
Art is deconstructed
all is film mist a digital stalking
let my finger do the walking!

He presses his remote to . . .
Ed and Slapper walking to the very edge of the roof.

Slapper
Let's jump!
Ed
I'd like another option!
Cheviot
Make it snappy
I can hardly hold her, Captain!

They nearly jump, they nearly fall . . .

Ronan
Now . . . where's 'rewind'?

Ronan presses 'rewind'.
They reverse backwards away from it.
He puts them on 'hold'.
Then to Serena and Hal running up the stairs.

Hal
There they are!
Grab them, ya!

Serena
Rip orf his nuts
And ruin her hair!

*Ronan presses 'reverse'. Serena and Hal run
backwards down the stairs . . . 'Hold'.
    Presses remote for Towler and Brotherton bringing
their rifles to their shoulders, aiming.*

Brotherton
Shall I take the little bleeder out?

*Ronan presses remote.
    Towler and Brotherton take rifles down, walk
backwards.
    Pog and Snoop get up, run to the door.*

Snoop
Arfarfarf!

Reverses, runs back and lies down again.

Ronan
Freeze-frame!!

*Everybody in freeze-frame. Slightly distorted, slightly
quivering, but still.*

TWENTY-FIVE
WHAT A PIECE OF WORK AM I . . .

Ronan
What a piece of work am I
How noble in reason
How infinite in faculties!
In form and movement
how express and admirable!
In action how like an angel!

In apprehension how like a god!
A fallen angel!
A god with a remote!
As me villain, you audience
and in this modern play
we get to pick.
Here's our choice of viewing
Select one, quick!

A large Satellite and Cable *viewing magazine appears.*

(*Reads.*) 'The suicide of a prince
a love story
she loves him he loves him'

Plays . . .

Slapper
Let's jump!
Ed
I'd like another option!

Hold . . .

Ronan (*reads*)
'An action thriller
a hot young prince uprises kills'

Plays . . .

Hal
There they are!
Grab them, ya?
Serena
Rip orf his nuts
And ruin her hair!

Hold . . .

Ronan (*reads*)
'Sci-fi
an alien spaceship lands

its only passenger a sweet but unearthly girlthing
who saves the undeserving human race'

Plays . . .

Cheviot
Make it snappy
I can barely hold her, Captain!

Hold . . .

Ronan
Or
(*Reads.*) 'Fantasy fable . . .
a rabid dog breaks loose
humans terrified to a frenzy'

Plays . . .

Snoop
Arfarfaarfarfarfarf!

Hold . . .

Ronan
A spy thriller perhaps
(*reads*) 'A Le Carré tale of unreliable operatives'

Plays . . .

Brotherton
Shall I take the little bleeder out?

Hold . . .

Ronan
A multiple love story
'Posh girls meet homeless boys'

Plays . . .

Totties
Streeties!

Streeties
  Totties!
Ronan (*reads on*)
  'A musical'
Tottie/Streeties (*sing/dance*)
  Ooo
  I wanna dance with somebody
  wanna feel the heat with somebody
  Ooooo
  I wanna dance with somebody
  with somebody who lo-oves me . . .

  Hold . . .

Ronan
  Well, apart from re-runs repeats
  (*Reads.*) *Friends*, *Sex in the City*, *Dawson's Creek*
  Reality shows docu-soaps
  the constantly bad bad CNN BBC SkyNews
  There's your choice, you choose . . .
  Which channel shall we zap upon?

He encourages the audience to pick one of the options.
  Whichever one they pick, he goes with . . .

Okay, (*title of choice*), here goes.

He presses the remote . . .
  We get one line then . . .
  Everyone shot by a huge electric shiver.
  They are still.
  Then . . . nothing.

Oh . . . what's going down?

A flash of lightning.
  A clap of thunder.
  We get the same line then . . .
  Everyone shot by a huge electric shiver.
  They are still.

Work! Channel! Play!

He points remote. But something's happened.
He gets . . . subtitles carded . . . languages highlighted.

Cheviot (*in Iraqi*)
Tha canneh fenneka,
Ya Abeti Al-Azeez
Anal hathi al-meyah al ha-ejatu
[If by your art, my dearest father
you have put the wild waters in this roar,
allay them . . .].

Ronan
Sound's all distorted . . . !

Ed (*in Afghani*)
The sky, it seems,
would pour down stinking pitch . . .

Ronan
I must have pressed some *foreign* DVD
option . . .

Slapper (*in Serbian*)
Divan brod's mekim plemenitim
Bicem na sebi
[A brave vessel
who had no doubt some noble creature in her]

Serena (*Ruandan*)
Dashed all to pieces!

Hal (*Somali*)
O the cry did knock against my very heart.

Towler (*Matabele*)
Unmuntu ongamyanga
[Poor souls]

Brotherton (*Matabele*)
Owatshayo
[They perished]

Ronan
What *is* this?

O what *is* this?
Rewind!
Where's the English?
Cheviot (*in Iraqi*)
If by your art, my dearest father
you have put the wild waters in this roar,
allay them . . .
Ronan
Sound's all distorted . . . !
Ed (*in Afghani*)
The sky, it seems,
would pour down stinking pitch . . .
Ronan
I must have pressed some *foreign* DVD
option . . .
in English, *English*!!

They replay . . . in English . . .

Slapper
A brave vessel
who had no doubt some noble creature in her.
Ronan
Ah good!
Serena
Dashed all to pieces!
Hal
O the cry did knock against my very heart.
Towler
Poor souls.
Brotherton
They perished.
Ronan
O brilliant! (*not*)
The *Discovery* Channel!
Cheviot
Crew!

Flash Mob group magnificently around her.

Had I been any god of power, I would
have sunk the sea within the earth or ere
it should the good ship so have swallowed and
the fraught souls within her.

Storm-makers throw a magnificent, tremendous storm.

Ronan
  Technology!
  Wickedness!
  Entertainment!
  Ruined by the weather!!
All
  Oh typical England!
Serena
  Henley Regatta one needs sunshine.
Ed
  Polo. Shooting.
  Rain comes you're stuffed.
Greenie
  Burglary.
  Rain. The silent policeman.
Cheviot
  It's the same even in space.
  We're at the mercy of meteors.
Pog
  Dogwalking ditto.
  So.
  All's F-star-star-ked!
  MacDonald's BurgerKingKFC
  Pizza Hut Pizza Express
  Yo Sushi Happy Noodle Indian Chippy?

*All make different catering choices. At last! Your only
chance to improvise your own dialogue!*

Big Mac Green Thai Fish
Deep Pan Pizza Dough Balls
Curry Sashimi Deep Fried
Mars Bar Kebab Doner . . .

Everybody exits, checking purses, money, as . . .
  Ronan smashes his huge remote . . .

Ronan
  Everything lets me down!!
Cheviot
  We're in the stratosphere, earthling
  No air
  Things burn up
  The strain on both the human body
  and technology's too much
  even a starship's chassis gets fatigued
  and if you watch it over and over again . . .
  it's the crew that really keeps it up aloft . . .
Ronan
  What are you drivelling on about?
Cheviot
  I'm doing the message, wombat.
  Be *human*, dude.
  Improve the technology
  develop better strategies
  grow up
  have a come-back series with
  a new cast in sharper clothes.
  It's *over* Ronan . . .
  Rain stopped play.
  The world wobbles on
  but
  good's prevailed.
  Doner kebab?

Ronan (*giving in*)
Chilli sauce?
Cheviot
That would be logical . . .
Ronan
But evil's still *lurking* . . .
Cheviot
Oh, *always*, Dude.

Cheviot and Ronan exit past Snoop Doggy-Dogg, who goes for him.

Snoop
Ararfararfarfararfarf!!
Ronan
Shut up! Sit down! Sit!!
Stay!
Wait!!

Snoop Doggy-Dogg does. Ronan points his remote at the lights. Blackout.

End.

Comedy Based on Appalling Truths

Bryony Lavery interviewed by Jim Mulligan

Discontented Winter: House Remix is the third play Bryony Lavery has had commissioned for the *Connections* project. It is also a major departure from her previous work in that her other plays, while relevant to young people, could be performed by adults in the mainstream theatre.

> *Remix* is absolutely for young people and needs the energy of the age group it is written for. This is especially for them. It is something they can do better than anybody else in the world. It is also a comedy, and while you're writing it you have the black dog on your shoulder snarling, 'It's got to be funny.'

The discontented winter of the title is a clear reference to *Richard III*. The language of Ronan's opening rant, as in Richard's first soliloquy, is raw and self-abusive, with a self-loathing that is the justification for the actions to come. In this play, however, the villainy is shared out among the hoodlums, and it leaves room for Ronan to have grace and to do some good. The squabbles for power between the warring factions and the willingness to bump off rivals (in this play only contemplated) also resemble the violence of Shakespeare's play.

Remix in the title gives companies the chance to remix the words using scratching, blending and repeats – all the techniques young people are familiar with from DJ-ing and rapping.

> The only music I don't care for is rap music, but I decided to pay it some attention and I discovered it is

actually very interesting. It is where the meat of protest and disturbance lies. Now obviously I couldn't just put raps in. I had to do it my own way. So I conceived the idea of sampling the play. The analogy of a video is apt here. The words are there but the production can cut words or repeat them or use effects. I've bled in bits of Shakespeare and *Friends* and *Dawson's Creek* so, if I can do it, they can do it. I find that really exciting.

The comedy of *Remix* lies in the situation, the language and the characters. These elements combine in moments that are hilarious but not so funny seen in the light of the stratification of our society, the violence, the terrorism and the ring of steel that surrounds our politicians and royalty – which can be penetrated by a comedian dressed up as Osama bin Laden. The story is that two princes are to be kidnapped by two groups, one of whose leaders, Serena, wants to marry her prince, while the other, Ronan, wants a ransom. In the confusion and mix-up, Slapper and Ed fall in love and Hal decides that Serena is the tart whose legs he can get between. He might as well, in other words, marry her. Thus the high plummet, the low leap.

This comedy is both tongue-in-cheek and serious. It is based on some appalling truths. I'm a republican. I think the notion of us still kow-towing to a group of individuals because of the family they were born into is ludicrous. I can't believe we're still doing it. It makes my blood boil, but I need that kind of anger to fuel my designs and endeavours. I want my play to subvert people, to alchemise them or at least to get them to change their minds.

The characters in *Remix* are clearly divided into three groups: the Princes, the Top Totties and the Low Streeties, while Cheviot is on a different plane from them all – a detached observer, a girl anorak, absolutely isolated in a world of fantasy, but who in the end emerges to save people. All these characters, coming from social groups that are divided by chasms of wealth, influence and privilege, use very similar language, characterised by a foul-mouthed lewdness which heightens poetic rhythms, images, contrasts and verbal shock. What will distinguish them on the stage will not be the words they use but their accents, demeanour, gesture, body language and dress.

If there is one quality that permeates *Remix* is must be incongruity. There is a manic dog, upper-class women who behave like sluts, princes who behave like gangsters, a slapper who is generous and loving, bodyguards who are tempted to rise up as the New Model Army, and other characters who swirl around creating chaos or order as required. The play appears to be about young people trying to control their circumstances by kidnapping authority figures. Both Serena and Ronan have clearly expressed dreams, huge aspirations for celebrity and respect; but their versions of these are flawed because society is flawed. Serena wants to be the Queen of Hearts with all the references and overtones that concept carries, and Ronan wants to be the Stephen Hawking of hoodlums, which for a disabled person is a poignant role model. Their solution to society's ills will be sorted if the world is ruled by the Teen-Green Government.

In control of all the action are the storm-makers of the Flash Mob who rule the entire world of the play. They are anarchic technological wizards who could if they wanted, simply by using mobile phones, organise a rave for ten thousand people in a field in Hertfordshire, or gridlock a city on a whim. As Ronan uses his massive remote control to fast-forward, to repeat, to reverse, the storm-makers bring on the storm that ends the play.

Bryony Lavery encourages those who are involved in *Remix* to go mad with invention and to be sane with caution. Everything in the play has to be invented, but at the same time there has to be selection so that it is both adventurous and artful.

I called it *House Remix* because I want each theatrical house to remix it in their own way. This is a big show for a big stage and I want all the most adventurous directors to go for it. I've made it daunting for the faint-hearted and enticing for the bold of heart.

Production Notes

Discontented Winter is Bryony Lavery's third play for
Connections, following *More Light* in 1997 and *Illyria* in
2002. It is more comedic than the other two, and has real
theatrical challenges, which will enhance its appeal for the
truly bold of heart. Bryony encourages you to 'go mad
with invention and sane with caution' over set, lighting,
costume, staging – and even with her own dialogue.
Actors with non-English speeches should find their own
translations. The part of the Endangered Wrinkly is good
for a guest appearance by an adult who deserves it. The
cast is of twenty-plus with some flexibility of gender. The
Flash Mob can be as big or small as the numbers
available, and the play is suitable for a wide age range.

Bryony always starts from something that makes her
angry, and is fervently opposed both to the monarchy and
a class-stratified society With this play she also wanted to
create challenges she couldn't herself solve – including the
video clips and sampling, in both of which she lacks exper-
tise. She started out thinking she was going to do a rewrite
of *Richard III* for young people, but then decided that by
pushing this idea she would get something even more
interesting. So the sources the characters sample and remix
range from Shakespeare all the way to *Dawson's Creek*.

CHARACTERS

RONAN There are parallels between Ronan's speech
on pages 215–16 and Buckingham's first soliloquy in
Richard III ('Now is the winter of our discontent . . .').

Both characters talk about the rejection of their mothers, which has led, in part, to their decision to act against normal moral codes. As far as Ronan's deformity is concerned, you'll need to decide whether he's carrying an internal or external hurt. The remote control (which is a symbol of power like an orb or a sceptre) could be an extension of Ronan's hand, and so part of his deformity. 'A lot of the character's speech is sampled from TV and film. Ronan is a really bright boy and at some point he's seen *Richard III* and thought, 'I'll be like that.' Like Richard, Ronan is aware of the prevailing forces within society and knows how to manipulate them to his own advantage.

SLAPPER is a particularly tough character, who has to contend with and try to break from society's expectations of a girl who has been so-labelled. She wears 'secret spectacles' because she relies on her looks and image and doesn't want people to know she needs glasses.

RONAN and SLAPPER There are parallels between this relationship and Richard's wooing of Lady Anne in Act One, Scene Two of *Richard III*. Here Ronan has devised a plan to get Slapper's boyfriend 'banged up' so that he can woo her himself – the only way he can win a girl, he believes, because of his physical disadvantages. Slapper is drawn to Ronan not through desire for him, but out of a need to have a protector in a dangerous world.

SERENA If you explore Serena's speech in Scene Sixteen beginning 'I get people . . .' (page 249) and explore what each of her lines means, you'll understand the character's intentions. Despite the reference to Princess Diana, her motives are not romantic but planned and calculated. 'I get to go round Africa holding damaged babies' may appear to mean 'I get to give love', but its cynicism is revealed by the key line, 'I get respect.' Later, in Scene

Nineteen, Serena is comparable with Lady Macbeth as she urges Prince Hal to murder his older brother, heir to the throne.

RONAN and SERENA Scene Sixteen is about attraction, flirtation and a struggle for power between the two – particularly the following moment on page 250:

> **Ronan** Let's see yer tail then, Roland,
>
> *Serena lifts her skirt, shows him.*
>
> (*looking*) Or we could team up
> I get into you
> You open up to me . . .?

Ronan's main weapon is his intelligence, which he uses to compensate for his deformity. Serena, equally intelligent, adds beauty to her armoury. Serena's showing off her tail is an act of defiance. Decide how Serena lifts her skirt: at the front or back? The actions have different implications. Don't over-complicate the scene, and particularly Serena's speech on page 249. This isn't a romantic encounter: the two come together to pool their considerable brains.

CHEVIOT We meet her and think: here's the bright, brainy girl who's a bit nerdy and reads a lot of books. In fact she watches a lot of TV, like the Discovery Channel. She's a very ambitious girl and wants in some ways to be other than human, like a Vulcan in *Star Trek*. Cheviot is linked to and able to control the natural forces of the Flash Mob. She might be likened to Prospero in *The Tempest*, marshalling the elements.

THE FLASH MOB The term refers to a group of people who receive text messages telling them to meet at a given time and place and await further instructions. A second message details a task they must all perform, then afterwards they're told to 'vanish'. In the play the Flash

Mob arrive, set up the scenes as quickly as possible and then disappear. Decide if they are part of the world of the play or facilitators on its periphery – a force that makes things happen. The eventual revealing of the Flash Mob as members of the Starship *Enterprise* crew gives the group an identity, but they are active throughout the play. They could, for example, be used in Scene Five as servants to Princes Ed and Hal, suggesting simply and effectively the privileges of royalty.

ED and HAL The two are based upon our own royal princes, and present a physical contrast to the poorer characters within the play. Hal's speech in Scene Nineteen (pages 255–6) 'samples' Henry's speech before Agincourt in Act Three, Scene One of *Henry V* ('Once more unto the breach, dear friends, once more . . .') In this scene Hal effortlessly becomes the alpha male by sidelining Ronan, who has to revert to another role and plan. It would be good for the actors playing Ed and Hal to explore the well-documented details of royal lifestyle.

POG and GREENIE They are the lieutenants of Ronan's army, and not particularly bright. You might want to look at the 'droogs' in Stanley Kubrick's *A Clockwork Orange* for clues to these characters. Don't play Pog and Greenie for laughs: they're very dangerous, and should be genuinely menacing.

SNOOP DOGGY-DOGG is based upon a real dog who belongs to Bryony's sister. He should have a full character.

TOWLER *and* BROTHERTON are hired thugs who stand behind the royal family. You see such functionaries all the time on the news, protecting royals and politicians, and they're as much killers as the Streeties,. They should be looking around constantly for potential hazards and danger – at exits and gangways.

STAGING AND TECHNICAL NOTES

The staging of the play is its biggest challenge, but offers exciting possibilities for flexibility and inventiveness. It's a perfect vehicle for students to do the creative solving with the director. Be really adventurous about the solutions. There isn't a definitive way of doing this play, it's about brainstorming and sharing ideas.

- Decide how much can be done with virtually no technical resources at all: for example, a toilet on its own or even the sound effect of a toilet flushing would establish the setting for Scene Seven (page 228).

- There are many power failures and blackouts in this city, so its denizens use searchlights, neon signs, candles, polluted suns, computer screens, stars to light the scenes.

- When Bryony wrote the play she intended no scene to have anyone standing on just one level. In thinking about the setting of the play, you might imagine a future or parallel world bombarded by different influences: popular culture, high art, etc. Take a look at Ridley Scott's *Blade Runner* and at *A Clockwork Orange* – particularly the borrowed and invented language in the latter.

- Physically the two towers can be represented in a number of ways. Experiment with different proportions in different spaces. Looking up at a tower block, as several characters do during the play, means you have to assume a particular physical stance.

- The play has a particularly heightened style, so you need to find ways of helping the audience with the locations. Experiment with Bryony's suggestion that the Flash Mob should 'card' (display a title for) each of the scenes to tell you where you are. Other stage directions might be incorporated into the dialogue – for example, 'Another miraculous, youth-organised disappearing trick' (page 237).

EXERCISES

Divide the cast into smaller groups of about five to work on different sections of the play. The task is to do some collective scene-solving exercises. Use these sections and work for fifteen minutes on them:

- Scene Eleven, page 238 (*Flash Mob provide an exciting chase sequence with dinky cars*).

- Scene Fourteen, page 246 (*Flash Mob bring on some planks . . . Ronan and Greenie walk along a plank, step onto, then down into a bobbing boat*).

- Scene Nineteen, page 255 (*Flash Mob add a capella martial music*).

- Scene Twenty-Two, page 261 (*Streeties and Totties join the bus queue with mobiles, ghetto-blasters, personal radios. Switch on and listen to . . . the house remix*).

This is what happened when the play was workshopped at the Keswick retreat, but you'll have other ideas.

CHASE SEQUENCE The group considered several possibilities, from using remote-control cars to torch beams suggesting headlights. Eventually four actors sat on chairs, as if in a car, and mimed driving – turning steering wheels, changing gears – while two others ran around the space pretending to hold toy cars. The two sets of actors synchronised their movements, one responding to the actions of the other. All the while the group provided appropriate sound effects – brakes screeching, etc.

BOBBING BOAT The group used wooden poles to represent the sides of the boat. These were raised when actors 'step onto, then down into' the boat to indicate the change in levels. The actors' movement demonstrated the bobbing of the boat as they walked tentatively along, swaying from side to side. The group's sound effects of creaking timbers added to the overall effect.

A CAPELLA MARTIAL MUSIC The group underscored Hal's speech by providing stirring vocal renditions of the theme to *The Dambusters* plus the *Three Lions* football song. One person provided the bass, another the melody. Different pieces of music were introduced at the start of each new thought within the speech.

GHETTO-BLASTERS The group played the action on a number of levels, some of the actors standing on chairs while the others remained on the floor. The actor who played the rapper provided a bass beat while the others talked or riffed over the top. Although the speeches of Serena, Ronan and Hal are written as voice-overs, they should still be performed live, in keeping with the overall spirit of the piece. Experiment with the proportions of the various ghetto-blasters – they get progressively bigger as more actors come on stage. This scene demonstrates the power of people listening to others.

SCENE TWENTY-FOUR with its repeated samples and episodes presents one of the biggest challenges. The staging of this scene is all about logistics. Work on the 'rewinds' and 'freeze-frames', such as 'Pog and Snoop get up, run to the door . . . reverses, runs back and lies down again' (page 271) – to include reverse dog-barking! Be completely authentic and accurate in the repetition of these sections. So for instance, repeated lines must be exactly the same. When rewinding a DVD the result is a stuttering reverse motion, and this is something to experiment with. Get the cast to see what happens when you play a video at double or triple speed to achieve the impeccable, precise staging required for this scene.

NOTES ON THE TEXT

When an ellipsis (. . .) appears within the text, it suggests a changed direction of thought within a character.

All the stage directions are there to help Bryony write the play, but ultimately they are negotiable. They're not definitive, but guidelines. You can use them in different ways. The words, are generally not negotiable, but the sub-title of the play – *House Remix* – indicates an allowance for cultural variations – you might find local variations on words such as 'wotcha'. Some of the slang has been invented and is therefore not specific to any one locale. It's a mongrel language.

In Scene Six (page 227) Slapper and Cheviot can actually hear each other.

In Scene Ten (page 236). the dance doesn't have to be Kathakali, so long as a story is told through the use of hands.

In Scene Fifteen the Top Totties are masked and don't speak, so that they can't be identified later.

In Scene Sixteen (page 246) the reason why Ronan wants to kidnap Hal isn't logical (he believes he can't be tried for treason if he kills only the second in line to the throne).

In Scene Nineteen, Ronan's joining forces with Serena and Hal may seem out of character. But he's only pretending to go along with them to suit his own ends.

In Scene Twenty-One (page 260) Slapper's line 'He's dead/A MacNugget his goodbye meal' is a prediction: she also wants it to appear that she's still on Pog's side.

REHEARSAL GAMES AND EXERCISES

Status and changes of status are very much in evidence in the characters of this play. Keith Johnstone's seminal book *Impro* (Methuen, 1981) is valuable here, in particular the 'Master–Servant' exercises. On page 69 Johnstone quotes from *The Human Zoo* by Desmond Morris (Cape 1969):

Desmond Morris . . . gives 'ten golden rules' for people who are Number Ones. He says, 'They apply to all leaders, from baboons to modern presidents and prime ministers.' They are:

1   You must clearly display the trappings, postures and gestures of dominance.
2   In moments of active rivalry you must threaten your subordinates aggressively.
3   In moments of physical challenge you (or your delegates) must be able to forcibly overpower your subordinates.
4   If a challenge involves brain rather than brawn you must be able to outwit your subordinates.
5   You must suppress squabbles that break out between your subordinates.
6   You must reward your immediate subordinates by permitting them to enjoy the benefits of their high ranks.
7   You must protect the weaker members of the group from undue persecution.
8   You must make decisions concerning the social activities of your group.
9   You must reassure your extreme subordinates from time to time.
10 You must take the initiative in repelling threats or attacks arising from outside your group.

- Start rehearsals with exercises exploring status as a good way into the characters and world of the play.

- Play the game 'The Court of the Holy Dido' with the cast (it's described in Keith Johnstone's book). The group sit in a circle quietly observing one another.

They are only allowed to move or speak by raising their hand and awaiting permission. For example:

Matt Permission to scratch my nose?
Judge Permission denied, Brother Matt.

As an extension of this the group, again presided over by an appointed judge, are only allowed to speak when holding a designated object, such as a rolled-up piece of paper.

A Permission to speak?
Judge Permission granted.
A May I sing a rousing chorus of 'Oh What a Beautiful Morning'?
Judge You may.

It's a good way into the Master–Servant exercises, and the cast will enjoy inventing new punishments.

- When developing Snoop Doggy-Dogg's character, you might find the following game useful. You ask one person from a group to pretend to be a dog and to wait outside the room. While they're gone the rest of the group decide what type of dog that person is – big, small, friendly, fierce, etc. On being allowed into the room the person has to work out what type they are as a result of the group's reaction.

REHEARSING THE PLAY

- To experiment with the beginnings and endings of scenes, rehearse from the middle of one scene to the middle of the next. This will help you create a fluid production.

- As a general note it's important to pace your actors throughout the performance. Make sure that the actors' thoughts and actions are simultaneous. Use exercises which encourage them to pick up cues.

- Explore the use of weather in detail and make it accurate. For example, in the storm it must look like someone is actually in a gale. It shouldn't be generalised 'storm acting'.

- Sampling is mixing two pieces of music together – extracting a melody or beat from one source and adding it to another. The skill is in doing it seamlessly so that the two sources make a completely new and fresh-sounding song. Have the cast experiment with sampling extracts.

RESEARCH

Several sources were referred to during the workshop:

Star Trek, the original TV series, starring William Shatner as Captain Kirk.

A Clockwork Orange, Stanley Kubrick's controversial film.

The Stepford Wives, the film made from Ira Levin's novel in 1974, remade starring Nicole Kidman in 2004.

Photographs could be another source of inspiration when exploring the world of the play. Nick Danziger's *British*, a photographic exploration of the British class system, is a good source.

based on a workshop led by Suzy Graham-Adriani
transcribed by Dominic Francis

ECLIPSE

Simon Armitage

Characters

Six friends

Klondike, the oldest
Tulip, a tomboy
Polly and **Jane,** twins
Midnight, male, blind
Glue Boy, a glue-sniffer

A stranger

Lucy Lime

SCENE ONE

A police waiting room. Seven chairs in a row. Glue Boy, Polly and Jane, Midnight and Tulip are sitting in five of them. Klondike enters the room and sits on one of the empty chairs.

Klondike Tulip.

Tulip Klondike.

Klondike Midnight.

Midnight Alright.

Klondike Missed the bus, then couldn't find it. Sorry I'm late.

Midnight Are we in trouble?

Klondike Anyone been in yet?

Tulip No, just told us to sit here and wait.

Klondike Oh, like that, is it? Glue Boy.

Glue Boy Klondike.

Klondike Extra Strong Mint?

Glue Boy Bad for your teeth.

Midnight Klondike, tell me the truth.

Klondike And how are the split peas?

Polly *and* **Jane** We're the bees' knees.

Polly Yourself?

Klondike Could be worse, could be better.

Midnight Klondike, we're in bother, aren't we?

Klondike Three times. Who am I? St Peter?

Off, a voice calls 'Martin Blackwood'.

Midnight Me first? I thought we'd have time to get it straight.

Polly Say as you speak . . .

299

Jane . . . speak as you find.
Klondike Say what you think, speak your mind. Clear?
Midnight Not sure.
Klondike Glue Boy, show him the door.
Tulip Klondike, why don't you tell him what's what?
  He's pissing his pants.
Klondike Let's all settle down. Midnight, stick to the facts.
  The oldies were up on the flat with the van,
  we were down in the crags.
  They were waiting to gawp at the total eclipse of the sun,
  we were kids, having fun.
  It was August eleventh, nineteen ninety-nine,
  they were pinning their hopes
  on the path of the moon,
  they were setting their scopes and their sights
  on a point in the afternoon sky
  where the sun put its monocle into its eye.
  The first and last that we saw of her. Right?
Tulip Right.
Polly *and* **Jane** Amen.
Midnight Just tell me again.

  Off, a voice calls 'Martin Blackwood'.

Tulip Stick to the facts. You were down on the sand . . .
Midnight I was down on the sand.
  The mothers and fathers were up on the land.
  Was it dark?

  Exit Midnight into the interview room.

Tulip What a fart.
Klondike Oh, leave him. Blind as a bat. Sympathy vote.
  He'll be alright. Anyway, who's said what? Tulip?
Tulip No fear, kept mum like those two did.
Klondike Polly, Jane?
Polly Thought we'd keep schtum till you came.

Klondike Good move.

Glue Boy What about you?

Klondike What about me? What about you?

Glue Boy No, nothing.

Klondike Well, that's alright then.

Jane What can you hear through the crack?

Polly He was egging himself, I know that.

Tulip Shh. No, not a word.

Klondike Can you see through the glass?

Tulip Give us a leg-up . . . No, it's frosted.

Polly Moon came up. Sun was behind.

Jane Nothing to say. Nothing to hide.

Klondike Correct. Let's get a grip. No need for anyone losing their head.

Tulip The copper who came to the house said we're in this up to our necks . . .

Klondike FOR CRYING OUT LOUD . . .
    They were on the tops,
    we were down in the rocks.
    Stick to the facts.
    Pax?

Tulip Pax.

Polly *and* **Jane** Pax.

Glue Boy Pax.

Klondike Stick to what we know and we'll be fine.
    Now a moment's silence for Lucy Lime.

All For Lucy Lime.

SCENE TWO

A police interview room.

Midnight Martin Blackwood, they call me Midnight –
    it's a sick joke but I don't mind. Coffee please, two
    sugars, white – don't ask me to say what I saw, I'm

profoundly blind, but I'll tell you as much as I can,
alright?

Cornwall, August, as you know. There's a beach down
there, seaside and all that, cliffs with caves at the back,
but up on the hill there's a view looking south, perfect
for watching a total eclipse of the sun. The mums and
dads were up on the top, we were down in the drop –
we'd just gone along for the trip, killing a few hours.
You see, it's like watching birds or trains but with
planets and stars, and about as much fun as cricket in
my condition, or 3D. There was Glue Boy, Polly and
Jane, Tulip and Klondike and me. Thing is, we were
messing around in the caverns when Lucy appeared.
Her mother and father were up with the rest of the
spotters; she wasn't from round here. Thing is, I was
different then, did a lot of praying, wore a cross, went
to church, thought I was walking towards the light of
the Lord – when it's as dark as it is in here, you follow
any road with any torch. Lucy put me on the straight
and narrow. There's no such thing as the soul, there's
bone and there's marrow. It's just biology. You make
your own light, follow your own nose. She came and
she went. And that's as much as I know.

We were just coming up from one of the smuggler's
coves . . .

SCENE THREE

*A beach in Cornwall, 11 August. At the back of the
beach a broken electric fence dangles down from the
headland above. There are cave entrances in the cliff face.
Polly and Jane are sitting on a rock, combing each other's
hair etc. They are heavily made-up and wearing a lot of
jewellery.*

Polly Your turn.

Jane Okay. The three materials that make up Tutankhamun's mask.

Polly Easy. Solid gold, lapis lazuli and blue glass.

Jane Yes.

Polly Hairbrush. Thanks.

Jane Now you.

Polly Proof of man's existence at the time of extinct mammals.

Jane Er . . . artwork carved on the tusks of mammals.

Polly Correct.

Jane Nail-file. Thanks.

Polly These are a doddle. Ask me something harder.

Jane Who swam through sharks with a seagull's egg in a bandanna?

Polly A bandanna?

Jane Alright, a headband.

Polly The birdmen of Easter Island. Easy-peasy.

Jane Lemon-squeezy.

Polly Cheddar-cheesy.

Jane Japanesey.

Polly Pass me the compact.

Jane Your go, clever clogs.

Polly On the same subject. The statues were studded with . . . which mineral?

Jane Er . . . malachite. No, marble.

Polly No, white coral.

Jane Sugar. When's the test?

Polly Monday next, I think he said.

Jane Oh, I should be alright by then. (*Pause.*) What time do you make it?

Polly Twenty past. Another couple of hours yet, at least.

Jane Mine must be fast.

Polly Let's synchronise, just in case.

Jane It might be yours. Yours might be slow.

Polly I don't think so. Anyway, it's solar-powered – it's been charging up all summer.

Jane Look out, here come the others.

Klondike, Tulip and Glue Boy come running out of one of the caves. Glue Boy is sniffing glue from a plastic bag, and continues to do so throughout. Klondike wears a leather bag on his back and is carrying the skeletal head of a bull. Tulip is wearing Dr Marten boots and a red headscarf like a pirate's.

Klondike Bloody hell, it's a cow's skull.

Tulip How do you know it's not from a sheep?

Klondike You're joking. Look at the size of it. look at the teeth. Some caveman's had this for his tea. Hey, girls, fancy a spare rib?

Polly Take it away, it stinks.

Jane And I bet it's crawling with fleas.

Klondike It's a skull, you pair of dumb belles, not a fleece.

Tulip He found it right at the back of the cave.

Klondike I reckon it fell through the gap in the fence – it's been lying there, waiting for me.

Polly It gives me the creeps.

Glue Boy It's a dinosaur. Ginormous Rex.

Klondike I'm going to frame it or something. Put it in a case.

Tulip takes off her red head-scarf, unfurls it and uses it as a matador's cape.

Tulip Come on Klondike. Olé. Olé.

Polly Where's Midnight?

Tulip Still coming out of the hole. Let's hide.

Jane Don't be rotten. That'd be really tight.

Polly Why don't we just stay here like statues? He can't see us.

Klondike He'd hear us, though. He's got ears like satellite dishes.

Glue Boy Like radar stations.

Tulip Everyone scarper and hide.

Glue Boy Everyone turns into pumpkins when Midnight chimes.

Exit Glue Boy, Polly and Jane.

Tulip Wait, my scarf.

Klondike Leave it.

Exit Klondike and Tulip, leaving the scarf behind. Enter Midnight from the cave, wearing dark glasses and a crucifix around his neck, which he holds out in front of him in his hand.

Midnight Klondike? Tulip? That skull, what is it?

Enter Lucy Lime.

Klondike? Glue Boy. Come on, don't be pathetic. Tulip? Tulip?

Lucy Selling flowers are we?

Midnight Polly? Jane?

Lucy Penny Lane? Singing now, is it?

Midnight I'm Midnight. Who are you?

Lucy I'm twenty-to-three. Look. (*She makes the position of a clock's hands with her arms.*)

Midnight I can't look. I can't see.

Lucy Oh, you should have said. I'm Lucy. Lucy Lime.

Midnight I thought you were one of the others. They said they'd wait for me somewhere around here.

Lucy No, I'm not one of the others. And you can put that thing down. I'm not Dracula's daughter either.

Midnight What, this? Sorry, I'm a believer. It's Jesus, watching over.

Lucy Well, don't point it at me. It's loaded.

An animal noise comes out of one of the caves.

What was that? A bat?

Midnight More like Klondike messing about.

Lucy Klondike?

Midnight Him and Tulip and Glue Boy and the twins. We all came here in a van to do this star-gazing thing, or at least everybody's parents did, but it's boring.

Lucy So you've been exploring?

Midnight Yes. Pot-holing.

Lucy How did you . . . ?

Midnight Go blind?

Lucy Lose your sight, I was going to say.

Midnight Looked at the sun through binoculars when I was ten.

Lucy By mistake?

Midnight For a bet. Burnt out. Never see again.

Lucy Sorry.

Midnight Not to worry. I've got Jesus, and the truth.

Lucy Truth? What's that?

Midnight When you can't see, it's better to follow one straight path.

Lucy Oh, right. (*Pause.*) Do you want them to come back?

Midnight I told you, they're written off.

Lucy No, the others, I mean.

Midnight Oh, they won't. They think it's a good crack, leaving me playing blind man's buff.

Lucy Ever caught moths?

Midnight What have moths got to do with it?

Lucy Oh, nothing.

She sets fire to the silk scarf and tosses it up in the air. It flares brightly and vanishes.

 Enter Klondike, Tulip, Polly and Jane.

Klondike Midnight, what's going on?

Tulip We thought we saw something burning . . .

Polly Or a meteorite falling . . .

Jane A maroon or whatever they're called, like a rocket . . .

Klondike Or sheet lightning.

Glue Boy Air-raid warning. Keep away from the trees.
The strike of midnight.

Midnight Er . . .

Lucy It was a will-o'-the-wisp.

Tulip Who the hell's this?

Midnight Er . . .

Lucy Lucy Lime. Mother and father are up on the top
with your lot. I've been keeping your friend company –
thought you'd be looking for him.

Klondike Er . . . that's right. We got separated.

Lucy Lucky I was around, then. Wouldn't have wanted
the electric fence to have found him.

Polly (*aside*) Strange-looking creature.

Jane Not pretty. No features. Hairy armpits, I bet.

Polly Yeah, and two hairy legs.

*Midnight sits on a stone away from everyone else and
puts on his Walkman.*

Lucy Mind if I join you?

Klondike Sorry?

Lucy Mind if I stay?

Tulip Feel free. Free country.

Jane I'm bored. Let's play a game.

Klondike Let's trap a rabbit and skin it.

Polly You're kidding. Let's play mirror, mirror on the
wall . . .

Jane Spin the bottle. Postman's knock.

Glue Boy Pin the donkey on the tail.

Lucy What about hide and seek?

Tulip British bulldogs. No, numblety peg.

Lucy What's that?

Tulip That's where I throw this knife into the ground
between your legs.

Klondike I know. We'll play bets. I bet I can skim this
stone head-on into the waves.

Polly We know you can. I bet if we had a vote, I'd have the prettiest face.

Jane I bet you'd come joint first.

Tulip I bet I dare touch the electric fence.

Klondike Easy, you've got rubber soles. What do you bet, Evo-Stik?

Glue Boy Tomorrow never comes.

Klondike Sure, you keep taking the pills.

Lucy I can get Midnight to tell a lie. That's what I bet.

Tulip You're off your head. He's as straight as a die.

Glue Boy Straight as a plumb-line.

Klondike You've got no chance. He's a born-again Mr Tambourine Man. A proper Christian.

Polly Says his prayers before he goes to bed . . .

Jane Goes to church when it's not even Christmas.

Lucy I don't care if he's Mary and Joseph and Jesus rolled into one. He'll lie like anyone.

Tulip What do you bet?

Lucy I bet this. Two coins together – it's a lucky charm – a gold sovereign melted to a silver dime.

Klondike It's Lucy Locket now, is it, not Lucy Lime?

Lucy It's worth a bomb.

Tulip We can sell and split it. Okay, you're on. I bet this knife that you're wrong.

Lucy I've no need of a knife. I'll bet you your boots instead.

Polly I'll bet you this bracelet. It's nine-carat gold.

Jane I'll bet you this make-up case. It's mother-of-pearl.

Glue Boy I'll bet Antarctica.

Lucy You can do better than that, can't you?

Glue Boy Okay, the world.

Tulip What do you bet, Klondike?

Klondike My skull.

Lucy Not enough.

Klondike And these Boji stones, from Kansas, under an ancient lake.

308

Lucy Not enough.

Klondike Alright, if you win – which you won't – you can kiss this handsome face.

Lucy Everybody shake on it.

Klondike All for one, and once and for all.

Glue Boy And one for the road. And toad in the hole.

Lucy Glue Boy, is that your name?

Glue Boy One and the same.

Lucy Come with me, you're the witness.

Polly Why him? He doesn't know Tuesday from a piece of string.

Lucy Sounds perfect. Everyone else, keep quiet.

Lucy and Glue Boy approach Midnight. Lucy taps him on the shoulder.

Listen.

Midnight What?

Lucy Can you hear a boat?

Midnight Nope.

Lucy Listen, I can hear its engine. I'm certain.

Midnight I think you're mistaken.

Lucy There, just as I thought – coming round the point.

Midnight There can't be. Which direction?

Tulip (*to the others*) What's she saying? There's no boat.

Lucy Straight out in front. Plain as the nose on your face. See it, Glue Boy?

Glue Boy Er . . . ? Oh, sure.

Lucy It's a trawler. Is it greeny-blue, would you say?

Glue Boy Well, sort of sea-green, sort of sky-blue, sort of blue moon sort of colour.

Lucy I'm amazed you can't hear it, it's making a real racket.

Midnight Well, I . . .

Lucy Too much time with ear-plugs, listening to static.

Midnight My hearing's perfect.

Lucy Fine. Okay. Forget it.

Midnight I'm sorry. I didn't mean to be rude.

Lucy You weren't. I shouldn't have mentioned it. It's my fault – I should have thought. You can't hear the boat for the sound of the seagulls.

Midnight Seagulls?

Polly (*to the others*) There isn't a bird for miles.

Jane This is a waste of time. It's her who's telling the lies.

Lucy All that high-pitched skriking and screaming. Must play havoc with sensitive hearing like yours.

Midnight How close?

Lucy The birds? Three hundred yards, five hundred at most. Black-headed gulls, Glue Boy, don't you think?

Glue Boy Well, kind of rare breed, kind of less common, kind of lesser-spotted type things.

Lucy Don't say you're going deaf?

Midnight Who, me?

Lucy Glue Boy can hear them, and he's out of his head. Come on, Midnight, stop clowning around. I bet you can hear it all. I bet you can hear a cat licking its lips in the next town, can't you?

Midnight I don't know . . . I think sometimes I filter it out.

Lucy Yes, when you're half-asleep. But listen, what can you hear now?

Midnight Er . . . something . . .

Lucy That aeroplane for a start, I bet.

Midnight Yes. The aeroplane.

Lucy I can't see it myself. Where would you say it was?

Midnight Er . . . off to the left, that's my guess.

Lucy What else? That dog on the cliff, half a mile back. Can you hear that?

Midnight Yes. The dog. Sniffing the air, is it? Scratching the ground?

Lucy Amazing. Wrap-around sound. What else? The boy with the kite?

Midnight Yes, the kite.
  The wind playing the twine like a harp.
  It's a wonderful sound.
Lucy And Klondike and Tulip, coming back up the
  beach. What are they talking about?
Midnight They're saying . . . this and that, about that
  eclipse, and how dark and how strange it'll be.
Lucy And down by the rock pools, the twins?
Midnight Chatting away. Girls' things. Boyfriends, that
  kind of stuff. It's not really fair to listen in on it.
Lucy You're not kidding. You're absolutely ultrasonic.
  Glue Boy, how about that for a pair of ears?
Glue Boy Yeah, he's Jodrell Bank, he is.
Lucy And one last noise. A siren or something?
Midnight Car alarm.
Lucy No. Music.
Midnight Brass band. 'Floral Dance.'
Lucy No. It's there on the tip of my tongue, but I just
  can't place it. You know, sells lollies and things.
Midnight Ice-cream van. Ice-cream van. I can hear it.
Lucy You can?
Midnight Can't you?
Lucy No. Not any more. What was the tune?
Midnight Er . . . 'Greensleeves.'
Lucy 'Greensleeves', eh? Thanks, Midnight, that should
  do it.
Midnight Sorry?
Tulip Nice one, stupid.
Midnight What? I thought you were . . .
Tulip Yeah, well, you know what thought did.
Polly Pathetic, Midnight.
Jane You should see a doctor, you're hearing voices.
Midnight But, all those noises . . .
Klondike She made them up, you soft bastard. I tell you
  what, you should take more care of those ears.
Midnight Why's that?

Klondike 'Cos if they fall off, you won't be able to wear
  glasses.

Midnight I didn't invent them.

Polly You lying rat.

Jane You just lost us the bet, Dumbo. Do us a favour –
  stick to your Walkman.

Lucy Midnight, I'm sorry.

Midnight Get lost. Keep off me.

Polly Where are you going?

Midnight Anywhere away from here.

Klondike Well, get me a ninety-nine will you, when
  you're there.

Tulip And a screwball as well.

Midnight Go to hell.

*Midnight takes off his crucifix and throws it in the
direction of Lucy. Lucy picks it up and puts it in her
bag.*

Lucy Well, I think that clinches it, don't you? The
  bracelet, the case, the boots, and the skull and the
  stone, if you please.

*Everyone hands her the items. Lucy puts on the shoes
and puts everything else in her bag.*

Klondike Forgetting something?

Lucy I don't think so.

Klondike A kiss from me, because you did it.

Lucy No thanks, Romeo. I was only kidding.

Polly What a cheek. Not to worry, in the glove
  compartment I've got more jewellery, too good for that
  gold-digger.

Jane But you've got to hand it to her. I'll come to the car
  park to check out the courtesy light and the vanity
  mirror.

Exit Polly and Jane.

Glue Boy What did I bet?

Lucy The Earth.

Glue Boy I've left it at home in my other jacket. Double or quits?

Lucy No, I'll take it on credit.

Glue Boy A whole planet. In a top pocket.

Tulip Hey, where do you think you're going?

Lucy To see Midnight, make sure he's okay.

Tulip You've got a nerve.

Lucy Why? It was only a game.

Glue Boy Klondike, the sun . . .

Klondike Don't you think you've lost enough for one day?

Glue Boy No, the shadow. Here it comes.

Lucy It can't be. It's too early to start.

Tulip He's right, it's going dark. Klondike?

Klondike ECLIPSE, ECLIPSE. EVERYONE INTO POSITION. EVERYONE INTO POSITION.

Tulip We're short.

Klondike Who's missing?

Tulip Midnight. Gone walkabout. And the twins, where are the twins?

Klondike Get them back. Polly. Jane. POLLY. JANE.

SCENE FOUR

The police interview room. Polly and Jane make their statement, sometimes talking in unison, sometimes separately, one sister occasionally finishing the other sister's sentence.

Polly *and* **Jane** They were up on the tops, we were down on the deck, kicking around in pebbles and shells and bladderwrack. They were watching the sky, we were keeping an eye on the tide, hanging around, writing

313

names in the sand, turning over stones, pulling legs from hermit crabs.

We're two of a kind, two yolks from the same egg, same thoughts in identical heads, everything half and half, but it's easy enough to tell us apart: I'm the spitting image; she's the copycat.

They were up on the top looking south, we were down on the strand looking out for something to do. She came and she went in the same afternoon, saw the eclipse, like us, but musn't have been impressed, so she left. Straight up. And a truth half-told is a lie. We should know, we're Gemini.

Oh, yes, and we liked her style and the way she dressed. We were something else before daylight vanished. Whatever we touched was touched with varnish. Whatever we smelt was laced with powder or scent. Whatever we heard had an earring lending its weight. Whatever we saw was shadowed and shaded out of sight. Whatever we tasted tasted of mint. Whatever we spoke had lipstick kissing its lips. We were something else back then, alright, muddled up, not thinking straight, as it were. But now we're clear.

Same here.

SCENE FIVE

The beach. Klondike, Tulip, Glue Boy and Lucy are standing looking at the sky.

Tulip False alarm. Just a cloud.
Klondike Thought so. Too early.
Tulip What now?
Glue Boy I-spy.
Tulip Boring. Hide-and-seek. Come on, Klondike, hide and seek.

Klondike Okay. Spuds up.
Lucy What, like this?
Klondike Yes, that's it.

They all hold out their fists, with thumbs pointing skyward.

One potati, two potati, three potati, four,
Five potati, six potati, seven potati, more . . .
Tulip There's a party on the hill, will you come?
Bring your own cup of tea and a bun . . .
Glue Boy Ip dip dip, my blue ship,
Sails on the water, like a cup and saucer . . .
Klondike It's here, it's there, it's everywhere,
It's salmon and it's trout,
It shaves its tongue and eats its hair,
You're in, you're in, you're in . . . you're out.

The dipping-out lands on Lucy.

Tulip You're it.
Lucy Okay, how many start?
Klondike Fifty elephants and no cheating.
Glue Boy Fifteen cheetahs, and no peeping.
Lucy Off you go then.

Lucy turns her back and begins counting. Exit Tulip and Klondike.

One elephant, two elephant, three elephant . . .
Glue Boy Filthy underpants and no weeping.

Klondike returns and drags Glue Boy off. Enter Polly and Jane.

Polly Hey, there's what's-her-face.
Jane What's she playing at?
Polly Practising her times-tables, by the sound of it. Let's tell her to get lost.
Jane No. I've got a better idea. Let's give her a shock.

Lucy . . . fifty elephants. Coming ready or not.

Polly *and* **Jane** BOO!

Lucy Don't do that. You'll give someone a heart attack.

Polly We're the two-headed . . .

Jane . . . four-armed . . .

Polly . . . four-legged . . .

Jane . . . twenty-fingered monster from the black lagoon.

Lucy And one brain between the pair of you.

Polly Now, now. No need to be nasty.

Jane Yeah, no one's called you pale and pasty, have they?

Lucy I just meant it's hard to tell you apart.

Polly We like it that way.

Jane It's scary.

Lucy Anyway, this is the natural look.

Polly What, plain and hairy?

Lucy No, pure and simple. Basically beautiful.

Jane Says who?

Lucy Says people. Boys. Men.

Jane You got a boyfriend then?

Lucy Yes. Someone. What about you two?

Jane No one to speak of . . .

Polly We're not bothered. All those round our way are
filthy or ugly and stupid.

Lucy Maybe you should do what I did, then.

Polly What was that?

Lucy Well, three men fishing on the towpath wouldn't let
me past; called me a tramp, threw me in and I nearly
drowned. I was down in the weeds with dead dogs and
bicycle frames. Couldn't move for bracelets and beads
and rings and chains. Don't know why, but I ditched
the lot in a minute flat, took off my clothes as well:
cuffs and frills and scarves, heels and bottoms and
lace and buckles and shoulder-pads, climbed out
strip-jack naked on the other bank, white-faced and
my hair down flat. The three men whistled and
clapped but I stood there, dressed in nothing but rain.

316

They stopped and threw me a shirt and a big coat,
which I wouldn't take. One of them covered his eyes,
said it was somebody's fault; a fight broke out and
I watched. All three of them cried, said they were
sorry, said they were shamed. I asked them to leave,
and they shuffled away to their cars, I suppose, and
their wives. I put on the coat and shirt, and walked
home, but never went back to dredge for the gold or
the clothes. This is me now. Be yourself, I reckon, not
somebody else.

Jane What a story.

Polly Jackanory.

Lucy Well, that's what happened. You should try it. You
might be surprised.

Jane You're kidding. Us?

Polly Not on your life.

Lucy Why not?

Jane How do we know we'd look any good?

Polly We wouldn't.

Lucy You would. Well, you might. Anyhow, better to
look the way you were meant to be than done up like
a tailor's dummy and a Christmas tree.

Polly Better to look like us than something the cat
wouldn't touch.

Lucy No cat curls its nose up at good meat.

Polly No, but I know what they'd go for first if it's a
choice between semi-skimmed or full cream.

Lucy Suit yourselves.

Polly We will.

Lucy Don't blame me when you're twenty-three or
thirty-four or forty-five, and left on the shelf.

Polly We won't.

Klondike (*off*) You haven't found us yet.

Lucy Am I warm or cold?

Klondike (*off*) Cold as a penguin's chuff.

Tulip (*off*) Cold as an Eskimo's toe.

Glue Boy (*off*) Yeah, cold as a polar bear's fridge. In a power cut.

Klondike *and* **Tulip** (*off*) Shut up.

Jane (*to Polly*) Why don't we give it a go?

Polly No.

Jane Why not?

Polly Because.

Jane It won't harm. Just for a laugh.

Polly I haven't put all this on just to take it all off.

Jane Come on, sis, do it for me.

Polly What if we're . . . different?

Jane What do you mean?

Polly What if we don't look the same? Underneath?

Jane Don't know. Hadn't thought. Put it all on again?

Polly Straight away?

Jane Before you can say Jack Robinson. Before you can say . . .

Polly Okay.

Jane Lucy. We're going to give it a whirl.

Polly Just for a laugh, though. That's all.

Lucy Excellent. Down to the sea, girls. Down to the shore.

> (*Sings.*)
> Oh ladies of Greece
> with the thickest of trees,
> covered with blossom and bumble,
> snip off the bees
> and there underneath
> two apples to bake in a crumble.
>
> Oh ladies of France
> with warts on your hands,
> come down, come down to the waters.
> And where you were gnarled
> at the end of your arms
> two perfect symmetrical daughters.

Oh ladies of Spain
at night on the lane
in nightshirts and mittens and bedsocks,
strip off those duds
and ride through the woods
on horses carved onto the bedrock.

*While singing, Lucy strips them of their jewellery and
some of their clothes, and washes their hair in the sea.
She puts the jewellery and a few choice items into a
bag.*

How does it feel?

Jane Unreal. I feel like someone else.

Lucy Polly?

Polly Not sure. Up in the air.

Jane I feel lighter and thinner.

Lucy Polly?

Polly See-through. Like a tree in winter.

Lucy You look great. You look like different people.

Polly Sorry?

Lucy I mean . . . you still look the same, alike. Just
different types.

Jane Here come the others. See if they notice.

Polly Oh no. Let's hide.

Lucy Say nothing. Just smile. They'll only be jealous.

Enter Klondike, Tulip and Glue Boy.

Klondike Couldn't you find us?

Lucy No. You win.

Tulip We were down in the caves with the dead pirates.

Klondike How hard did you look?

Lucy Oh, about this hard. Feels like I've been looking for
hours.

Tulip We were camouflaged.

Glue Boy Yeah, we were cauliflowers.

Tulip Oh my God.

Klondike What's up?

Tulip It's those two. Look.

Klondike Wow. I don't believe it.

Jane What's the matter with you? Never seen a woman before?

Tulip Never seen this one or that one. What happened? Get flushed down the toilet?

Lucy They've changed their minds.

Tulip You mean you changed it for them. That's all we need, three Lucy Limes.

Glue Boy Three lucky strikes. Three blind mice.

Polly Shut it, Glue Boy.

Klondike I think they look . . . nice.

Tulip Nice? They look like bones after the dog's had them.

Lucy They had a change of heart.

Glue Boy Heart transplant.

Klondike I think they look . . . smart. Sort of.

Tulip Yeah, and sort of not. They don't even look like twins any more. Don't look like anyone.

Polly I told you we shouldn't have.

Jane Don't blame me. You don't look that bad.

Polly Me? You should see yourself. You look like something out of a plastic bag.

Jane So what? You look like an old hag. You loo like a boiled pig.

Tulip Glue Boy, what do they look like? Mirror, mirror on the wall . . .

Glue Boy
Mirror, mirror on the wall,
Who's the worstest of them all? . . .

Jane Glue Boy . . .

Glue Boy This one looks like a wet haddock . . .

Jane I'll kill you.

Glue Boy But this one looks like a skinned rabbit.

Polly Right, you've had it.

Polly and Jane pull Glue Boy's glue bag over his head and start to kick him. He wanders off and they follow, still kicking him.

Klondike They'll slaughter him.

Tulip He wouldn't notice.

Lucy What a mess.

Tulip Yes, and you started it.

Lucy Me? It was all fine till you came back and started stirring it. Now it's a hornets' nest.

Klondike Leave it alone. It'll all come out in the wash.

Lucy (*holding up some of the clothes left on the floor*) What about these? Needles from Christmas trees.

Klondike Tulip, go and put leaves back on the evergreens.

Tulip Why me? What about her – Tinkerbell?

Klondike I don't think that'd go down too well. Please?

Tulip Okay, give them here.

Lucy Take this, a brush for back-combing their hair.

Tulip Beach-combing more like. How kind.

Lucy That's me. Sweetness and light. Lime by name, but sugar by nature. Isn't that right?

Klondike Eh? How should I know? Got everything?

Tulip S'pose so.

Klondike Won't take a minute.

Tulip (*to Klondike, privately*) You'll wait here, won't you?

Klondike Course.

Tulip Don't let her . . .

Klondike What?

Tulip Doesn't matter.

Klondike Go on, what?

Tulip Talk to you, you know.

Klondike No, I won't do.

Tulip Don't let her . . . Lucy Lime you.

Klondike Don't be daft. Go on, I'll time you.

Exit Tulip.

Enjoying yourself?

Lucy I've had better.

Klondike Where are you from?

Lucy All over. (*Pause*) I'm a walking universe, I am. Wherever the best view comes from, wherever Mars and the Moon are in conjunction, wherever the stars and the sun are looking good from, wherever the angles and the right ascensions and declinations and transits and vectors and focal lengths and partial perigons are done from, that's where I come from. Traipsing round with mother and father. What about you lot?

Klondike Yorkshire. Came in a van.

Lucy Bet that was fun.

Klondike I meant it, you know.

Lucy Meant what?

Klondike About that kiss. If you want to.

Lucy What about her? Don't you think she'd mind?

Klondike Tulip? No, she's alright. She's just . . .

Lucy One of the lads?

Klondike Something like that. Well, what about it?

Lucy Ever played rising sun?

Klondike Don't think so. How do you play it?

Lucy Well,
A light shines bright through a sheet or blanket,
Somebody follows the sun as it rises,
It dawns at daybreak above the horizon,
The one looking east gets something surprising . . .

Klondike Really?

Lucy Something exciting. Something to break the ice with.

Klondike Let's try it.

Lucy Sorry, no can do. We need a torch for the sun.

Klondike (*producing a torch*) Like this one?

Lucy And we need a sheet.

Klondike (*taking off his shirt*) You can use this shirt.

Lucy And it needs to be dark. Sorry, can't be done.

Klondike I'll put this blindfold on. (*Without taking it off, he lifts the bottom front of his T-shirt over his head*).

Lucy Okay, here it comes.

Klondike kneels on the floor and holds his T-shirt up in front of his face. Lucy, on the other side, presses the torch against the shirt and raises it very slowly. Klondike follows the light with his nose.

Rain in the north from the tears of Jesus,
Wind in the west with it's knickers in a twist;
Flies in the south sucking blood like leeches,
Sun coming up in the east like a kiss –
(*Whispers.*) – from Judas.

Repeat.

SCENE SIX

The police interview room.

Tulip When she left us for good I was nine or ten. Ran off with the milkman, so Dad said. Ran off with the man in the moon, as far as I care. Grew up with uncles, cousins, played rugby football, swapped a pram for a ten-speed drop-handlebar, played with matches instead, flags and cars, threw the dolls on a skip and the skates on a dustcart, flogged the frills and pink stuff at a car-boot sale, burnt the Girl Guide outfit in the back garden, got kitted out at Famous Army Stores and Top Man. And Oxfam. I'll tell you something that sums it up: found a doll's house going mouldy in the attic – boarded it up, kept a brown rat in it. Put it all behind now, growing out of it, Dad

323

says, says I'm blossoming, and I suppose he must be right. Klondike? No, not a boyfriend, more like a kid brother, really, known him since as far back as I can remember. Kissed him? Who wants to know? I mean, no, sir, except on his head, just once, on his birthday. Him and Lucy? Well, she took a shine to him, he told her some things and I think she liked him. She just showed up and wanted to tag along, make some friends, I suppose, mess about, have fun; she had a few tricks up her sleeve, wanted . . . alright, if you put it like that . . . to be one of the group. It's not much cop being on your own. Which was fine by us. It's not that we gave it a second thought, to tell you the truth. She just turned up that afternoon like a lost dog. She was one of the gang. Then she was gone.

SCENE SEVEN

The beach. Lucy and Klondike playing rising sun.

Lucy Rain in the north from the tears of Jesus,
　　Wind in the west with it's knickers in a twist;
　　Flies in the south sucking blood like leeches,
　　Sun coming up in the east like . . . piss.

Lucy throws water in his face.

Klondike You bitch.
Lucy Something to break the ice, you see. It's a riddle.

Enter Tulip, unnoticed.

Klondike It was a swindle.
Lucy Oh, come on. You can take it. Here, dry off on this.

She hands him his shirt and kisses him on the forehead.

Klondike You shouldn't joke.

Lucy What about?

Klondike Rhymes and religion. Old things. Things in the past.

Lucy I don't believe in all that claptrap.

Klondike It's just the way you've been brought up.

Lucy Yes, in the twentieth century, not in the dark. Anyway, what about your lot? They're up there believing in science and maths.

Klondike No, with them it's the zodiac.

Lucy Oh, I see. It's like that.

Klondike They've come to take part, not take photographs.

Pause.

Lucy What's in the bag?

Klondike Bits and pieces.

Lucy Show me. Or is it a secret?

Klondike Just things I've collected.

Lucy Suit yourself. Only, I was interested.

Klondike Well, it's just that . . .

Lucy Oh, forget it then, if it's so precious. Makes no difference.

Klondike Alright then, since you've asked. (*Klondike opens his bag, and reveals the contents, slowly.*)
This is the skin of a poisonous snake,
this is a horse stick, cut from a silver birch,
this is bear's tooth, this is a blue shell,
this is a wren's wing, this is a brass bell,
this is a glass bead, this is a fax tail,
this is a boat, carved from a whale bone,
this is a whistle, this is a goat's horn
this is driftwood, this is a cat's claw,
this is a ribbon, a mirror, a clay pipe,
this is a toy drum, this is a meteorite,
this is fool's gold, this is buffalo leather –

SIMON ARMITAGE

Lucy All done?
Klondike And this is the moon and the sun:
  a hare's foot and an eagle's feather.
Lucy How do you mean?
Klondike That's what they stand for.
Lucy Well, quite a bagful. When's the car-boot sale?
Klondike You couldn't afford them.
Lucy Wouldn't want them. Anyway, what are they for?
Klondike They're just things, that's all.
Lucy Things from a mumbo-jumbo stall?
Klondike Things for dreaming things up.
Lucy What?
Klondike I said, things for dreaming things up.
Lucy Tommy-rot. You're just an overgrown Boy Scout.
  Next thing you'll be showing me a reef knot.
Klondike Get lost, Lucy.
Lucy Dib-dib-dib, dob-dob-dob.
Tulip Klondike, show her.
Klondike No.
Tulip Why not?
Lucy Because he can't.
Tulip Show her.
Klondike Why should I?
Lucy Because he's a big kid, playing with toy cars.
Tulip You don't have to take that from her.
Lucy But most of all, because he's full of shite. Eagle's
  feathers? Chicken more like.
Klondike Alright.
Lucy This is the eye of a bat, this is a leprechaun's hat,
  this is the spine of a bird, this is a rocking-horse turd –
Klondike I said alright.
Lucy This is a snowman's heart, this is a plate of tripe –
Klondike ALL RIGHT. Pick something out.
Lucy Well, well, well. All this for little old me. I don't
  know where to start.

326

Eenie, meanie, meinie, mo,
put the baby on the po . . . no, not my colour.

Scab and matter custard, toenail pie,
all mixed up with a dead dog's eye,
green and yellow snot cakes
fried in spit,
all washed down with a cup of cold sick.
Here's what I pick.

Klondike The eagle feather.

Lucy None other.

Klondike Put it in the bag, then on the rock, then –

Lucy Let me guess. Light the blue touch paper and stand
well back?

*Klondike performs a ceremony around the bag. There
is a deafening roar and a brief shadow as a low-flying
jet passes overhead.*

Is that it?

Tulip What?

Lucy Is that it? A jet.

Tulip Oh, only a jet. What do you want, jam on it?
Klondike, you were brilliant. That was the best yet.

Lucy Hang on, let's get this straight. It's the feather that
counts, right? You made that plane come out of the
clouds by doing a voodoo dance around a bit of feather
duster in an old sack?

Klondike Not quite. Something like that.

Lucy Well then, how do you explain . . . this. (*She
produces a rubber duck from the bag.*) Quack, quack.

Klondike What . . .

Tulip Where did you get it?

Lucy Down on the beach, washed up. Klondike, say
hello to Mr Duck.

Tulip You're a bitch.

Lucy Sails on the water, like a cup and saucer. So much for the jet, lucky you didn't conjure up the *Titanic*, we might have got wet.

Tulip I'm going to break her neck.

Klondike No, Tulip.

Lucy Rubber Duck to Ground Control, Rubber Duck to Ground Control, the signal's weak, you're breaking up, you're breaking up.

Tulip You think you're really fucking good, don't you?

Lucy I'm only having some fun. What else is there to do?

Tulip Oh, it's fun, is it? Well, I've had enough. I hope you're either good with a knife, or I hope you can run.

Klondike Tulip, leave her.

Lucy Sorry, neither. You'll just have to do me in in cold blood. Mind you, I'm strong.

Tulip Where, apart from your tongue?

Lucy Here, from the shoulder down to the wrist. This right arm doesn't know its own strength.

Tulip Looks to me like a long streak of piss.

Lucy Ah, well, looks deceive. For instance, you don't have to look like a man to be as strong as one.

Tulip And what's that supposed to mean?

Lucy What will you do when your balls drop, Tulip? Grow a beard?

Tulip Right, you're dead.

Klondike Just stop. Knock it off, I said. If you want to show off, why don't you arm-wrestle or something, there on the rock?

Lucy No thanks, I don't play competitive sports.

Klondike Not half you don't.

Tulip Now who's chicken?

Lucy I've told you, I'm just not interested in winning.

Tulip Not interested in losing, more like. Come on, arm-wrestle, or maybe I just smash your face in anyway, for a bit of fun, for a laugh.

Lucy Alright, but don't say you didn't ask for it.

Klondike Both of you down on one knee, elbows straight and a clean grip. Ready?

Tulip Yep.

Klondike Lucy?

Lucy As I'll ever be.

Klondike When I say three. One, two –

Enter Midnight, carrying a melting ice cream in both hands.

Midnight Ice cream. I got the ice cream.

Klondike Not now, Midnight.

Midnight 'Greensleeves', up the road. A screwball and a ninety-nine. Or was it a cone?

Klondike Midnight, we're busy. Just wait there for a minute. And count to three.

Midnight Why?

Klondike Just do it.

Midnight Okay then. One. Two. Three.

With her free hand, Lucy takes hold of the electric cable. Tulip is thrown over backwards with the shock.

What was that? Lightning?

Lucy No, something like it. Is she okay?

Klondike Just frightened, I think.

Lucy Ten volts, that's all. Hardly enough to light a torch, but it's the shock I suppose.

Klondike How come?

Lucy Meaning what?

Klondike How come her, and not you?

Lucy Easy. Insulation. Good shoes.

Klondike She was the earth?

Lucy Yes. Here, she can have them back – not my style, rubber boots. (*She takes off the boots and tosses them on the floor.*)

Klondike She was the earth.

Lucy Certainly was.

Klondike Just for a laugh.

Lucy No, self-defence.

Klondike I see. (*He picks up Tulip's knife.*) Well, that's enough.

Lucy What do you mean?

Klondike I mean enough's enough.

Lucy Klondike, that's real. That's a knife.

Klondike That's right. That's right.

Midnight (*facing the opposite way*) Klondike. No heat.

Klondike No heat. Ice cream. That's right.

Midnight No, no heat, on my face. No . . . no light.

Klondike No light?

Midnight No light. No sun.

Lucy Eclipse.

Klondike Eclipse? ECLIPSE. Everyone into position. Who's missing?

Tulip The twins.

Klondike Polly. Jane. POLLY. JANE. How long left?

Tulip A minute. No, fifty seconds. Less.

Klondike Who else? Midnight?

Midnight Here, right next to you.

Enter Polly and Jane.

Klondike Six of us. Six of us.

Tulip Glue Boy. Where's Glue Boy?

Klondike Where's Glue Boy?

Polly We saw him up by the tents.

Jane Out of his head.

Klondike Idiot. How long left?

Tulip Twenty. Less.

Klondike Okay, okay. (*to Lucy*) You. It'll have to be you.

Lucy I'm going back to the –

Klondike Stay there and don't move.

Tulip Where shall we stand?

Klondike Don't you remember, the plan? (*He begins to move them into position.*) You there, you there, you there . . .

Midnight What about me?

Klondike You stand here.

Lucy Look, I'm not really sure . . .

Klondike Just stay put. You've had it your own way all afternoon, now let's see what you're made of.

Tulip Ten seconds.

Lucy Huh, me at the back, then?

Klondike Pole position. Right where it happens.

Facing towards where the sun grows darker, they stand in a triangular formation, with Tulip, Klondike and Midnight at the front, Polly and Jane behind them, and Lucy at the back.

Polly Look out, here it comes.

Jane (*elated*) Oh yes.

Polly Time for the shades. Time for the shades?

Klondike Yes, the shades. Put them on.

Klondike, Tulip, Polly and Jane put on their protective glasses.

Midnight What?

Polly The specs.

Midnight Oh yes. (*He takes his off.*)

Tulip Five seconds, less. Three. Two. One.

Except for Lucy, they begin to chant.

All Fallen fruit of burning sun
Break the teeth and burn the tongue,
Open mouth of the frozen moon
Spit the cherry from the stone.

SCENE EIGHT

The police interview room.

Klondike Dusk and dawn, like that, in one afternoon.
  For all the world, this is as much as I know.
  We were standing there watching the most spectacular
     show
  on earth, a beam of light from the bulb
  of the sun, made night through the lens of the moon;
  ninety-three million miles – point-blank range. Strange,
  the moon four hundred times smaller in size,
  the sun four hundred times further away;
  in line, as they were for us for once for a change,
  they're the same size. We were set. We were primed.
  Like the riddle says, 'What can be see as clear
  as day, but never be looked in the face?' This
  was a chance to stand in a star's shade,
  to catch the sun napping or looking the wrong way –
  the light of all lights, turning a blind eye.
  I'm getting ahead of myself – it's hard to describe.
  When the shadow arrived from the east like a stingray,
  two thousand miles an hour, skimming the sea spray,
  two hundred miles across from fin to fin,
  we felt like a miracle, under its wingspan.
  We said nursery rhymes, like frightened children.
  Midnight bats came out of the sea caves, calling,
  birds in the crags buried down in their breasts
  till morning, crabs came out of holes in the sand
  with eyes on stalks to watch for the tide turning.
  When it was done . . . we looked about, and she'd gone.
  Never thought for a second she might be lost,
  just reckoned she wasn't impressed with planets
  and stars and shadows . . . figured she wasn't fussed.
  Thought that she'd taken her lime-green self up top,

sidled away, shuffled off. Came as a big black shock
when they called and said she never showed up.
She wasn't us although we liked her well enough.
She told us things, showed us stuff. It's almost
as if she did us a good turn by putting us all
on the right track. Sad. And that's the whole story.
I wish I could tell you more but I can't. I'm sorry.

SCENE NINE

*The police waiting room. Tulip, Polly and Jane, Midnight
and Glue Boy, sitting, waiting. Enter Klondike from
interview room.*

Tulip Well?
Klondike Well what?
Tulip Any problems, or not?
Klondike No, none.
Polly What did you tell them?
Klondike Same as everyone else, I presume.
Jane What do they think?
Klondike How should I know? I'm not a mind-reader.
Tulip Well, I don't care. I don't see what else we're
    supposed to say.
Polly Nor me.
Jane Me neither.
Midnight So we can go home?
Klondike No.
Midnight Why not? We're all done, aren't we?
Glue Boy Except for one.
Midnight Oh yes. Sorry. Forgot.

Off, a voice calls 'Paul Bond'.

Glue Boy That'll be me, then.
Tulip Why are they asking him?

333

Klondike It's his turn. Everyone has to go in.

Polly Fat load of good that'll be. He can't remember his own name at the best of times.

Jane He was out of his brain that day, weren't you, Glue Boy?

Glue Boy High as a kite. Cloud Nine.

Off, a voice calls 'Paul Bond'.

Oh, well. Cheerio.

Klondike Glue Boy?

Glue Boy What?

Klondike Whatever you know, get it straight.

Glue Boy Like you, right?

Klondike Right.

Exit Glue Boy into interview room.

Tulip See the news?

Polly No. In the paper again?

Tulip Yes, and on the telly as well this time.

Midnight *News at Ten*?

Tulip Don't know. I was in bed by then, but I saw it at six on the BBC.

Jane What did it say?

Tulip Said that they'd called off the search. Said they'd had aeroplanes over the sea, locals walking the beach, boats in the bay, dogs in the caves and all that for over a week, but they'd called it a day. Said that she might be thousands of miles away by now.

Polly Anything else. Anything . . . new?

Tulip No. Oh yes, they showed her mum and dad.

Klondike I saw that. Him in the suit, her in the hat, going on and on and on.

Jane How old?

Klondike Don't know, but you could see where she got it from.

Pause.

Tulip They're talking about a reconstruction.

Jane What's one of those when it's at home.

Tulip We all go back to the place and do it again, see if somebody remembers anything or seeing anyone.

Polly And they do it on film, don't they?

Jane Oh yes, and someone will have to dress up as her, won't they?

Polly With her stuff, and her hair.

Tulip That won't be much fun.

Pause.

Klondike Not a problem, can't be done.

Midnight You sure.

Klondike Certainly am. Not without the moon, and not without the sun.

Pause.

Tulip Anyway, when's the next one?

Polly Next what?

Tulip Eclipse. Klondike?

Klondike Don't know, I'll have to look at the list. Why, are you up for it?

Tulip Can a duck swim?

Klondike Polly? Jane?

Polly In.

Jane In.

Tulip What about him in there – Mr Pritt-Stick?

Klondike Mr Dipstick more like. Don't worry about him, he'll be alright.

Tulip What about you, Midnight?

Midnight Sorry, I wasn't listening.

Tulip Don't play the innocent with me, sunshine. The next eclipse – yes or no, sir?

Midnight Lunar or solar?

Klondike Solar. Total.

Midnight Two days in a van with my mum's barley
sugars and the old man. Two minutes at most of
afternoon night when I'm already blind. Hanging
around with you lot calling me names, playing tricks
of the light and stupid games, then egging myself for a
week, can't eat, can't sleep, then twenty questions by
the police, and all the rest, enough to put a normal
person in the funny farm . . . go on then, you've
twisted my arm.

SCENE TEN

The police interview room.

Glue Boy

I suppose you've heard it needle and thread five times.
Saying it over and over again – not much point, right?
Any road, I was all of a dither back then, disconnected,
fuse blown in the head, loose ends, nobody home,
fumes on the brain – know what I mean? Hard to think
of it all in one long line, it's all squiggles and shapes.
Fits and starts. Kills the cells, you see, after so long, so
that you can't tell. Well, nothing to speak of coming to
mind just yet. Except . . . no, nothing, nothing. All gone
funny. Not unless you mean the bit between the last bit
and the rest? You should have said. Let's think. Let's
think. No point saying it over and over to death, no
sense wasting breath. Bits and bobs. Chapter and
verse. Unless . . . no, nothing. What the others said.
Just that. Oh yes, then this . . .

SCENE ELEVEN

The beach. Klondike, Lucy, Tulip and Midnight, as before.

Lucy Klondike, that's real. That's a knife.
Klondike That's right. That's right.
Midnight (*facing the opposite way*) Klondike. No heat.
Klondike No heat. Ice cream. That's right.
Midnight No, no heat, on my face. No . . . no light.
Klondike No light?
Midnight No light. No sun.
Lucy Eclipse.
Klondike Eclipse? ECLIPSE. Everyone into position. Who's missing?
Tulip The twins.
Klondike Polly. Jane. POLLY. JANE. How long left?
Tulip A minute. No, fifty seconds. Less.
Klondike Who else? Midnight?
Midnight Here, right next to you.

Enter Polly and Jane.

Klondike Six of us. Six of us.
Tulip Glue Boy. Where's Glue Boy?
Klondike Where's Glue Boy?
Polly We saw him up by the tents.
Jane Out of his head.
Klondike Idiot. How long left?
Tulip Twenty. Less.
Klondike Okay, okay. (*to Lucy*) You. It'll have to be you.
Lucy I'm going back to the –
Klondike Stay there and don't move.
Tulip Where shall we stand?
Klondike Don't you remember the plan? (*He begins to move them into position.*) You there, you there, you there . . .

Midnight What about me?
Klondike You stand here.
Lucy Look, I'm not really sure . . .
Klondike Just stay put. You've had it your own way all
afternoon, now let's see what you're made of.
Tulip Ten seconds.
Lucy Huh, me at the back then?
Klondike Pole position. Right where it happens.

*Facing towards where the sun grows darker, they stand
in a triangular formation, with Tulip, Klondike and
Midnight at the front. Polly and Jane behind them,
and Lucy at the back.*

Polly Look out, here it comes.
Jane (*elated*) Oh yes.
Polly Time for the shades. Time for the shades?
Klondike Yes, the shades. Put them on.

*Klondike, Tulip, Polly and Jane put on their protective
glasses.*

Midnight What?
Polly The specs.
Midnight Oh yes. (*He takes his off.*)
Tulip Five seconds, less. Three. Two. One.

Except for Lucy, they begin the chant.

All Fallen fruit of burning sun
Break the teeth and burn the tongue,
Open mouth of the frozen moon
Spit the cherry from the stone.

*Enter Glue Boy from opposite direction, still with glue
bag on his head. He collides with Lucy, who takes him
to one side and takes the bag from his head. She holds
his hands as he hallucinates.*

Glue Boy Seeing things. Dreaming things.

Glue Boy blurts out his dream as Midnight leaves the group, retrieves his crucifix from Lucy's bag and puts it on.

head through a noose dreams
  lasso roping a horse
needle threading itself
  bat flying into cave
mole coming up through a grave
  cuckoo's head through the shell of an egg
dog on a leash dreams

Midnight rejoins the group, who are still facing the eclipse, chanting. Tulip leaves the group and begins putting on her boots. She produces another red head-scarf from her pocket, and ties it around her head.

sea-horse trying on its shoes
  tom cat tortoiseshell stood up
mermaid scaling the beach
  finding its feet ditching its tail
square of the sky shepherd's delight
  pulled down worn as a crown
poppy blazing in a field of corn
  dead volcano blowing its top
matchstick wearing heat to its head like a hat
  dream things things like that

Tulip rejoins the group. The twins go to the bag to retrieve clothes, jewellery and make-up.

double-vision dream two trees
  Dutch elms coming back into leaf
two snow-leopards trying on furs
  leggings coats of sheep that were shorn
two African rhino stripped to the bone
  locking horns

nude Aunt Sally   birthday suit on a tailor's dummy
    rose-petal lips   ivory teeth
dreams   dolled up like Russians
    dressed to the nines   clothes of their mothers
those dreams   others

*The twins rejoin the group. Klondike goes to the bag
to retrieve the skull and the Boji stones.*

nutcracker man coming out of his shell
    great auk treading thin air
phoenix roasting   driftwood fire
    unicorn meeting its match   point of a spear
head of a griffin   worn as a hat
    beak of a dodo worn on a boot
as a spur
    tusk of a mammoth torn from its root
a tooth a tree
    white hart hung by its hooves
Franklin's men   out of the deep-freeze
    dream things those   these

*Lucy and Glue Boy have become stuck together with
the glue. They spin round violently trying to free
themselves from each other.*

Lucy Let go.
Glue Boy It's the glue. It's the glue.
Lucy LET ME GO.

*The rest of the group are still chanting. The total
darkness of the eclipse descends, then sunshine returns
and Glue Boy is found to be standing in the position
where Lucy stood.*

Klondike That's it.
Tulip Blown away.
Polly That was strange. Really strange.
Jane Funny, I've gone all cold.

Midnight I feel sick.

Klondike Happens to some people. I've read about that.

Tulip Come on, everyone up to the top.

Klondike Glue Boy?

Glue Boy Hello.

Klondike Where did she go?

Glue Boy Where did who go?

Tulip Princess Muck. Lady Di. Who do you think? Lucy Lime.

Glue Boy Er, don't know. Lost her in the light.

Polly (*picking up Lucy's bag*) She left her bag.

Jane Here, Glue Boy, better give it her back.

Glue Boy walks off with her bag.

Klondike Come on. We're wasting time.

Jane It seemed to go on for hours. How long did it last?

Tulip Two minutes thirty-five.

Polly Not according to mine. Yours must be fast.

Tulip So what did you make it then?

Polly Well . . . less.

Klondike Come on. Last one to the top gets a Chinese burn.

Midnight I feel sick.

Klondike Somebody give him a hand. Polly and Jane.

Tulip Hang on.

Klondike Now what?

Tulip (*looking around*) Nothing. Just checking.

As everyone pauses, Tulip runs in front of them.

Last one up's a chicken!

They all exit, Polly and Jane dragging Midnight with them.

SCENE TWELVE

*The interview room. Glue Boy holding Lucy's bag,
examining it.*

Glue Boy
Sorry, I just wanted to be sure. Yes, this is the one,
the one that she had on the beach. It's been a bad week.
We're all cracking up with thinking what to think.
We've made up a rhyme to say at the service tonight,
something that fits, we reckon, kind of a wish or a
    prayer
to cover whatever's gone on, wherever she's gone.
I could run through it now, if you like? You'll say
if you think we've got it all wrong? Okay then, I will.

*As he begins, he is joined in the chanting at various
intervals by the others in the waiting room.*

under the milk token of the moon
under the gold medal of the sky
under the silver foil of the moon
under the Catherine wheel of the sun
born below the sky's ceiling
at home with the moon's meaning
nursed on the dew's damp
twilight for a reading lamp
tribe of blue yonder
Cub Scouts of Ursa Minor
the east wind for a hair-dryer
Mercury for a shaving mirror
a-bed afoot Jacob's ladder
head down on Jacob's pillow
Heaven's sitting tenants
meteorites for birthday presents
Masai of the stone deserts

stage-lit by daffodil heads
Orion's belt for a coat peg
Uranus for an Easter egg
tumbleweed of the world's park
hearers of the world's heart
ears flat to the earth's floor
thawed by the earth's core
needled by Jack Frost
high priest of the long lost
passed over by Mars
pinned down by the North Star
some type of our own kind
branded with real life
Lobby Ludds of the outback
seventh cousins gone walkabout
Navaho of the tarmac plains
snowdrifts for Christmas cakes
groupies of the new age
Venus for a lampshade
Jupiter for a budgie cage
Saturn for a cuckoo clock
guardians of the joke dogs
Jack Russells in tank tops
Sirius for a pitbull
Pluto for a doorbell
Neptune for night-nurse
civilians of the universe
Eskimos of the steel glaciers
St Christopher's poor relations
citizens of the reservations
under the bullet-hole of the moon
under the entry wound of the sun
under the glass eye of the moon
under the bloody nose of the sun
under the cue ball of the moon
under the blood orange of the sun

under the sheriff's shield of the moon
under the blowtorch of the sun
under the stalactite of the moon
under the nuclear blast of the sun
under the hammered nail of the moon
under the cockerel's head of the sun
under the iceberg tip of the moon
under the open heart of the sun
under the cyanide pill of the moon
under the screaming mouth of the sun
under the chocolate coin of the moon
under the chocolate coin of the sun

End.

The Biggest Geometric Event You Could Witness

Simon Armitage interviewed by Jim Mulligan

Simon Armitage writes extensively for film, radio and TV.
He is also a novelist, and has recently received the Ivor
Novello Award for his musical *Feltham Sings*, based on
creative writing done with young offenders. But funda-
mentally he is a poet. So it is not surprising that, when
he was commissioned by the National Theatre to write
Eclipse for *Connections*, the language he used should be
crafted and range over many registers.

> When I came to writing *Eclipse*, initially I was going
> to write about something that happened in Hebden
> Bridge where a girl had been abducted. She was young
> and was hanging about with other young people. The
> incident happened on Bonfire Night, and there was a
> feeling that the kids knew something that they either
> wouldn't or couldn't tell. That was the territory I wanted
> to get into: knowledge without being able to see it,
> intuition, instinct. But I realised there were too many
> agonies associated with writing about a real event,
> so I found a venue and a time for an exploration of
> disappearance: a beach on 11 August 1999 when we
> would witness the last total eclipse of the sun of that
> millennium – the biggest geometric event you could
> ever witness.

Only children appear in the play; adults are present but
are not seen. Each child in turn goes into an interview
room and makes a statement about a version of events,
which is either the one being remembered or the one
being created. Between the monologues there is a series
of flashbacks to the day when the eclipse occurred and

345

Lucy Lime appeared and disappeared. Each person has a different version of the event, and the four children give us their versions up to the point of the eclipse, telling us about themselves and moving the narrative on. After the eclipse there are two more monologues.

I am aware that children can tip from being child-like into having adult sensations and sayings, and back into being children. I think very young children have a particular special quality that relates to a primitive and ancient knowledge. As they grow old they lose this intuition just as the human race has lost some of its instincts. Lucy Lime is not meant to be a celestial creature who arrives on earth only to create havoc. Neither is she meant to be an ordinary child. She is somewhere in between. She brings modern ideas to the other children who are still caught up in old-fashioned ideas.

Lucy Lime is not entirely truthful. When she tells the story about her rebirth, emerging naked from the canal with a new self-knowledge, it is because she needs to convince the twins that they need to abandon their make-up and fripperies; she cheats at arm-wrestling; and she wins the children's treasures by lying to Midnight.

Everyone lies up to a certain point. Lucy Lime says what she needs to say in order to be herself and to get others around her to accept her version of herself. I think we all have different versions of ourselves based on other people's ideas. Lucy certainly manipulates, but then we all manipulate. She's just very good at it. They are frightened of her because, as a complete stranger, she is able to get them to do things they didn't think possible. They recognise she has power over them and they aren't sure where that process will end.

Simon Armitage uses different language-registers in
Eclipse: there are realistic scenes which veer off into the
language of rhymes, dreams and fantasies; the monologues
mix up the version of the eclipse with early-life memories,
earthy humour and carefully polished images; there is a
song that mixes balderdash with resonances of losing
something and gaining something; and there is Glue Boy's
final monologue.

> The whole play is about occlusion, what is behind
> and what is in front, and I tried to write it so that
> some motifs came up constantly – disguise, masks,
> being in the dark, future present and future past. The
> last monologue is supposed to exist somewhere between
> a prayer and an alibi. Glue Boy explains that it is
> something they have concocted to say at a memorial
> service, so it is a token of their concern. But it is also
> an alibi in the sense that something as difficult to
> fathom as this could be concealing something else.
> Many of the elements are of people living without a
> roof under the stars. The very real is set against the
> very abstract. Some parts are the here-and-now, others
> are cosmological.

Simon Armitage believes that we have become disconnected
from the world we came from, and one way to make the
reconnection is through the language used by poets. He
sees poets as shamans who can communicate with other
realities of the self and, in a sense, he became the nation's
shaman when he was commissioned to travel the UK in
the millennium year and write a poem that reflected on
the experience. In that poem, *Killing Time*, he dealt with
the eclipse, but also took a sombre look at the shooting at
Columbine High School, the London nail bombs and the
Paddington rail crash. Now that *Eclipse* has been revived
for *Connections*, Simon Armitage is hopeful that young
actors will once more gain insights from his play.

Most poets are after some version of the truth, not all
of them and not all the time and not always success-
fully. I hope the young people who perform in *Eclipse*
will realise that every character has a duality and can
be played as completely innocent or completely guilty.
There are a number of ways this play can be balanced.
If they try to look for deep meanings it might be too
difficult. The best way is just to dive in and have a
go. That's what I did. I held my breath and dived in.
I don't think I've come up yet.

Production Notes

Eclipse began as a story about a town full of extreme characters: on the one hand, New Age travellers; on the other, very old people who had never left the town and whose family had been living there for generations. It was inspired by a true story about a young girl who went missing on Bonfire Night. There was a sense that, because she was a child and Bonfire Night belongs to children, the children of the town knew something but wouldn't reveal it to the adults.

To ensure a similar level of mystery the play was located in Cornwall during the solar eclipse of August 1999. Ultimately the play is about the closeness of friends and what happens when something comes along to threaten that. The group start as children but end as adults, and the concept of change and transformation was very important in developing the play. This process is heightened by the technique of past, present and future being interwoven and scattered throughout the script.

CHARACTERS

The play is written for seven characters, four boys and three girls. The following notes suggest some of the points to consider and questions that need be to answered about each of them.

POLLY and JANE (the twins) They realise that they are sick of being one but are scared of being separate. They begin painted and bejewelled – their make-up is a mask.

349

There is a moment when they try to scare Lucy Lime and they are more entwined than they have been before. They become the monster from the Black Lagoon.

Lucy Lime introduces instability to Polly and Jane; they start almost as one and end by questioning their relationship.

They are referred to as trees: a tree in leaf is adorned and covered up so you can't see its quality and detail. Lucy Lime helps the twins to shed their leaves. But when they take their clothes off there is no middle ground of safety: one of them finds this sexy, the other finds it scary. They take back their jewellery and clothes to regain their leaves.

During the police interview are they together or apart? It could be that they are separately interviewed but they say the same thing. This is a decision that you need to make.

TULIP Nicknames stick and she's stuck with Tulip. Nicknames inform your character in real life; they help to establish a particular world and environment. Tulip is a closed flower, but there are glimpses of openings.

Tulip adores Klondike and behaves like 'a boy' and 'a girl' to find what he prefers so that she can gain his affections. She is jealous of Lucy Lime because Klondike fancies her. Tulip is happy to be a tomboy until Lucy arrives and threatens her position. There are tensions of unrequited love between Lucy, Klondike and Tulip.

There is a lot of hidden aggression in Tulip that feels as though it could explode at any point. She is described as a 'volcano' in Scene Eleven.

MIDNIGHT He uses blindness as a power, and gets very distressed when his senses are distorted and played with in Scene Two. Although he is the first victim of Lucy Lime, she doesn't set out to abuse him but to mock the others and win their prize possessions. She favours Midnight and Glue Boy the most. The children demonstrate how cruel they can be when they play blind man's bluff with Midnight.

KLONDIKE is a mining term, associated with the Gold Rush, implying hidden depths of something precious. He leads the group and brings them together, and is described later as 'nutcracker man' – the hardest nut for Lucy Lime to crack. She tries three times to get him riled but he ends up threatening her with a knife.

He cares about Tulip. (If Tulip is the earth, who is everyone else?) Tulip is described as his match. When she is electrocuted Klondike realises how much he cares for her. Lucy Lime is therefore getting at him indirectly. But there is a moment between Tulip getting electrocuted and when he says 'That's enough.' Why?

Lucy Lime manages to find the one thing that flips him out. It is a loss of control. All of the characters dance to Klondike's tune, but Lucy Lime gets too close to his power.

GLUE BOY He is the biggest challenge to Klondike's authority. As soon as Lucy Lime appears he disappears. Glue Boy and Lucy Lime are a happy balance. Decide whether Lucy Lime sacrifices herself for Glue Boy. The only time they encounter each other is when they get stuck together. What happens between Glue Boy and Lucy Lime is between them.

During the police interview Glue Boy appears to have changed. He knows what has happened (or seems to). Is he likely to lose his friends if he tells the true story?

Glue Boy allows you to suspend reality. He is poetic and truthful and can cut through all of the rubbish that people have said or are saying, but some of the characters don't give him the time to develop his ideas. Glue Boy must take time over his language to enjoy it. He has been able to remain part of the group because he's funny, he adds to the group dynamic.

Glue Boy has a parallel set of thoughts and morals. And is actually the most moral character in the play.

LUCY LIME Lucy is the patron saint of blind people, and lime can produce the brightest light in the world. Lucy Lime has an aura about her. She is confident and is very different from the group. She is a catalyst for change, transforming everyone around her.

It seems to be an accident that she is where she is during the eclipse. Is she a ghost? Real or unreal? Good or evil? Does she represents what everyone has to go through when growing up?

Lucy challenges people, but has moments of tenderness. She holds Glue Boy's hand as he goes through his hallucinating, and while in all the other characters' monologues Lucy Lime is referred to in the past tense, Glue Boy refers to her in the present tense. He is also the last person to have seen her, when they become stuck together with glue. Then Lucy Lime disappears. Beyond this no one knows what actually happened.

THEMES

MAGIC Throughout the play there is a blurred line between myth and reality, a dream-like state and wakefulness. The appearance of the ice-cream van could be a coincidence, but the characters perceive it as magic – a childlike ideal. Consider the scarf and the jet flying past: the scarf being set alight and becoming very bright; the jet flying in front of the sun, making everything very dark, a prologue to the eclipse itself.

THE ECLIPSE Thousands of people came together to take part in something they didn't really understand, and in the play we have a group of young people dabbling in something they don't really understand.

- In the eclipse formation all the other characters are facing the other way.
- During the play there are points when all the characters are planets and move and rotate around one another.
- The triangle during the eclipse is a solid formation for two minutes, then spins out of control again.

POETRY Rhyme and rhythm are an integral part of life. Poetry is an anthropological necessity: there is something elemental about it, and its language is the way in which the universe enters the mind.

- Old people can't remember their own past but can remember nursery rhymes.
- We are surrounded by noise 24/7. Poetry is one person saying something they really believe in.
- All the characters are bound together through language. They have spent a long time together and can make shared references to this common past. They play games with the language to create closer relationships with the people who can relate to it.
- Football chants grow organically from a body of people. There is a magical sense surrounding this. The group's chant during the eclipse grows from

Klondike, and the characters absorb the words each of them says.

- Lucy Lime's language is more realistic because she is an outsider.
- Simon Armitage is writing with rhythm throughout the play. His language doesn't have a metre and there is no strong rhythm, but a lot of the words rhyme in some way.

EXERCISES

Eclipse includes a series of dares and challenges set for the individuals within the group by the outsider, Lucy Lime. But the first dare we learn of was set up by Klondike, and caused Midnight to go blind when he looked at the sun through a pair of binoculars. Ask the actors about the greatest dare they would ever perform.

All the bets the characters make involve harm. Ask the actors what sort of effect placing bets might have. Organise a series of bets for the company which aren't self-harming.

The characters play a number of different games, involving: arm wrestling; potatoes; and blind man's bluff. These have a cult-like quality to them, with one character setting out rituals for the others.

The preparation for the eclipse, the plan and formation they put themselves in is very ritualistic. This is also instigated and led by Klondike. The others fall into and pick up the chant. Have your actors play the games outlined above as well as some of their own.

STAGING

SCENE ONE There is an empty chair for another person: someone who is missing. The first part of the scene is full of questions. Where are they? What town are they in? Does this matter? The action moves between a police station and a beach, two completely contrasting environments. How can you make this work on stage?

The battle of the story is between Glue Boy and Klondike, and the whole story is encapsulated in the paragraph that Klondike speaks at the beginning.

From this point the director needs to decide on the following: how the characters are dressed; whether they are in the present or the past of their character; who has reverted and who hasn't.

SCENE TWO Midnight's relaxed air in the interview room contrasts with how he was in the corridor. The audience find out about his change – the change from child to adult. There is the sense that someone is manipulating Midnight – placing a blind person in a hugely visual experience such as an eclipse.

SCENE THREE There is an electric fence, a beach – the beginnings of a new location. Klondike, Tulip and Glue Boy are in the cave. Klondike is the hunter-gatherer – a mythical creature, the Minotaur, lost in the cave and leading people out.

How does Midnight enter? For the first time a stage direction tells us that he is wearing glasses. How does Lucy react? Our frst impression of Lucy is that she is quite sarcastic and says what she thinks. She doesn't

believe in God. She mentions moths, and when she lights
the scarf the characters, like moths to the flame, are
drawn to her. They begin to play and place bets. Each
character bets something that is precious to them.

Midnight will lie to gain Lucy's friendship. Lucy Lime
challenges him and flatters him. Midnight wants to
engage in the relationship, but goes too far because he
wants it to continue. Lucy Lime seduces and flirts with
him until she gets what she wants.

Midnight gives up his religion almost instantly. He has
lied and broken his relationship/bond with God. Each
character is affected differently by this moment.

When Lucy Lime is about to leave the stage, it is about to
go dark. She has a relationship with brightness.

SCENE FOUR Refer back to the notes on the twins. 'But
now we're clear' is about the past and a moment of
renewal. The next scene is about transformation.

SCENE FIVE The playing of childish games is like in a
primary-school playground. When Lucy Lime tells the
story of the canal, it's a trick: something similar might
have happened to her, but ultimately she is telling a story.
The twins react in very different ways: one convinces the
other to work together to rebirth themselves.

Lucy Lime makes them all feel vulnerable – especially so
while they are naked. The twins split and hate each other.
They have to learn to love each other anew.

SCENE SIX Tulip's speech: her transformation from girl
to woman.

SCENE SEVEN Klondike reveals everything about his life all at once. Lucy Lime tries to get to him and get inside his head, but when she stamps on his objects and he is not riled, she has lost. He is the nutcracker man.

The one person Lucy Lime doesn't manage to get to is Glue Boy – until he is sitting in the police interview and realises in hindsight the effect she has had.

SCENE NINE There is lots of rhyme in this scene and it creates lots of energy. Then the rhyme and rhythm disappear, causing everything else to tumble out quickly.

Bear in mind that the characters have probably moved around since the last police scene. Look at what's happened in the play so far. How does it inform the character formation on stage? The scene ends inside Midnight's head, and is an interior monologue.

THE ARROW FORMATION Who is at the front? The strongest experience is the person's standing at the front, the point of the arrow. Glue Boy is the natural choice for this, but Lucy Lime has to step in and do it instead.

The eclipse is the most amazing form of occlusion, with overtones of dabbling in the occult, whereas Lucy Lime has introduced adulthood, science and rationality. Combining the two creates a chemical reaction.

The moment of eclipse is supposed to be dark: how dark? But it is also a moment of enlightenment, of waking dreams or nightmares. The darkness is the darkness of childhood that is also magical. The eclipse is a metaphor for this.

AFTER THE ECLIPSE Lucy Lime has disappeared. Tulip starts to look for tracks. Glue Boy is covering up that he was the last person to see her. The most incriminating piece of evidence is the knife that is in Lucy's bag.

The characters go back to get the things they have been stripped of and what they betted away. They all revert to being young again when something has gone wrong.

The characters have wanted to get rid of Lucy because she reveals all their flaws and exposes their insecurities. Each character has a prop or mask to hide behind, and she takes all those things away so that they feel exposed and vulnerable.

The ritual they were performing was done in ignorance. They weren't looking when Glue Boy came back, which turns out to be important and significant.

THE POEM The group make up a poem to read at the memorial service. Why have they done this? The play doesn't tell you what happens, there is no straight answer.

Is the rhyme an excuse or a kind of commemoration? There are images of people living outside under the stars and of the lost people – a heartfelt prayer for the missing. It is an attempt to try and fit the omniscient and unexplained into the material and the domestic. But it could also represent the collective guilt of the group.

RESEARCH

Similar themes are discussed in Simon Armitage's novel *Little Green Man*, which is about a group of school friends who carry out a series of dares with one another.

based on a workshop led by Lawrence Till
transcribed by Imogen Kinchin

HEADSTRONG

April De Angelis

Characters

Rose Anne Phillips, fifteen

Lila Mae Lowe, seventeen

Mrs Lowe, her mother

Captain Lowe, her father

William Isaac, a young doctor, twenty-four

Mr Oliver, a poet, twenty

First Mate, Jim Salmon, seventeen

Mrs Stevens, a pregnant woman, twenty-eight

Mr Logan, a ship-owner, twenty-eight

Miss Robena Logan, his sister, twenty

Dr Nichols, forty-five

A Woman

A Jailer

A Judge's Voice

Sea Witches, singing

PROLOGUE

1830. A young woman stands with a jailer beside her. She faces the audience. We hear a Judge's voice.

Judge's Voice Rose Jane Phillips, that is your name?
Rose Yes, sir.
Judge's Voice Crime against property ranks with that against the person and hurts a man just as grievously. The destruction you wreaked, the lives you put at risk, the capital you destroyed, mean that mercy cannot be afforded you. Some consideration will be given to your youth. Fifteen years. Have you anything to say for yourself? How you came to this path in life?

Pause.

The sentence of the court upon you is, that you be transported beyond the seas for the term of your natural life. Take her down.

Clank of keys turning. A door slamming. Rose steps forward.

SCENE ONE

A year earlier. A quayside. Rose speaks to the audience.

Rose I'd been to sea once before. I'd never dreamt in my wildest dreams that I would go, but I did. I was a servant. My mistress was a girl only a little older than I. They didn't tell me much about her except her name, which was Lila Mae. A name I'd never heard of.

363

Mother and Lila Mae enter.

Mother Lila Mae! Don't drag your skirts! They'll spoil.

Lila I hate the sea.

Mother What's wrong with it, my love?

Lila Everything, and it's got fish in it.

Mother They have to live somewhere, my pet. God gave us the land and fish the sea. That's only fair.

Lila I know that, you idiot.

Mother Don't talk to me like that, Lila Mae, I'm your mother.

She sees Rose.

Look now, from the description I had this must be our new servant. She was to wait for us here. Rose Phillips?

Rose curtseys.

Rose Ma'am.

Mother The letter from the Parish said you are a good girl, very obedient and willing to work hard. Is that true?

Rose Yes, ma'am.

Mother Welcome to our family, Rose. I am Mrs Lowe and this is Lila Mae Lowe who you are to help and you will help us all generally. You've not been aboard a ship before?

Rose No, ma'am.

Mother Well, I'm sure you will take to it.

Rose I know I will.

Lila You'll be sick.

Mother Lila!

Lila You'll be so sick it'll be coming out your nose.

Mother Don't say such things.

Lila There are waves the size of mountains and if you die they throw you over the side.

Mother To bury you, my love.

Lila Then the sea's a kind of grave.

Mother Why do you have to look at things in that peculiar way? You know your father doesn't like it. (*to Rose*) We are to sail to India where Lila is to meet her intended and become a wife.

Lila If I like him.

Mother There are plenty of beautiful silks in India for a wedding dress. And now we must board. Our luggage will follow.

Lila I'm not going.

Mother Don't make a scene, Lila.

Lila I said I'm not going.

Mother We have planned so long for this day!

Lila Now it has come I find I don't want it. Naturally my intended is very fond of me, but India is a long way off and very hot.

Mother That is just your nerves.

Lila You won't persuade me, Mother.

Mother Am I to write to your father in Bombay and tell him that! It will break his heart!

Lila WRITE WHAT YOU LIKE!

Mother (*dabbing her eyes with a handkerchief*) You see the trouble I am put to? Now what is to become of us? The ship is about to set sail. All our arrangements! Rose will have to return to the Parish officers . . .

Rose What is the name of Miss Lila's intended?

Mother His name is Mr Logan and he has written the most elegant letters. Once a week. Like clockwork.

Rose I expect he is handsome.

Mother By all accounts. He has a moustache.

Rose I expect he will be most disappointed if Miss Lila doesn't arrive.

Lila He will be heartbroken.

Rose For a bit. But gentlemen I've heard get over these things quicker than ladies.

Lila Nobody asked for your opinion!

Mother Don't raise your voice, Lila. I wish you could be more like Rose. She is a good, quiet, well-behaved girl.

Lila But maybe she will turn out like her mother in the end.

Mother You mustn't say such things! Rose is a hard worker and according to the Parish officers will turn out very well and a good servant. You must not mind Lila Mae, Rose. Apologise, Lila.

Pause.

Lila Let us go aboard, Mother. I would not like to break Mr Logan's heart after all.

She exits. Mother pats Rose's arm in approval.

Mother I think you will do very well.

Rose I hope to prove myself.

Mother It is very sad to think of your history, but with prayers and hard work you will keep to the right path. Could you take the brown box?

She follows Lila off. Rose picks up the cumbersome box, follows.

SCENE TWO

On board ship. A small cramped room. A storm, creaking, winds. The women sit looking afraid.

Mother There, it is not too bad.

A loud creak.

Don't worry about the creaking, that is only the wooden boards being hit a little by the waves.

Another loud creak.

The storm should pass off soon. How unfortunate that we should hit a storm so early.

A louder creak. The Mother gives a cry.

I am very foolish to cry out in such a manner.

An extremely loud creak, waves hitting side of boat. All three women cry out. Lila gets up and runs to the door.

Where are you going?
Lila Out of here.
Mother You'll be washed overboard. Rose, stop her. We've been told to stay in our cabins. The captain gave the orders.

Rose gets up and stand in front of the door.

Lila Get out of my way.
Rose I musn't.
Lila Out of my way! Do I have to pull your hair?

The door opens and the First Mate enters. A young man.

First Mate Ladies.

They all stop.

You mustn't be afraid.
Lila We're not afraid, we're bloody terrified.
Mother You must forgive my daughter. The creaking is very loud in this part of the boat. And this is our servant, Rose Phillips.
First Mate A pleasure. How do you do?
Rose Very well, thank you.
First Mate Jim Salmon. First Mate. Don't be alarmed. The storm will pass. This is a trusty ship.
Lila It's an old tub. My father is the captain of a clipper.

Mother My husband, Captain Lowe's ship is the *Sea Witch* and his partner Mr Logan has made a proposal to our daughter.

First Mate May I offer my congratulations.

Lila No, for at this rate I shall never get there!

Mother We're pleased to make your acquaintance.

Enter Poet.

Poet Greetings, ladies. Your cries of distress brought me precipitately – just like the dear squirrel rushing to defend its nuts from unwanted predators.

Mother We have no nuts here, sir.

Poet No, you have a poet. Allow me to introduce myself. Mr Terence Oliver. I have had the idea to read you some of my verse in order to alleviate your distress at the storm.

Lila It may make it worse.

Mother That would be charming.

Poet Ma'am.

The Poet pulls out a fat sheaf of papers. He prepares himself.

Poet O misery! O . . . I will start again. It is not easy to stand up without falling over on a ship, I find. O misery . . .

Lila Excuse me, our servant is about to be sick.

Mother Is she?

Lila Yes.

Mother (*to Rose*) Are you?

Rose I don't think so.

Lila Then I am about to be sick myself.

Poet Good Lord.

Mother The doctor must be called.

First Mate Ma'am. (*He exits.*)

Poet Poets are extremely sensitive to the suffering of others . . .

Lila makes a gagging sound.

And therefore should not hang around to witness it.
 Good day. (*He exits hurriedly.*)
Mother Poor child.
Lila I don't need a doctor.
Mother Nonsense. It could be serious.
Lila I won't see one.
Mother Don't have a turn, Lila.
Lila They are all hideous.

The Doctor enters. A handsome young man. A pause. Lila stares at the Doctor.

Doctor May I be of assistance?
Lila Are you a doctor?
Doctor Newly qualified.

Doctor shakes hands with them.

William Isaac.
Mother She seems a lot better already. You're obviously very good.
Lila I am not quite better yet, Mother. I think I do need a doctor.

Doctor feels her temples. Takes her pulse. Lila continues to stare at him.

Doctor No fever. A good and strong pulse.
Lila Are ladies supposed to have strong pulses?
Doctor If they want to be healthy they must have.
Lila I thought only servants should have them.
Doctor Servants and mistresses alike.
Rose Yes, for servants must do all the work.
Lila But that is what servants are for!
Doctor Who is this?
Rose Rose Phillips, sir.
Doctor You have strong opinions.
Rose No. sir. I have no opinions at all.

Doctor takes her pulse.

Doctor Your pulse is fine and strong as well.

Lila Do you want to see my tongue?

Doctor That won't be necessary.

Mother Is there no medicine you can give us, sir?

Doctor What for?

Mother Medicine is what doctors give people, or they did in my day.

Doctor Only if it is required, ma'am.

Lila Is there any more you have to do?

Doctor No. I am satisfied.

Lila Oh.

Mother Why do you travel to India, Mr Isaac?

Doctor There is a great call for doctors in the new clipper trade. I intend to try my fortune there. Now I must let you get some rest. The storm seems to be abating. (*He exits.*)

Mother Well now, Rose and I will do some mending and you may sit and write your letter to Mr Logan, Lila my dear.

Lila He can wait. I'll write it tomorrow. (*Lila sighs and stares at the door.*)

SCENE THREE

A sunny day on deck. Rose and Lila. Lila sits with an empty piece of paper in her hand. Rose holds pen and ink.

Rose I think you must begin to write, Miss Lila.

Lila I can't think what to say.

Rose You must say the usual things, I suppose.

Lila I'll say there is a new doctor on board. His name is William and his eyes are the colour of the sea when the sun shines on it.

Rose I don't think that is what Mr Logan would like to hear.

Lila Well, I can think of nothing else to say to him.

Rose Then we can never go in for lunch.

Lila You write it, Rose.

Rose I can't join up my letters.

Lila I'll copy it out in best, after.

Rose I don't think it's right that I should be writing to your fiancé, Miss Lila.

Lila You must begin 'Dear Robert'.

Rose It's wrong, Miss Lila.

Lila It's your place to help me and do as I tell you!

Poet enters with First Mate.

Jim Morning, Miss Lila, Miss Rose.

Both Good morning.

Poet Letter writing? Inspiration, ladies. That is what is needed. It's the key to all composition.

Lila You are full of it.

Poet It's true I am bursting with inspiration. Sometimes I have to run from a room, find a corner and scribble it all down. Words!

Lila Write my letter, then.

Poet I can't do that, it would be demeaning my gift, but I shall give you a technique, Miss Lila. You must close your eyes.

Lila I shall look silly.

Poet Trust me.

Lila You do it first, Rose.

Rose But it's not me that has to write the letter, miss.

Lila Go on.

Jim Go on, Rose.

Rose closes her eyes.

Poet Close your eyes and take a deep breath. In and out. Then let a picture come into your mind's eye. What do you see?

Rose gasps and opens her eyes.

Poet Well?

Jim Don't be shy.

Rose (*lies*) Nothing. I saw nothing.

Poet Ah! You haven't a poet's soul.

Lila Of course she hasn't.

Poet She lacks inspiration.

Jim She hasn't had a chance yet.

Rose I don't want inspiration. What good would it do me?

Poet Perhaps you're right. Inspiration. It's a poet's thing. Whatever comes into your head is what you should write about. I shall demonstrate . . . (*He closes his eyes. Breathes in and out. Pause. He tries again. He opens his eyes, disconcerted.*) It usually works. The rocking motion of the boat is perhaps not conducive to the imagination.

Lila I'll try it. (*She close her eyes. She breathes in and out.*)

Poet What can you see, Miss Lila?

Lila It is very dark. Midnight. There is a breeze. The sea is black and smooth. A hand is lying on a rail in the moonlight and it looks ghostly white. It is my hand! And then there is another hand reaching for it. A strong hand.

Rose That must be Mr Robert Logan.

Lila opens her eyes.

Lila It is not him!

Enter Doctor. He carries a few small hoops and a small stand.

Doctor Good morning.

All Good morning.

Doctor I have a plan for some exercise, which is very beneficial on long voyages. Have you ever tossed a hoop, Miss Lowe?

Lila No. But I should very much like to try.

Doctor Help me set up the game, Jim.

First Mate does so. They begin to set up the game.

Poet I shan't join you. I have a book of poetry to write on the subject of sea voyages. (*He exits.*)

Lila Write the letter for me, Rose.

Rose No offence, Miss Lila, but I don't think servants are supposed to have inspiration. I don't think your mother would like it.

Jim (*calls*) Do you want to try, Rose?

Lila Jim might not be so keen on you if he knew more about you, that your mother was a criminal.

Jim Rose?

Pause.

Rose No, thank you. I have a letter to write. (*Rose sits down.*)

Doctor Come and try, Miss Lila.

Lila Thank you, I will. (*She does so.*)

Doctor Very good.

Jim Well done, miss.

Doctor Now you must prove it was more than beginner's luck.

Lila You'll find once I put my mind to something, Doctor, I don't give up easily.

They laugh. Game continues as Rose begins to write.

Rose Dear Robert . . . (*She stops, thinks, then closes her eyes and breathes in and out. Opens her eyes. Writes.*) I miss you and long to see you every moment of the day.

SCENE FOUR

On deck. Mother, Rose supporting a Pregnant Woman.

Mother Are you sure?
Pregnant Woman (*panting*) Yes!
Mother It's not your first?
Pregnant Woman Seventh.
Mother Rose, fetch the Doctor.
Pregnant Woman Hurry!
Mother You need to lie down.
Pregnant Woman Want to walk.

They walk round together.

Mother Where's your husband?
Pregnant Woman Scared. With the kids.
Mother What are they called?
Pregnant Woman Billy is ten, Sara eight (Ugh!) John is
five and a half. (Ugh!) The twins Luke and Tabatha are
three. Baby is eighteen months. (Ugh!) I don't know
why I keep on doing it!
Mother Doctor won't be long now. It's God's will that
a woman should suffer. I was in labour twenty-four
hours. I did think that a little excessive.

Doctor enters.

Doctor We need to get you to your cabin.
Pregnant Woman Ugh!
Doctor Mrs?
Mother Stevens.

*Poet enters. Mrs Stevens grabs the Poet. Has a
contraction.*

Mrs Stevens Ugh!!
Poet Ow! That hurts.
Mrs Stevens I don't feel so glorious myself.

Doctor The contractions are coming with frequency?
Mrs Stevens Yes. Ugh! (*She grabs the Poet harder.*)
Poet Ugh!
Mrs Stevens Can you give me something, Doctor?
Poet (*holding his arm*) And me, Doctor!
Doctor I don't want you falling asleep, Mrs Stevens.
Mrs Stevens Just something for the pain.
Doctor Let's see how we go.
Mrs Stevens Have you given birth?
Doctor I'm not a medical miracle, madam.
Mrs Stevens Well, I have, and it's hell. So have a bit of consideration. Ugh!
Doctor Very well. I happen to believe that liberal doses of laudanum are harmful to the patient. Small amounts properly administered are acceptable.
Mrs Stevens Thank you.
Doctor (*to Rose*) Will you fetch something for me. The bottle marked laudanum, from the drawer in my cabin. Here is the key. (*He gives her the key.*) I can trust you.

Rose exits. Mother helps Mrs Stevens off.

Poet Can I have a moment, Doctor?
Doctor Not now.
Poet I am a poet.
Doctor I'd be delighted to hear your verse another time.
Poet I have invested a small inheritance on this voyage. Poets need a subject. The sea is mine.
Doctor This isn't the time, sir.
Poet What do you think of this, sir?

(*Reads.*) The sea sucks at the boat
Salt sears in the throat
It's a miracle we float
Like leaves tossed in a moat
Something something bloat . . .

It's shite, isn't it?

Doctor Good day, sir.

Poet (*calling after him*) Inspiration, sir, has deserted me and without it I am destitute.

Doctor exits. Rose runs on with the bottle. Poet stops her.

Poet Rose.

Rose I can't stop.

Poet Wait. I need some. Just a few mouthfuls.

Rose Your arm can't hurt that much.

Mother (*calling*) Rose!

Poet I need it to help me with my inspiration. I appear to have lost it.

Mother (*calling*) Rose!

Poet I have to write poetry, Rose, and in that bottle lies the key to lucidity and brilliance.

Mother (*calling*) Rose!

Rose The Doctor needs this for Mrs Steven's labour.

Poet Are you a machine?

Rose A machine?

Poet Always doing as people tell you and never thinking for yourself?

Rose But I'm not doing as you tell me.

Poet You won't help me?

Rose I must help the Doctor and Mrs Stevens. That is the right thing to do.

Poet What have you to do with right and wrong? You are a machine.

Voice Off (*calling*) Rose!

He grabs hold of her. Rose gets free, runs off.

Poet Damn. (*He crumples up the paper in his hand and throws it into the sea.*)

SCENE FIVE

Cabin. Evening. Rose gets paper, sits down, writes.

'Dear Robert – Everything here is calm and sunny. Just
   imagine, I will be with you in less than two weeks . . .'

*Closes her eyes. As she does so a figure of a woman
appears behind her, dressed in rural working clothes.
She holds a charred torch. Rose senses something
eerie. Rose is horrified. Gives a cry: 'No.' The figure
retreats as Lila enters.*

Lila Brush my hair, Rose. I'm almost late for dinner.

Rose gets brush and begins.

We stop again at port tomorrow. Fresh supplies will be
   taken on. I must deliver another letter for Mr Logan.
   You must finish it tonight.

Rose You haven't written one yet.

Lila I've been very busy. After dinner William has
   promised to show me the Pole Star. I shall pretend
   to be interested, but all the time I shall be looking at
   his profile, cut out sharp and delicious against the
   night sky. And his shoulders. Mrs Stevens says he is
   the best doctor she ever had.

Rose All the time Mr Logan has been getting letters and
   trusting them and falling in love with them and they
   have been lies.

Lila They are not exactly lies. They are what I would
   write if I could be bothered.

Rose Your mother would not be pleased if she knew that
   I was writing to Mr Logan and not you.

Lila I shall forget William when I am with Mr Logan.
   But for now William is here and Mr Logan miles away.
   If you make a little effort to join up your letters we can

send it off without me having to copy it out. You can eat dinner alone and write it.

Rose I won't write another letter for you. It's going against Mrs Lowe's wishes and I promised I would be good and honest.

Lila You must do as you are told. Your mother never did as she was told and look how she ended up.

Rose stops brushing.

Keep brushing, Rose. I'll be late for dinner. I didn't mean anything. I'm sure you are nothing like your mother.

Rose No, I'm not.

Lila She must have done something very bad to end up the way she did. Ow! (*Lila touches her hair.*)

Rose Sorry, was I pulling?

Lila The thing is, Rose, you have started now and you are already in trouble if I tell on you. I would be in trouble too, but not as much as you. It's only a few more weeks of letter writing and then I'll never ask it of you again. I don't think you can afford a black mark against you, can you, Rose? Let's be friends about it.

Rose pins up Lila's hair.

Thank you, Rose. I look very nice.

Lila exits. Rose gets paper, sits down, reads:

'Just imagine I will be with you in less than two weeks . . .'

She closes her eyes again. Opens them, writes:

'I hardly know how I can bear so long a time – it seems an eternity . . .'

As she does so the figure of a woman re-appears behind her. Rose again senses something eerie. Rose looks behind.

Leave me alone. I hate you. Leave me alone.

SCENE SIX

*Land. Everyone on deck looking out towards the
audience. Land – India. Mrs Stevens holds a baby. Lila,
Mother, Rose, Poet, Doctor and First Mate. Mrs Stevens
holds up baby.*

Mrs Stevens Look there, Katie. India.

Lila It will feel strange to leave the ship.

Jim Seventy-three days at sea. Not as fast as a clipper,
but not bad.

Mother I think I have got frightfully sunburned.

Poet O India, O something . . . something . . . yes . . .
there's a poem in there somewhere . . . if only I could
get to it.

Mrs Stevens Good luck to you, Doctor.

Doctor Thank you.

Lila Do we need a doctor on our ship, Mother?

Mother Father and Mr Logan will be waiting for us at
the port.

Lila But shan't we need a doctor on the *Sea Witch*,
Mother?

Mother That's your father's business.

Lila Father always listens to me.

Doctor It's been a pleasure throwing hoops with you,
Miss Lowe.

Poet I need words . . .

Mother You are very quiet, Rose.

Rose It's beautiful.

Jim Our Empire.

Poet Nothing rhymes with India.

Lila (*to Doctor*) You'll forget me.

Doctor I couldn't forget you.

They hold hands.

Lila Promise?

Doctor Your hands . . . are lovely.

They look at each other.

Mother Are you looking out for them, Lila? Can you see them?

Jim Well, Rose, this is goodbye.

Rose Yes.

Jim I might try my luck with the *Sea Witch*, too. Have you an opinion on that?

Rose I don't have opinions, but if I did I would think it would be a good idea.

Mrs Stevens (*to her baby*) She's smiling. That's it. India. India.

They continue to look out.

SCENE SEVEN

A house in Bombay. Captain Lowe, Mother, Mr Logan, Lila Mae, Rose and Miss Robena Logan. A tea table.

Captain Our business goes very well. Fortunes are being made. Our little ship is a gold mine.

Miss Logan Women understand nothing about business, although I have been keeping the accounts and it is wonderful to see ourselves growing so rich. My brother has promised me my own carriage. Mr Logan is so generous.

Mr Logan Robena! I fear my sister is too generous on my account.

Mother Nonsense. Shall I pour?

Captain There are servants to do that, my dear.

Mother But I like to do it. It's a homely touch.

Lila Let Rose do it, Mother. She is a servant.

Mother But I like to do it. Sugar, Mr Logan?

Mr Logan Three spoons.

She stirs in three spoons for him. Hands him the tea.

Mother You no longer have a moustache, Mr Logan. Lila Mae was quite taken with the idea of your moustache.

Mr Logan I'll grow another one if she likes.

Miss Logan My brother is a very considerate man.

Mother Well, that is an offer. Isn't it, Lila?

Miss Logan There are not many men that I know of who would arrange their facial hair so as to suit the ladies of their acquaintance.

Mother Very true. I am always on at the Captain to do something to his whiskers but he pretends he hasn't heard me.

Captain I haven't heard you many times on that matter.

Mother Captain Lowe likes to tease me.

Mr Logan I trust you did not find your voyage too arduous, Miss Lowe?

Lila No.

Captain I think Mr Logan deserves a fuller answer, petal.

Lila It was alright.

Mr Logan You wrote most elegantly of your observations.

Lila Did I?

Mother Of course you did. Who else?

Mr Logan I believe you have literary flair.

Lila I don't think so.

Captain Don't contradict Mr Logan, child, he will begin to think you are headstrong.

Mother Which she is not in the least.

Mr Logan You had a travelling companion – Miss Phillips. That was some consolation, I expect.

Lila She's not my companion.

Mr Logan Two young women of similar age cannot help but get along when they are thrown in one another's company.

Lila Not in this case.

Mother You make yourself seem too fierce, Lila. Rose is a good girl.

Miss Logan I find I make friends wherever I go. I cannot help making friends. People are drawn to my pleasant and open manner. Cake?

She offers. Mother accepts.

Mother Thank you.

Mr Logan Thank you for your letters, Miss Lowe. I looked forward to their fresh viewpoint exceedingly.

Mother I could hardly stop her writing them.

Captain Talk to Mr Logan, Lila. You have come a long way to keep silent.

Mr Logan I know you are not at a loss for something to say for yourself. Your letters showed me that.

Mother Say something, Lila.

Pause.

Lila Father, have you a ship's doctor? There was one on our ship looking for a post. I said I would mention his name to you at the earliest opportunity.

Mother This is not the time, Lila dear.

Lila I wish, Father, that you would answer me concerning the ship's doctor.

Captain That is no concern of yours!

Mother Lila!

Captain You are here to become acquainted with Mr Logan – so get on with it, child.

Lila He is not what I thought.

Mother Lila!

Lila He has no moustache, for a start.

Miss Logan But he has offered to grow one. I should be glad if any man were to grow a moustache for me.

Lila He wouldn't have to. You've one of your own!

Miss Logan Why! I shall forgive the impertinence of that remark seeing as you had so long a journey. Any shorter a distance and I would have been obliged to terminate our friendship.

Mother I think it is the heat that affects us!

Mr Logan It is hot. There are none of the sea breezes you wrote so eloquently of.

Lila I wrote eloquently of nothing!

Mr Logan You are modest. A good quality.

Lila Will you answer me concerning William, Father?

Captain Will you answer Mr Logan, Lila, and forget this William? I'm warning you.

Lila No. Rose wrote the letters.

Mother Rose?

Captain Explain yourself.

Rose I . . . I'm sorry.

Mother Impossible. I saw them posted myself.

Mr Logan Perhaps Lila dictated them to Rose?

Lila Rose wrote every word.

Mother Rose!

Lila I'm sorry to say, Mr Logan, that I do not love you.

Captain Take her home, Mrs Lowe.

Mother I do believe the sun has affected her most disadvantageously. Goodbye.

She curtseys, and ushers the girls out.

Mr Logan Goodbye, Miss Lowe.

They exit.

Mr Logan Your daughter is excitable.

Captain She's a good girl really.

Mr Logan She needs to get used to me, perhaps.

Miss Logan Is there a history of insanity in the family?

Captain Certainly not. Not on my side in any case.

Miss Logan One does hear such dreadful stories. It's better to get such things into the open. Can I persuade you to more cake before you leave? No?

Captain I'll take her with me to China. The trip will settle her down.

Mr Logan Let us hope so.

Captain Count on it. On our return she'll be more appreciative. (*He exits.*)

Miss Logan (*to Logan*) Don't hold your breath. Shall we take a trip to the Maharaja's palace this evening and watch the sunset? I should like that more than anything.

SCENE EIGHT

A cabin aboard the Sea Witch. *Rose sits on a chair by the door. On the bed Lila has been weeping. She gets up and looks out of a small window.*

Lila I shall go mad if I don't get out of here! When will I see him again? It's so unfair. It's cruel. Let me out! Murderers! (*She beats at the door.*)

Rose I think I am to lose my position.

Lila You'll get another one. My heart's broken.

Rose I won't get another. This was my chance.

Lila What will become of me?

Rose What will become of me? You didn't have to betray me. I was helping you.

Lila Haven't you ever been in love? It's like having a knife in your chest. William is on land and I am on this stinking ship!

Enter Mother and another Doctor.

Mother Lila my love! This is Dr Nichols.

Doctor Good day. How has she been, Rose? Any quieter?

Lila Turn this ship around and take me back to shore!

Doctor Not that quiet, I see. Let me help you, Lila. Can you tell me what ails you?

Mother She says she is in love.

Doctor Young women always fancy themselves in love.

Mother She is engaged to be married.

Doctor Well, that will sort her out. Marriage is the greatest antidote to romantic love ever invented!

Mother But she's not in love with her intended. It's someone else.

Doctor Well, that is unfortunate. And more serious. Does she have other symptoms? Does she use foul language?

Lila Because my heart is bloody breaking!

Mother Lila!

Doctor Let me take your pulse.

Lila Stay away from me.

Lila kicks Doctor.

Doctor Ow! Kicking is another sign. I've seen cases like this before.

Mother What is it, Doctor?

Doctor It afflicts young women in puberty. Her excessive excitability is a clue.

Mother What's wrong with her?

Doctor Nymphomania.

Mother That sounds dreadful.

Doctor It's treatable.

Mother Thank God.

Lila Nothing's wrong with me!

Mother The Doctor says there is, my love.

Lila Mother, I just don't want to be here.

Mother (*hugs her daughter*) The Doctor will make you better. Have you something to give her, Doctor?

Doctor Cold baths every three hours, and I will prepare a tincture for her. Two spoonfuls every four hours.

Mother Thank you.

Lila I won't take it.

Mother Yes you will, my love, and everything will be much better.

Doctor I've cured many nymphomaniacs in my time.

Mother I'm sure you have, Doctor.

The Doctor gets phial of laudanum out of his bag.

Here is your medicine, darling girl.

The Doctor pours some into a tumbler. Gives it to Lila. She swallows one mouthful. Recoils.

Lila It's bitter!

Doctor Opium is bitter but the effects are very strong and quick. (*He offers her more.*)

Lila I don't want it.

Doctor Just a few more mouthfuls.

Lila No! I'd rather be a nymphomaniac than swallow any more of that poison.

Doctor Then we must hold her down.

Mother Rose. You must help us.

Rose hesitates.

It will go better for you if you do. It's a chance for you to make amends.

They hold her down. Force her to drink.

Lila Ugh! It's foul.

She sits. Grows calm. They watch her. She lies down.

Mother She is calmer.

Doctor Opium charms the mind. Eases fretfulness and anxiety.

Lila lies still and does not say a word.

I'll leave her now. She must be left to sleep. (*He exits.*)

Mother Oh, Rose, I know you are a good girl really.
Sometimes a lamb strays from the fold only to return
to the light more strongly. (*She holds back a sob.*)
Watch over her, Rose. If she is saved I know the
Captain and I can forgive you.

Mother leaves. Rose looks at Lila, who is lying still.

Rose Lila? Lila?

Lila continues to lie still.

SCENE NINE

On deck. Morning. Rose sits alone.

Jim Rose?
Rose Jim!
Jim I was taken on in Bombay. Are you glad?
Rose Yes, of course.
Jim What do you think of the *Sea Witch*?
Rose Very fine.
Jim She is the prettiest vessel I've ever seen. As far as
ships go, I mean. (*He smiles at Rose.*) She's built of
the very best materials and although she has a light
appearance she is strongly constructed. She can present
more canvas than a man-of-war. That's why she's so
fast. What do you think of her figurehead? Come here
and you can see it very well.

He shows her. She follows him.

Rose A black dragon.
Jim Do you like it?
Rose It looks fierce.
Jim It's the symbol of the Chinese Empire. It puts us in
good favour to trade with them. And it scares off
attackers.

Rose Who wants to attack us?

Jim The Chinese.

Rose Why?

Jim They aren't so keen on our cargo. They have to pay us a lot of silver for it and we British are getting rich, but that is a good thing. For isn't it a good thing to be rich?

Rose I suppose it is. But I'm British and I'm not rich.

Jim That's a funny way of looking at things. I thought you said you had no opinions.

Rose That's not an opinion. That's a fact.

Jim How's Miss Lila?

Rose I better get back to her. She's not well.

Jim What's wrong with her?

Rose She's a nymphomaniac.

Jim Bloody hell. That sounds bad.

Rose Whatever it is, I think she was born that way. She's always been headstrong, so how come they've only found out now. I have to give her medicine and I don't like doing it. It makes her . . . strange.

Jim The Doctor knows best, Rose. You have to do what he says. It's like I must do what the Captain says. He knows what's best for this ship.

Rose Only I'm not used to her being so quiet.

Jim If the Captain sets the course into hostile waters we may not like it, but we trust him. We need to sell our cargo to keep our business going. He does everything in the best interests of that.

Enter Poet.

Poet To be a poet is the most beautiful thing. I'm full of words like sea, sky, fish. I am fulfilling my destiny. My imagination is as vast as this ocean. This ship's doctor is far more amenable to talent than the last. (*He drinks from a small phial.*) I have promised him a percentage of the sales of my first book of poetry. He is man who understands poetry and the demands of the romantic imagination.

Jim Write a poem about Rose for me.

Poet Ah! A love poem.

Rose He didn't mean that.

Jim Didn't I?

Poet As it happens, I can feel a poem coming on. Something piercing yet melting, joyful but sad . . . short but long . . .

He bows, exits.

Rose Did you mean it?

Jim I like you, Rose. One day I want to own part of a clipper myself and then maybe I will be rich. And then, who knows, maybe you will be too.

They kiss.

Rose When I do that I feel safe. I feel like everything else in the world disappears and nothing else matters.

Jim You'll have to do it more often then.

Rose exits to Lila. Jim watches her, leaves.

SCENE TEN

Cabin.

Rose Time for your medicine, Miss Lila.

Rose gets the bottle.

Lila Do you think I'm a nymphomaniac?

Rose You do swear. (*She approaches Lila.*) Just two spoonfuls.

Lila Take it yourself.

Rose Then you won't get better.

Lila I'm not ill.

Rose If you won't take it I'll have to fetch Dr Nichols. Then you'll be forced.

Lila I bet you'd love that, wouldn't you?

Rose Dr Nichols was talking about an asylum. He said they send girls there if the opium doesn't work. He said some girls deserve to go there because they don't try to get better.

Lila An asylum . . .

Rose Don't bring terrible things on yourself by your own stubbornness.

Lila You're just trying to frighten me. My parents wouldn't send me there.

Rose Your parents are at the end of their tether. Either you take this or I have to get the Doctor and he'll think the worse of you for it.

Lila I don't want to go to an asylum. When I feel angry I say things . . . Don't you ever feel like doing that?

Rose I should lose my job for sure if I did.

Lila How come you're not a nymphomaniac too?

Rose I close my eyes and I try to bring nothing to mind. Just blankness. No pictures. So I think nothing and feel nothing.

Lila I'm scared. Help me.

Rose Close your eyes.

Lila does so.

Rose Just see whiteness. Your feelings drift away. You're empty. Calm.

Lila opens her eyes.

Lila You've found a way to take opium without taking it!

Rose You won't have to take it for ever. Just take it for now and show them willing. (*She offers Lila the medicine.*)

Lila But what about William? If I close my eyes now I can see his face. It's like a torment, but a lovely torment. But when I take opium I don't care if I see him or not. When you take it for a bit you feel happy and nothing seems to matter, not even that your heart is broken. But my heart is broken.

Rose Maybe it's good to forget someone, if they bring you trouble.

She offers the medicine. Lila takes it, then spits it out.

Lila I don't want to forget William! Get out of my way!

Rose No.

Lila Do I have to pull your hair!

Lila pulls her hair. Runs out.

Rose No. Lila. Come back! (*She follows her out.*)

SCENE ELEVEN

Deck. Night. Lila stands on the rails of the deck. Poet, First Mate, Captain, Doctor, Mother, Rose gathered watching.

Mother Oh this is terrible! This is the worst night of my life since I discovered my daughter was a nymphomaniac.

Captain Lila Mae. You must come down, child.

Lila No! Not unless you promise.

Mother We promise.

Lila You don't know what to, yet! Liars.

Mother What are you going to do?

Lila Jump.

Mother But you hate the water.

Lila I hate this ship more.

Doctor Has she had her medicine?

Rose I tried to give it to her. She wouldn't take it.

Lila Turn the ship around.

Captain Child, that is impossible.

Mother You'll catch your death of cold.

Lila I'll be drowned, Mother. Who cares if I catch cold?

Mother Oh, help us.

First Mate I have a knife. I can whittle you a doll from driftwood.

Lila I don't want a bloody doll.

Mother Can you persuade her, Rose?

Rose She won't listen to me.

Lila Father, I will jump. I don't want to marry Mr Logan. I want to marry the Doctor.

Doctor I'm afraid I am already spoken for.

Lila Not you, you bald twit. William, I mean.

Doctor This is the worst case of nymphomania I ever saw.

Father Nobody will marry you at this rate, child. You'll be in an asylum.

Lila Then I'd rather die. I have a letter here for William. I want it sent to him. A proposal of marriage.

Mother Things are not usually done that way round, Lila my love.

Lila Yes, but I'm a nymphomaniac, we do things differently.

Mother Say you will give her what she wants.

Father Very well.

Lila That I will marry William. Your word of honour.

Father Word of honour.

She climbs down. Her Father seizes hold of her.

Father You've shamed me.

Lila Let go.

Father Get to your cabin.

Doctor We must double her dosage.

Lila NO! Liars! Liars!

She is taken off. Exit Doctor, Mother, Father.

Poet This must all be put into a poem. She is the sea witch incarnate. Yes, I can see it . . . But the vision is fading already. Slipping through my fingers . . . (*He takes out small bottle of laudanum. Drinks it.*) Just want to write a poem. Just one little itsy-bitsy one.

Jim comes up to Rose.

Jim Nobody blames you, Rose.
Rose They lied to her, Jim.
Jim For her own good. She'd have drowned herself probably. No man would want to marry a woman like that. No end of trouble I expect. She's not sweet like you. (*to Poet*) Did you write a poem for me? For Rose.
Poet I have it here.

He hands Jim a piece of paper. Jim hands it to Rose.

Jim Here. That'll cheer you up.
Rose Thank you.

He kisses her on the cheek. Exits. She opens the piece of paper out. Looks at it.

Rose It's empty.

Poet drinks again.

Poet Sublime feeling.

Wanders off. Rose exits.

SCENE TWELVE

Jim, Rose, Lila. Lila lies on the bed, sleeping, Rose is sewing. A knock. Jim enters. He brings a tray.

Jim We dock in an hour. You are to keep the door locked. We don't want her escaping again and jumping overboard.

Rose Not much chance of that. These last weeks she's
just laid on her bed. Since they doubled her medicine,
she's quiet.

Jim You're a good girl, Rose. Mrs Lowe says she doesn't
know what she would do without you. Sitting here day
in, day out. I miss you, though. It's not for ever. That
keeps me going.

Rose It keeps me going, too.

Jim Lock the door behind me.

*Jim exits. Lila wakes up. Now we can see Lila, she
looks ghostlike, with dark circles under her eyes.*

Lila What day is it?

Rose It's Saturday, Miss Lila. We dock in Canton today.

Lila Canton?

Rose In China!

Lila Is it time for my medicine?

Rose Not yet. Your mother says you are to eat something.

Lila I'm not hungry.

Rose I was thinking. Perhaps I could help you write a
letter.

Lila I don't care to.

Rose Not to Mr Logan. To William, I meant. I could get
Jim to post it for you when we get into port. It might
ease you to write.

Lila I don't care to write. I only care for my medicine, it's
time.

Rose Being in love makes you feel alive. You just want to
talk about the person you love all the time. You could
talk about William and then I could talk to you about
Jim. Jim knows everything about ships.

Lila Leave me alone.

They hear singing.

Rose There's someone singing.

Rose looks out of the small window. Singing gets louder.

It's a girl on a raft! She's got a long paddle. Someone's thrown something down to her. A bundle of clothes! And there's another bundle. It's laundry! That must be how they make their living. Jim's told me about them – those rafts are their homes. They sing to get our attention. She's wearing breeches. A red shirt. She's got a knife at her belt. There's a flower in her hair. Jim says they call them sea witches.

Lila It's time for my medicine, isn't it?

Rose hesitates.

Rose In a few minutes. I wonder what it would be like to be a girl like that.

Lila A lot of washing, I imagine.

Rose closes her eyes.

Rose You'd build your own raft from thick reeds. You'd sleep on your raft and wake in the morning when the sun rises. You set off and there's a breeze in your hair and on your face and it wakes you up like nothing else. You try it, Lila.

Lila If you promise to give me my medicine.

Rose Straight after.

Lila closes her eyes.

Lila It doesn't feel very safe.

Rose After a bit it feels as good as land.

Lila So much water. Where do you go?

Rose Any direction you choose. The paddle feels heavy at first but your arms get used to it. The sun warms your back. Pushing into the water is a beautiful feeling.

Lila opens her eyes.

Lila Like I said before, it's time I took my dose.
Rose I'm sorry I made you take it.

Lila stares at her.

I was scared. They don't always give people chances like
they gave me. To prove myself different. Not like my
mother.

Lila turns and faces Rose.

Lila What did she do? Did she murder someone?
Rose We come from Kent. My mother looked after us.
She worked every harvest. That's how we got by. Then
one year there was a machine instead. A thresher. They
didn't want hands any more. They didn't need them.
So people began to starve. Some went to cities to try
their luck, to be servants maybe, but Mum didn't want
to. So with some of the men she went out one night and
burnt all the crops the threshers had cut. They were
angry, they said, and they wanted their livelihoods
back. But they were caught and they were transported.
Lila She was?
Rose But I was allowed to stay here if I swore I would be
good and not headstrong like her.
Lila She sounds like a nymphomaniac! She was angry
like me.
Rose She wasn't thinking about me when she did it.
Lila She was working for you, wasn't she?

Pause.

Rose, I could escape! I'd go on one of those rafts. When
I got to the shore I'd sell my earrings. I'd send for
William. Dear William. Nymphomaniacs, I've
discovered, are very headstrong and don't take no
for an answer. I'd live secretly till he came to get me.
I don't want my medicine. I forget him when I take it!
Unlock the door, Rose.

Rose I can't. I've already had one chance.

Lila Bloody give it to me.

Rose That's more like the Lila I used to know. Rude and unpleasant.

Lila Your mother never did what she was told. You're like her.

Rose You're telling me what to do, aren't you?

Lila Look at me. I don't even know if I've got room in my heart for love any more. I just crave the medicine and that's all I am. That's not life. Swallowing and swallowing. It isn't right. Is it?

Pause.

Rose Here. (*She hands Lila the key.*)

Lila Thank you. I'm sorry you'll be in trouble. (*Lila goes slowly over to the door, unlocks it. Stands.*) I'll take my medicine with me, Rose, if you don't mind.

Slowly Rose gives it to her.

It's no good, Rose. I'm not free. (*Winces as she drinks it, because it's bitter.*)

Rose At least somewhere there's somebody free. We can imagine that. The sea witches.

Rose sits by Lila.

SCENE THIRTEEN

The hold. Boxes of cargo. First Mate, Rose enter. He carries a candle, which he places down on one of the boxes.

Jim We can be alone here. I wanted to talk to you, Rose. This business we are in, it's a good one. There are plenty of chances for advancement. I intend to take that chance. Make something of myself. I want to be captain of a clipper one day.

Rose I'm sure you will be.

He goes to kiss her. As she steps towards him she knocks over the candle. He stops and picks it up.

Jim Careful. We don't want a fire. Rose – do you think – do you like me enough, I mean?

Rose Yes.

Jim You do? This is a good time to be alive, Rose. There's a chance of a future. Money to be made. We could be happy.

Rose I like it when you talk about the future.

Jim Look around you, Rose. It is all around you. In these boxes.

Rose What is it?

Jim Something that once you start wanting you can never stop. White gold. That is what we sell here in China, and get a good deal of money for. That is making us all rich.

Rose Opium?

First Mate That is the clipper trade.

Rose But is that right?

First Mate That's not our place. You have an imagination, Rose, that's your trouble.

Rose I can imagine all the people that won't be thinking and feeling because of our cargo and I feel sorry for them. It might be too big a thing for me to forget.

First Mate No point in feeling anything for them, Rose. Feel for yourself.

Rose What about the sea witches? I suppose they might take the white gold, too.

First Mate Maybe. So what's it going be, Rose? Me and you? Yes or no?

Rose I just need to think for a bit.

He kisses her.

I do love you, Jim.

First Mate I know.

He leaves. Rose takes the candle and looks at the boxes. She closes her eyes. Behind her appears the vision of her mother with a lighted torch. She looks at the cargo.

Rose Fire.

The blaze of a fire is heard, crackling, shouting, cries of 'Fire in the hold!' Orange light.

Freedom.

White Gold

April De Angelis interviewed by Jim Mulligan

When she was at university April De Angelis won a competition for new young women writers with a prize of £400 and a production of her play. That was it: 'I loved writing. I had found what I wanted to do and, although I had wanted to be an actor when I was younger, I relished the hard work that writing entailed. I haven't stopped since.'

The paradox is that when she was at school April De Angelis was not allowed to do English O Level. She had liked her primary and middle school, but was not happy at her very traditional comprehensive school. 'If you showed any signs of not fitting in, of not being like the grammar-school girls they were used to, you weren't allowed to do O Levels.' So she left and went to a college of further education, and from there to read English at Sussex University. She was, it would appear, showing signs of being headstrong.

Headstrong starts with a young woman being sentenced to deportation for a crime against property, and moves immediately to a scene with the same young woman speaking to the audience: 'I have been to sea once before.' As the audience is taken through the journey of the play, they have to refer back and make connections. The events they are witnessing cast light on that first scene.

In essence *Headstrong* is a simple story about headstrong women.

> I really wanted to write a play for young people that had strong women. Both Leila May and Rose are headstrong in their own ways. In the nineteenth

century a woman who was obeying orders and convention was seen as good. But actually if you are headstrong you make your own judgements about things. You have to be strong in the head to say no to what you think is wrong and yes to what you think is right. In that society it was a woman's role to behave, and even today politicians expect us to condone what we know is wrong.

Lila Mae is manipulative and a little minx, but she knows what she wants and is not prepared to compromise. She can be horrible to her servant Rose, downright rude to her mother, flirtatious with a handsome doctor and coy with her father; but she will not budge on the question of marrying Mr Logan. The only thing that can tame her is opium administered as medicine for her 'nymphomania'. Rose also has her opinions, although like a well-trained parish waif she denies this. In the end, once she realises what an evil opium is, she is more headstrong than anyone and chooses to commit arson rather than settle for a steady marriage to Jim. The third headstrong woman, seen only in ghostly flashbacks, is Rose's mother, who had been deported for her part in the farm workers' protests at the introduction of threshing machines.

April De Angelis has set these relationships against the historical and political background of the development of the British Empire. The Industrial Revolution, alluded to in the threshing machines that were driving workers from the land to the factories, was sustained in large part by the wealth derived from slavery. By extending its control of India, Britain was also extending a monopoly of opium production that made merchants fabulously wealthy and forced open markets in China and the Far East. Without wanting to preach about the evils of heroin, April De Angelis wants young people to be aware of some of the history behind it.

My starting point was that there is this drug which seems quite cool and hip but, when you actually look at it, is used to oppress people and control them. I wanted to make the point that there is nothing liberating about taking a drug. At the time the play is set, the Romantic poets were taking opium in the hope that it would give them inspiration, and there is a reference to that in the play. But drugs don't do that. They rob you of creativity. It was used then to rob people of their autonomy and if you use drugs now you are the last poor sod in a long chain of people getting rich. You are not the user. You are the used.

Everybody on board the *Sea Witch* looks upon opium as a perfectly normal commodity and medicine, but they are well aware that it is 'something that once you start wanting you can never stop'. To the merchants it is white gold, to the doctor a medicine, to Jim a perfectly acceptable way of climbing the social ladder. Lila is the only one who is actually addicted: 'Look at me. I don't even know if I've got room in my heart to love any more. I just crave the medicine and that's all I am.' As she goes to make her escape she takes the medicine with her, saying: 'It's no good, Rose. I'm not free.'

In the final scene the full evil of the opium trade dawns on Rose. She is given the choice that everybody else in the chain has been given. They have chosen the route to riches, but Rose has her inspiration. Her mother appears behind her with a lighted torch and she makes her headstrong decision. There is the sound of crackling flames and the last word of the play is 'Freedom.'

I don't think young people will find this a difficult play. It's always fun to take the words on a page and work out how it's going to become a three-dimensional production, with humour and passion. It is possible that because it is set in the past with different social conventions and protocols, that little bit of distance may allow the young people to understand their history and in doing so to understand more clearly some of the issues they are confronted with in their lives today.

Production Notes

Headstrong is mainly set on a nineteenth-century opium clipper, a fast sailing ship that transported opium from India to sell in China. It is written for eleven actors to perform. If you absolutely have to, you might cross-cast depending on the make up of your company; but don't change the gender of a character because of the issues arising in the play. For example, the use of opium was allowable as a source of inspiration for the male poet, whereas Lila Mae is forced to take it as 'medicine' for her unacceptable behaviour.

April De Angelis decided that her play would have two good parts for young actresses. She didn't set out to write an historical piece but that is how it evolved, and it was an approach that she had taken before in her writing. Heroin was her starting point, but her brief was that, although she could write about anything, she should be careful in writing about drugs. April thought that sub-consciously she had taken this on board and so wanted to take up the challenge of writing about them. She didn't know what journey the subject would take her on, but she became interested in the huge deficit we owed to India through the import of large quantities of tea from the subcontinent, and how the export of opium became our trade to balance this deficit.

She was also concerned by the oppressive history of the drug – how it was given to people to control them. When the National's Youth Theatre read the play for the first time, they made a link with the drug Ritalin, used to control behavioural problems in young people. April thought by examining this oppressive history of the drug opium in a theatrical context, it might make people think twice about taking drugs today. She also wanted to include other interesting elements of historical research that she discovered, such as the coining of the medical term 'nymphomania'.

THE CHARACTERS

Use accents to differentiate class and the world of the play rather than worrying about naturalistic details of individual characters. Use regional differences in your own actors' voices to do this. When actors don't use their own voices, it is hard for them to connect with the emotional energy of a play. That takes a lot of training. The world of the play is strong in terms of the relationships between characters. It is a history play, but is also connected with the present, so don't try too hard to create a 'period piece'. In her use of language April has not created an 'old' world. This is a play about now: the historical world is just a relevant construct.

ROSE PHILLIPS   Fifteen years old (probably twelve when her mother was transported). Desperate to prove that she is compliant and not like her mother. Intelligent, hard-working, honest. She fears the part of herself that wants to think independently: she sees her imagination as something that may cause disobedience. She's frightened by what happened to her mother, and hurt by what she sees as her mother's betrayal. She probably witnessed the fire, which is the event she recalls in flashback at the end of the play.

LILA MAE LOWE Sixteen years old. A spoilt only-child, she's used to getting her own way. Passionate and sharp. She's no coward and has never learnt to hide her feelings. April chose this name for her because it's sweet-sounding, and she wanted the name to be different from Lila Mae's personality.

WILLIAM ISAAC Ship's doctor. Handsome, charming. Forward-thinking in his practice of medicine. Honourable.

MRS LOWE Lila Mae's mother. Dotes on her daughter, but afraid Lila may upset her father and so the household. She's not as sharp as her daughter, or maybe she's just grown used to suppressing her intelligence.

MR LOGAN Rather unimaginative. A businessman who has a very manipulative sister. He's sharp at business, not so much at home – but then he doesn't need to be.

MISS ROBENA LOGAN A woman who has discovered that it is better to appear compliant in order to get her own way. She's power-hungry and sees Lila as a threat.

DR NICHOLS A doctor of the old school. Wants to please his clients by giving them what they want. He's quite a dogmatic character and probably afraid of women.

JIM SALMON At seventeen, he is quite advanced in his career. He has risen from a seaman to be First Mate, and aspires to be a captain. Attractive and hard-working. Idealistic and loyal, but would never disobey authority. He could have been sailing since he was ten.

CAPTAIN LOWE Lila's father. Wishes he had a more compliant daughter. Sees his role in life as providing well for his family. Would think anyone a fool who did not capitalise on opportunities to make money.

MRS STEVENS Gives birth on board ship. Forthright, stoic, brave.

POET Twenty-two. Highly idealistic, and a follower of Romantic poetry. An opium addict. There is a rock star's bohemian self-consciousness about him (Adam Ant modelled himself on a Romantic poet). As with Byron, inherited money gives him the freedom to live an unconventional life. If he has invested his inheritance in his poetry, this increases the ugency of his need for the inspiration he believes laudanum to give him.

THE TEXT

OPENING SEQUENCE April defined this as the play's prologue. The most important thing to do here is to clarify to an audience that this is the future. In terms of the set, do what you need, but keep the momentum and the rhythm of the play in terms of its design. It should be clear in this sequence that we are not yet in Scene One, which opens with Rose's speech: 'I'd been to sea once before . . .' This is the transition from 1830 back to 1829.

SCENE ONE Back story: Captain Lowe has arranged a marriage of convenience – for business purposes – of his daughter, Lila Mae, to his business partner, Logan. The marriage is a way of cementing their partnership. There was a lot of new money in the merchant trade, many of whose members would have put on 'airs and graces' suited to their raised status. The Logans are greater snobs than the Lowes. The Captain is quite practical and down-to-earth, not at ease around the tea table. He would be a practical man on his ship – there's not much sentiment about him. He makes a good contrast to Logan, with all his servants around him.

Lila Mae is a pawn in the contract, to ensure that the money stays in her family. But her parents are not being unduly Machiavellian – this was common practice at the time, and the match is a good one.

Rose's mother is a convict. Traditionally, children were transported with their mothers, but Rose has promised not to be like her mother, and has stayed behind, working in the Parish, training to be a servant. Once on board ship, though, she doesn't want to go back – so she practises reverse-psychology to get Lila Mae aboard. There would have been less separation between master and servant on board a small ship.

SCENE TWO We are introduced to many characters in this scene, and there are lots of stories set up. Lila Mae and the Doctor fall in love, and Rose and Jim also clock each other, but in a more measured way.

At first the Doctor is being professional. He probably quite likes both women. Only in the next scene with the hoops does he begin to reciprocate Lila Mae's advances. You can decide if the Mother sees everything, but tries or chooses to ignore it, or is oblivious to what's going on. Maybe she's just not very bright. Try both choices and see what happens to the dynamic of the scene.

Note the settings in these scenes. We go from big, open spaces to tight, claustrophobic ones. Light moving back and forth is good to show the sense of movement on the ship. The characters inhabit an unsteady world.

SCENE THREE We have gone from a storm to a sunny day and from a cabin to the deck. The hoops and stands are played like quoits (where a hoop is thrown at a peg in the ground with the aim of encircling it). The stand would have hoops made out of wood or rope.

At some point in this scene, there has to be a moment when Lila Mae clocks that Rose likes Jim – it is your choice when this happens – so that she can blackmail

Rose into writing letters for her. When Rose closes her eyes, she says she sees nothing, but she's really seeing her mother. (Don't have the mother appear literally here, it would make the moment too big.)

The Doctor makes his decision about which woman he's going to go for, and the Poet is trying to find out why he's not inspired.

SCENE FOUR There is a lot of urgency in this scene, and no one should have any time. The pregnant woman screaming off stage and the Mother calling put pressure on Rose as the Poet is trying to keep her on stage. For the scene to work, the Poet has to be rooted – we need to feel his urgent need for the opium. The young doctor in the play is more forward-thinking and won't give out laudanum as freely as the older doctor (laudanum was even given to babies at the time, to keep them quiet).

SCENE FIVE The relationship here between Rose and Lila Mae is clear. Less immediately so is how the figure of her mother haunts Rose. Remember when you are staging this that it is a dream. Think of your use of space – perhaps using a piece of the stage that has not been used before, signifying the out-of-body experience through lighting, sound or smoke. Just how do you make a person appear on stage like a ghost? Perhaps they are not lit so brightly. Find a place that the audience's eye is not drawn to until it is necessary. Rose's reaction will tell the audience when the ghost is there.

SCENE SIX The Doctor does have feelings for Lila Mae, but they are not as intense as hers for him. He doesn't have the plans Lila has. Maybe it's a holiday romance. The relationship hasn't gone far. They've kissed. They haven't consummated the relationship. They've probably already had a conversation about Lila getting him a job on her father's ship.

As far as blocking this scene is concerned, where the Mother is placed is very important. Try keeping her slightly isolated stage right, as she's the least important character. Put Lila and the Doctor together centre stage. Every time a character says a line, ask them to draw attention to themselves just prior to it, so that the focus is pulled slightly towards them. When Jim talks about the Empire and India, try having everyone focus out front – to India – allowing Lila and the Doctor an intimate moment. Of course, there could be movement in the scene. Find out what would happen if Lila and the Doctor started at opposite sides of the stage. It can make it more intense for characters to need to find their way to each other. With a 'public' scene like this, you need to decide which lines are heard publicly (i.e., by others on the stage).

SCENE SEVEN This is a pivotal scene, where Lila's destiny is shifted. Think about the tension for Lila. Everybody wants something from her in this scene. What drives her to say Rose wrote the letters? And think about the silences. Mr Logan and Rose don't say much, but both have a powerful presence and affect the dynamic. How truly does Logan actually love Lila? Think of the heat, the alien culture – all of these would be oppressive.

All the characters have very strong relationships in this scene, so be clear what every character thinks about every other. When your cast is familiar with the scene, try playing it with different 'points of concentration' – on the weather, or with the Mother as everyone's focal point.

We are now approaching Scene Eight and we have already been to six different locations. The best way to create the world is through the actors' responses. Props are magnified in their importance – the opium bottle, the teacups.

SCENE EIGHT The laudanum bottle should look the same as it did in Scene Four. One of the last lines, spoken by the Mother – 'Watch over her, Rose. If she is saved I know the Captain and I can forgive you' – is a pressure point on Rose, a real conflict for the character to play.

Opium makes you ill at ease, and so you want more. It robs you of your spirit. Lila falls asleep quickly because she has been so hyperactive. The doctor has given her a strong dose as a start to obliterate her.

The Victorians invented and also categorised things, and any behaviour by a woman in the nineteenth century that appeared socially challenging was linked to her sexuality. Lila is expressing desire: this was seen as a mental illness, and warranted the use of opium as a cure for nympho-mania. Don't worry about the laughter the term will evoke – go with it. April wrote knowing what its present associations are. But you are playing with the irony that no one understands the meaning of the word in the world of the play.

SCENE NINE This is the first scene in which Rose and Jim get together – it is their first kiss. Textually, a lot happens. April is setting up the political context for the rest of the play, with information about the clipper and China. Make sure that you clarify Jim's intentions – he wants to impress Rose – otherwise the scene may appear too cluttered with dialogue.

This is the first time that the Poet has been seen on the clipper – a moment that needs to be acknowledged.

SCENE TEN There is a sadness, a naivety and pain in this scene, which make it very moving. We see Rose's vulnerability, bur also Lila for the first time admitting her feelings, so we see both girls as they really are. The turning point is when they are sharing something and we think they'll get through it – then Lila changes her mind and the gear of the scene shifts.

SCENE ELEVEN Place Lila at a height, very isolated from the others so that they can watch her. It is interesting that there is so much comedy in the scene undercutting the tragedy. For example, at this time of danger and distress, the First Mate can only come up with the suggestion: 'I have a knife. I can whittle a doll from driftwood.' But don't play the comedy – the Mother should be in pain. Make the humour come out of a place of truth. Lila is an intelligent, bright woman and the system can't accept her.

This is quite a dark scene for the Poet. He wants to write, but he's gone into a place where the the drug that at first assisted creativity has now taken over and destroyed him. Rose sees this, although she doesn't comment on it – and she has seen her friend be taken over by the drug and threaten suicide.

Make your choices to get the shape of the journey – and make choices as to which makes the strongest journey. For example, the Poet has two choices – has he given up or is he angry with frustration?

SCENE TWELVE Rose says 'These last weeks . . .' so the time lapse between this scene and the last is probably about two weeks, during which Rose has been sitting with Lila twenty-four hours a day, seven days a week.

The song of the sea witches comes from Lubbock's 'The Opium Clippers', and refers to young women who, when ships came into port, would call up and sing to attract the attention of the sailors, whose washing they would collect thrown down in bundles. The singing might be part of a charm or a street cry, it could be melodious or supernatural. But it's about the outside world, so it needs to be something in contrast to, or in counterpoint with, the emotional quality of the scene.

Lila doesn't leave the scene. Heroin is the most addictive drug on the planet and she's trying to kick it. She has realised that she is weakened by the drug but also tied to it. This is the last time that we see her – the end of her journey as we see it. We also get Rose's story and the pinnacle of the girls' relationship. Work out where they start their relationship, because this is where it ends in the play. It is interesting that in Rose's journey so far she has fought being like her mother; but now, in giving Lila the keys, she is doing what she believes is right not what she has been told. Both girls challenge notions of who they are in this scene. They both have to face themselves.

SCENE THIRTEEN This scene can be lit by a lantern or an oil lamp, it doesn't have to be a candle.

The best drama in terms of storytelling comes from moments of conflict – for example, if Rose really cares for Jim, but can't accept moral responsibility for what's happening to Lila.

Rose's future has been clear from the beginning. This is because April likes the idea that you know what the consequences are – that property is destroyed, but no one dies. The question is – how does this girl who tries so hard for acceptability at the start get to this point?

The important thing to take from this scene is the order of events in Rose's final journey: Jim and Rose part; she

413

closes her eyes, and her mother appears – a voluntary vision, a choice of reconciliation; from the vision Rose looks at the candle: she sees and accepts the proud choice of her mother holding a lighted torch.

Play with echoing the beginning, reminding the audience of Rose's life sentence. Perhaps just place Rose in the same position as in the opening scene – sometimes we need as little as this to remind us. Or use more elaborate reminders – keys jangling, doors slamming, etc. Endings are really difficult in new plays. Even with a writer in the rehearsal room, you only set the ending at the close of the rehearsal process. What is the last moment you want to leave the audience with? Don't try to get to it from the start of rehearsals.

based on a workshop led by Indhu Rubasingham
transcribed by Sophie Ward

MOONFLEECE

Philip Ridley

*There is no greater agony
than an untold story inside you*

Maya Angelou

Characters

Link

Gavin

Tommy

Curtis

Alex

Jez

Sarah

Nina

Zak

Wayne

Stacey

A derelict flat on the top floor of a tower block. The peeling wallpaper and decrepit furniture (coffee table, sideboard, armchair) indicate the place has not been 'officially' lived in for many years. There are, however, signs of more contemporary – if 'unofficial' – occupation: cans of lager, remains of fast food, a radio, a few books, sleeping bag, etc.

The boards covering the windows have been removed to reveal cracked, broken or missing glass (and afternoon sunlight). A few doors: to kitchen, balcony and the front door (broken off at hinges). A hallway in the flat leads, presumably, to bedrooms, bathroom and toilet.

A political banner can be seen. It has a family photo on it: smiling middle-aged couple, two teenage sons and a teenage girl (who, judging from the held hands and engagement rings, is the eldest son's fiancée). They are all neatly dressed and (very, very) smiling. Also, a pile of fliers and a box of badges (everything emblazoned with the cross of St George and 'VOTE AVALON') and a megaphone.

The sound of distant barking can be heard. This is loud to begin with but rapidly fades away.

Link stands in the middle of the flat. He is fourteen years old and wearing scruffy jeans and trainers. His hair, like the rest of him, is in need of a wash.

Link Who d'ya think you are? Eh? You can't just march in here and do what you like. You don't own the bloody place.

Tommy has come in from kitchen. He is seventeen years old and wearing a neat, dove-grey suit. His hair, like the rest of him, is slick and tidy. He is muscular and tall for his age, a graceful giant at home with tea-cups and sledgehammers. He looks round room as –

Link You scared the bloody dogs. Hear 'em? They go on for hours like that sometimes – Oi!

Tommy has picked up a book.

Slight pause.

Tommy puts book down.

Gavin enters from hallway, brushing dust from his dove-grey suit. He is sixteen years old and, like Tommy, immaculately groomed. Unlike Tommy, the effect is totally incongruous. Short, stocky and generally ungainly, he's like a Rottweiler in a tutu.

Link I'm not here alone. My mate lives here too. If he comes back and catches you there'll be trouble. I can go and get him, ya know. I know where he is. He's down by the supermarket.

Tommy gets mobile phone from pocket.

Gavin My turn to call!

Gets mobile from pocket.

What'll I say?
Tommy Tell him we're in the flat.
Link My mate's older than me. Bigger. He looks after me. He can do things with his little finger you couldn't do with your . . . with a grenade-launching bazooka.
Gavin Voice mail.
Tommy Message.
Gavin Curtis. Gavin. Place secure. Awaiting further instructions. Over and out.

Link 'Over and out'? Who's he think he is? The SAS?

Gavin Oi! Shut it!

Link Why should I?

Gavin 'Cos you value your kneecaps.

Tommy Gav!

Gavin It's him!

Tommy (*to Link*) Listen. Why don't you make yourself scarce for an hour? Here's some money. Get yourself something to eat.

Link Stuff ya money! This is *my* place.

Gavin Your *squat*!

Link I've still got rights!

Gavin You've got nothing! I bet you're a refugee. What's ya name?

Link Ain't telling you!

Gavin What's ya bloody name?

Link Rumple – bloody – stiltskin.

Gavin Foreign!

Tommy He's playing with you, for chrissakes.

Gavin Eh?

Tommy It's a kid's story!

Gavin You bloody –

Makes a dash for Link.
    Link darts out of the way.
    Tommy holds Gavin back.

Tommy Oi! Stop it!

Gavin He's winding me up.

Tommy You're winding yourself up! Now cool it . . . Cool it, I said!

Gavin calms down.
    Tommy lets go of him.
    Slight pause.

Tommy Okay. Now . . . Let's take a deep breath and start again, shall we?

Slight pause.

My name is Tommy. This is Gavin. What's yours?

Silence.

Okay. We're sorry we knocked down your door. That was wrong of us. Wasn't it, Gav?

Silence.

Okay. We knocked it down because we didn't know anyone was living here.

Link You should've knocked.

Gavin It's a derelict bloody tower block, you foreign bloody –

Tommy Alright! I accept – *we* accept – we should've knocked. We're sorry. We weren't thinking. We've been very busy lately and –

Link Hang on! *Now* I get it!

Looks at banners, etc.

Tommy We're campaigning for next week's by-election.

Link Yeah, yeah, but you ain't put them on any of this lot, have ya?

Gavin What?

Link That's what fooled me, ya see. If you'd *shown* 'em to me when you huffed and puffed me bloody door down I'd've known *exactly* what party you're with and your behaviour would've been – Tattoos! That's it! Show me! Go on.

Gavin (*with Tommy*) What?

Tommy (*with Link*) What?

Link Your swastikas.

Gavin It's prejudiced comments like that get ya head kicked in!

Tommy Gav!

Gavin He's ignorant.

Tommy Well, we ain't gonna educate him by shouting.

Link I don't need educating about you lot.

Tommy We're an official political party.

Gavin We take old people on day trips to Southend.

Link *White* old people!

Gavin So bloody what?

Tommy Gav! Remember what Mr Avalon says. 'Don't heckle a heckler. Educate through –' Gav? What does Mr Avalon say? Educate through . . .?

Gavin . . . reasonable debate.

Link Oh, you can *reasonably* debate, can you?

Gavin Yes!

Link This I must see!

Slight pause.

Tommy Go on, Gav.

Gavin . . . Good evening, ladies and gentlemen. Afternoon. Gentleman. I want to thank you all for coming out on such a chilly night. Warm day – he's laughing at me!

Tommy Perhaps you should skip to the family photo . . . 'I'd like to introduce you to –'

Gavin I know!

Grabs banner.

I'd like to introduce you to a family. They've been an important family in my life and I hope they'll become an important family in yours. This is Mr Avalon. You might have seen him around. He's lived in East London all his life. His dad lived here before him. Mr Avalon can trace his family roots back to William the Conquerer.

Link Who was French.

Gavin Says who?

Tommy Just . . . carry on.

Gavin This is Mrs Avalon. She's lived here all her life too. East London born and bred. She's the perfect

423

mum and wife, is Mrs Avalon. No one cooks roast beef like her. This is their eldest son. His name's Wayne. And this is Wayne's fiancée, Stacey. They got engaged when they were sixteen. Childhood sweethearts. Next year, when Wayne's twenty-one, they're gonna get married. It's gonna be the biggest bash East London's seen in years. Who knows? If you're a friend of the family like me you might get an invitation too.

Link Is *Mein Kampf* on the wedding list?

Tommy Why don't you give him a chance?

Gavin This is Curtis! Curtis is the youngest son! He's eighteen. He's left school now and is working in his dad's double-glazing business down Mile End Road. Curtis is a bit of a thinker. He's got a shelf full of books in his room –

Link yawns and walks away.

Gavin Oi!

Grabs megaphone and yells through it –

We believe in the history and tradition of this great nation. Our aim is to give this nation back its self-respect. To do that we've got to rediscover the spirit and values that made us rule the waves.

Tommy Go for it, mate!

Gavin The family as the central unit in society. A man and wife having children. Moral values. Christian values. The Bible.

Tommy Work ethic!

Gavin Respect for the law!

Tommy Neighbour helping neighbour.

Gavin A clean doorstep!

Tommy The Blitz spirit reborn!

Gavin This is the future I see.

Tommy Who can give us this future?

Gavin (*chanting with Tommy*) Avalon . . . Avalon . . .
Avalon . . .
Tommy (*chanting with Gavin*) Avalon . . . Avalon . . .
Avalon . . .

Distant dogs, disturbed by the noise, start barking as –

*Curtis arrives in doorway, holding a torch. He is
eighteen years old and wearing a dove-grey suit that
fits him too perfection. He is fair-haired, glossily good-
looking, as slick and smooth as a shark in baby oil. He
watches as –*

Gavin (*chanting with Tommy*) Avalon . . .
Tommy (*chanting with Gavin*) Ava –

Sees Curtis.

Oh . . . Hello, Curtis.
Gavin Hello, Curtis.

Curtis You've set the dogs off!
Tommy Sorry, mate. We . . . er . . . we got a little carried
away.

The noise of the dogs starts to fade.

Gavin I've been educating, Curtis. Like ya dad says. I've
just given him the full Gav treatment.
Link It worked! Come on! Let's chuck a pig's head in a
synagogue – *Sieg heil*, Curtis!
Gavin Oi! Respect! – And keep ya distance!

Stands between Curtis and Link.

Link Hear that?

Indicates the fading dog noise.

The first few floors are full of 'em. Wild dogs all over the
joint. They can sniff out a Fascist at twenty paces.

Dog noise fades away.
Slight pause.

Curtis Tommy?

Tommy Says he lives here. Two of them apparently. Other one's out somewhere.

Gavin Begging probably.

Link He's a street entertainer.

Gavin Exactly! – You get my message, Curt? I left a message with an update. Did you get it?

Curtis No.

Tommy I've informed this individual we'll only be requiring the premises for a short period but he refuses to vacate.

Curtis I'm sure he'll go if you ask him nicely.

Link Bollocks!

Gavin Oi! Don't forget who you're talking to.

Link I ain't! Bollocks!

Curtis I'll deal with you later.

Link Ooo, you're turning me on!

Gavin Don't be disgusting!

Curtis starts looking round the flat.

Link So what's ya story, eh? You lot? Wanna use this place for a secret HQ or something? Print ya hate mail? Make petrol bombs?

Curtis Where's the table and stuff, Tom?

Tommy What table and stuff?

Curtis The fold-up table. The one at the back of the meeting hall. And chairs. They're supposed to be here.

Tommy First I've heard.

Curtis stares at Gavin.
Tommy follows the stare.

Tommy Bloody hell, Gav.

Gavin I put everything in the back of the car. I swear.

Curtis So where's the car?

Gavin Down by the flower market.

Curtis Well, it ain't doing much good there, is it?

Gavin It's him!

Points at Tommy.

Tommy Me?

Gavin We were in the car, Curtis. I was giving it the ol' 'Vote Avalon' business out the window. Going great guns, I was. We had some time to spare. *He* suggested we park the car and walk through the market. There I was! 'Vote Avalon!' Flyers! Badges. All the way down to the Town Hall we got. Twenty people told me we had their vote. Twenty, Curtis! Twenty!

Curtis Cut to the chase!

Gavin *He* said it was quicker to walk here than go back for the car.

Tommy I didn't know there was stuff in the boot we needed, did I!

Gavin You didn't ask!

Tommy Gimme strength!

Curtis Don't say you both walked up the stairs in the dark.

Tommy I've got this.

Takes small pocket torch from pocket.

And Gav's got his lighter.

Curtis You said you'd quit smoking.

Gavin I'm trying!

Curtis No ciggies. No drink. No nothing, Gav. We've got to be squeaky clean. You hear? Jesus!

Tommy Want me to go back for them, Curt?

Curtis Eh? What?

Tommy The chairs and –

Curtis There's no time. It's gonna kick off any minute.

Link What's gonna 'kick off'?

Gavin You're head if you don't hop it!
Curtis Gavin! A word, mate – Come here.

Slight pause.

Gavin goes over to Curtis.

Curtis puts his arm round Gavin's shoulder and takes him to one side.

Curtis If you use any more language like that I will be forced to tell Dad and –
Gavin But, Curt –
Curtis No, no, listen, mate. You've been warned before. Wayne won't come to your rescue every time.
Gavin The party's everything to me, Curt.
Curtis I know, mate. Now, put your thinking cap on and let's solve the table and chairs situation. Can you do that for me?
Gavin Sure thing, Curt!

Looks at Tommy, then indicates Link.

Curtis Give him some money.
Link Stuff ya money. This is *my* place!
Curtis No. It's not.
Gavin What about this?

Points at coffee table.

Curtis Too low, mate. We need to sit around it.
Gavin Armchair?
Curtis No.
Gavin Two people can sit on the arms and –
Curtis No! We need a proper table with proper chairs like I told you to bloody – Jesus! Tommy?
Tommy We'll check the other flats. Might strike lucky. How many chairs?
Curtis Three.
Tommy No worries – Oi! Mr Memory!

Tommy and Gavin leave.

Link is looking at the Avalon family photo on the banner.

Link What's it like having ya family photo used as a piece of political propaganda?

Curtis It's fine.

Link This your garden?

Curtis Eh?

Link Where the photo was taken.

Curtis Yeah, yeah. Our garden.

Link The roses look . . . a bit odd.

Curtis They were put in afterwards.

Link How d'ya mean?

Curtis On computer. The roses were . . . sort of pasted on or something. I dunno the ins and outs. That's Wayne's department.

Link Your brother?

Curtis *Step*-brother.

Sound of distant door being kicked in.
Dogs start barking.

Link You're mate's turned door-kicking into an art form.

Curtis He's a trained athlete.

Link Crowbars're easier. You just get it under the lock and – krack! Open says-a-me.

Curtis The crowbar and other useful items are in the car. As you heard.

Link Neither of them are the sharpest tools in the tool shed, are they.

Curtis Oi! Tom's alright! Watch it!

Curtis has been dialling on his mobile phone and now –

Curtis Hi. It's me . . . I'm in the flat . . . Yeah, yeah, odd . . . I was just wondering if everything's going to plan at

429

your end . . . I thought you finished at two on
Saturday . . . Oh, right . . . Don't take a bus, Sarah.
Grab a taxi . . . I'll pay . . . Call up when you arrive
and I'll send the money down . . . Okay . . . Good . . .
And Sarah! Thanks.

Hangs up.

Link Who's Sarah?

Sound of dogs has faded now.

Curtis looks round flat.

Link Girlfriend?

No answer.

Link You want her as a girlfriend?

No answer.

Link Ex-girlfriend!
Curtis Shut it!

Another door kicked in.
  Dogs bark.

Link Why's your ex-girlfriend coming here?
Curtis What's it to you?
Link I have a natural curiosity in every Fascist who
occupies my home!
Curtis It's *my* home!
Link Of course. Everything belongs to you.
Curtis No. Not everything. But *this* flat – You see that
armchair? There was another one like that. Here. A
sofa – there. Telly in the corner. There was a big mirror
up here. Photos on the mantelpiece. Ornaments. A snow
globe. And in the bedroom at the end of the corridor –

Rushes for bedroom, then reconsiders, hesitates.

The end room? Are there . . . paintings on the wall?

Link Yeah. Fairy-tale stuff.

Curtis My brother painted 'em.

Link My mate thinks they're amazing. He loves the
Prince. Loves fairy tales. We've got a book with 'em in.
See? We look at one a night.

Curtis How old're you?

Link He's teaching me to read. He's a great teacher.
When he tells a story . . . everything just floats away.
It's like you're *in* the story. You know?

Curtis . . . Yeah.

Link He tells stories on the street, Zak does. That's his
name. Zak. I help him sometimes. I'm the official
Storyteller Apprentice. I say, 'Ladies and gentlemen!
Roll up, roll up. Spare us a few minutes of your time
and enter a world of enchantment and wonder. We
bring you stories! Fantasy. Thriller. Thriller-fantasy.
Comedy-weepie-fantasy! Zak here will spin a tale of
surprise and magic before your very eyes. Nothing is
prepared. Just call out three things and Zak will spin a
web of a story to take your breath away.'

Curtis And does he?

Link Yeah. Always. Most people clear off. Some stay to
hear the whole thing, though. I go round and collect
money.

Curtis Not much by the looks of it.

Link Enough!

Slight pause.

Tell ya one thing. Your brother's better at painting than
photo-whatsit?

Curtis Eh –? Oh, not *him*, for chrissakes. That's Wayne.
I told you. He's my *step*-brother.

Link So who did the paintings?

Curtis Jason. My *real* brother.

Link So . . . who's ya step-parent?

Curtis . . . No more questions.

Link Why not? I ain't going anywhere. I'm naturally inquisitive. My mate says I'm the chattiest chatterbox he's ever met. Gets me in trouble sometimes.

Curtis It's getting you in trouble now.

Link I just wanna know who your step-parent is. What's the big deal? I bet it's ya mum.

Curtis No.

Link Gotchya!

Another door.
More dogs.

Slight pause.

Link Where's Jason got to, then?

Curtis What d'you mean?

Link No real brother Jason with real mummy in propaganda family photo.

Curtis You've got three seconds to disappear.

Link Or what?

Curtis One!

Link Real brother Jason disagree with the family politics, eh?

Curtis Two.

Link doesn't move.
Slight pause.

Link Two and a half?

Curtis What's wrong with you?

Link What's wrong with *me*?

Curtis All I'm asking you to do is clear off and –

Link This is *my* place!

Curtis Jesus Christ, ain't you heard anything I've said, you bloody stupid –? Listen! My gran was the first person to move into this block. They were still laying cement. If you go to the basement there's handprints in the floor. My gran's. My mum – she was born in this

432

flat. She had her wedding reception in this flat. My
mum and dad lived in this flat. My first dad. My *real*
dad. When Gran died she was buried from this flat.
The big bedroom down the hall? That's where Jason
was born. Me too. The four of us lived here and we
were bloody happy. Mum, Dad, Jason and me.
Everyone respected Mum and Dad. They came to them
for advice and stuff. If anyone had a complaint against
a neighbour they didn't go to the council or anything.
They went to Mum. They went to Dad. *They* sorted it
out. Always. When Dad died – I tell ya, the whole
bloody block stood outside to pay their respects. And
the flowers! The car park was covered. You could
smell 'em right down to the supermarket. Local papers
took photographs. We had drinks and sandwiches in
here afterwards. Neighbours queued up for hours –
hours! – to pay their respects. You see this armchair?
Mum sat here and cried so much the cushions were
wet for weeks. Months. Dad's death ripped her to
bloody pieces. You ever seen that happen to someone
you love? Eh? It's shit! I'd rather kill myself than see
that again! My brother had to look after me. He was
seven years older. He washed my clothes and got me to
school and . . . and cooked my dinner and . . . Don't
you *dare* refer to this flat as yours! Hear me? Don't
dare! It'll *never* be yours. It'll never be anyone's except
mine. Even when they dynamite the place – and it's
nothing but rubble – the rubble that makes up this flat
will have my name running through it!

Alex (*off, calling*) Sarah?

Link Who's that?

Alex Sarah?

Curtis Oh, Jesus . . .

*Alex strides in, holding torch. She is eighteen years old
and wearing combat trousers, T-shirt and denim jacket*

433

tied round her waist. Her hair is short and tousled.
Confident and swaggering, she seems to be constantly
on the precipice of an argument and relishing the
prospect of jumping in head first.

Alex Blimey, what's this? The Fascist version of
Halloween? Dress up like a respectable person.

Curtis What you doing here?

Alex Sarah not turned up yet?

Curtis What you bloody –?

Alex I'm here for Sarah!

Curtis Did she ask you to come?

Alex I'm surprising her.

Curtis Why're you always sticking your big bloody nose
in?

Alex Let's think. Perhaps it's like . . . Yeah! Like when
I'm watching *Sleeping Beauty*. The bit where the
Princess is using the spinning wheel. Ya know? The
wicked whatever has put poison on the prick on the
needle. Every time I watch that scene I can't help
sticking my big bloody nose in and calling out, 'Don't
go near the poisoned prick!'

Link laughs.

Alex Oh, wotchya, mate – Oh, hang on, don't tell me.
You live here, right?

Link They kicked my door in.

Alex (*at Curtis*) Pig!

Holds hand out to Link.

Alex.

Link Link.

Alex Oh?

Link When I was a kid I always went missing. Ya get it?
Eh? Missing Link.

Alex I like it.

434

Link Me too.

Alex You and me'll stick together, Link. We'll be the underground freedom fighters against the Imperial Storm Troopers.

Curtis What did Sarah tell you?

Alex About?

Curtis This!

Alex Everything.

Curtis She promised she wouldn't tell anyone.

Alex I'm not *anyone*, pal.

Link What they doing here, Alex?

Curtis Not a word.

Alex Viking youth's been seeing ghosts.

Link Ghosts!

Gav and Tommy can be heard struggling in with table.

Alex Oh, no. Don't tell me. Not all three ugly sisters in one room. This is too good to be true.

Gavin and Tommy appear with table.

Hello, ladies.

Gavin What's she doing here?

Curtis Nothing to do with me.

Tommy You're not welcome, Alex.

Alex From you, that's a compliment.

Link What ghosts you been seeing?

Curtis Shut it!

Alex Pig!

Gavin and Tommy are having trouble with the table.

Tommy Careful!

Gavin It's you!

Jez (*calling, off*) Al – lex?

Curtis Jesus! Who's that?

Alex Jez! – You alright, babe?

Jez Where are you?

Alex Go down the corridor after the lift shafts. By the vomit. See?

Jez Nah.

Alex Hang on, love.

Tries to get past Gavin and Tommy.

Curtis Who the hell's Jez?

Alex You bringing that table in, boys, or is this some sexual fetish?

Gavin Don't be disgusting!

Curtis Who's Jez, Alex?

Alex A mate!

Goes to grab table.

Gavin Hands off!

Curtis This ain't some bloody free-for-all, you know. Sarah won't want – Jesus!

Starts dialling on mobile.

Alex Go on! What d'ya think she's gonna say? 'Ooo, tell that pesky Alex to clear off, Curt-baby?' You arrogant pig! I'm surprised she's here at all after what you did.

Curtis What did *I* do?

Alex You can't be serious?

Curtis *She* stopped talking to *me*! No reason!

Alex No *reason*? You want the full essay or just the bullet points? You lied! You're full of hate! You preach hate! Your views stink! You're a pig! You'll breed pigs! Want me to carry on? You bloody self-deluded pile of – You took that precious thing – the most precious thing in the whole world – and you crapped on it from a great height. 'Oh, you should see us when we're alone, Al. He's so affectionate. I look into his big eyes and –' Big eyes. The wolf had big eyes! And teeth! The teeth you lied through, you poisonous – 'Oh, I'm not really part of all this Avalon stuff. I'm not political. I just go

436

along with it 'cos I don't wanna upset Mum.' Then what happens? A little secretive rally in the middle of Epping Forest. A family day out with smiley grannies and toddlers chanting, 'England for the white!' I told her not to go. I *warned* her. I was standing next to her when she heard you speak – Pig! Her world fell apart. And who picked up the pieces? You? Ha! Not even a bloody phone call. She was on medication for months. Ya know that? Course ya don't! Not even a card when she jumped in the canal and nearly . . . Shit!

Curtis Jumped?

Alex . . . Forget it.

Curtis No. I heard she slipped and fell into – Tom?

Tommy That's what I was told.

Gavin That's what Wayne said. A bit of a laugh.

Alex Laugh?! (*at Curtis*) If you'd shown your face that night I swear I would've –

Jez (*calling, off*) Alex?

Alex Yes!

Alex strides over to table and effortlessly lifts it high. She plonks it down and leaves.

Pause.

Tommy Okay. Let's get the table in place, shall we?

Gavin Yeah, right.

Gavin and Tommy pick up table.

Tommy About here, Curt, mate?

Slight pause.

Curt?

Curtis What? Oh, yeah, fine.

Tommy and Gavin put table in place.

Tommy (*at Curtis*) You okay?

Sarah (*calling, off*) Curtis!
Curtis Oh, Jesus! Tom?
Tommy It's alright.

Goes to balcony.

Hi, Sarah. We'll be right down.

Comes back in.

Everything's under control, mate. Come here.

Rubs Curtis's shoulders.

Curtis There's no time, Tom.
Tommy No one wins a fight when they're tense.
Gavin I'm tense.
Tommy That's how you're meant to be! – Better, Curt?
Curtis Thanks, mate.
Tommy (*at Gavin*) Come on, Mr Tense!

Tommy rushes out followed by Gavin.
Slight pause.

Link Was it . . . someone you knew?
Curtis What? Who?
Link The ghost.
Curtis Yeah, yeah, someone I knew.
Link Your real dad?
Curtis No.
Link Gran?
Curtis No.
Link Then who?
Curtis None of your bloody business.
Link I saw a ghost once. The last foster-place. A kid
from years ago. Said he'd been chopped up and buried
in the cellar. Foster-couple looked so kind and cosy.
But you never can tell. The bloke collected beer mats
so something weren't right.

438

Curtis Look! Don't take this the wrong way, but nothing about your pathetic little life interests me in the slightest bloody way so just – Oh, Christ! The taxi money! Tommy! Tom!

Rushes out as Alex and Jez come in. They collide.

Alex Don't let us get in your way, will ya! Pig!

Curtis has gone.

Jez is seventeen years old. His stylish and casual clothes are, perhaps, more suited for clubbing than for the present surroundings. Like Alex, there is something brave and fearless about him. He is carrying a small bag and a torch.

Link Sarah's downstairs.
Alex Oh, Jez!

Rushes to balcony.

Jez Look at this place! Am I Aladdin in the cave or what? – Oh! Link, I presume.
Link Us three against the Imperial Storm Troopers, eh?
Jez You bet, baby.

Talks into microphone.

I am talking to Link, who is the current occupant of 107 Sunrise Heights – now commonly known as Wild Dog Heights – the birthplace of Curtis Avalon. Tell me, Link, how long have you been here?
Link Er . . . a week.
Jez And what's your first impression of Curtis?
Link He's a pig.
Jez Do you think he's good-looking?
Link Eh?

Alex has come back in looking a little shell-shocked.

Jez Babe? What's up?

439

Alex She's wearing that new dress.

Jez Oh, babe.

Alex I don't get it, Jez. I just . . . don't.

Jez It's like my mum says about Dad. Sometimes the worst presents come in the best wrapping paper. And Curtis, he's *some* wrapping paper!

Link What's all this for?

Indicates tape recorder.

Jez What –? Oh, I'm doing a – how shall I say? – a study of Curtis.

Link Why?

Jez He . . . intrigues me.

Alex *Obsesses* you more like.

Jez Like sharks obsess.

Alex Or boy bands.

Jez My, someone ate a big bowl of wisecracks for breakfast.

Alex Jez has a theory about Curtis.

Link What?

Jez Dead-daddy guilt.

Link How d'ya mean?

Jez Curtis has followed Mr Avalon – his new daddy – so closely because Curtis feels some kind of guilt about the night his own father – his *real* daddy – was killed.

Link Killed?

Alex Curtis's real dad was murdered.

Link What happened?

Alex He went down to the –

Jez Wait, wait! Details please.

Alex I've told you all this before, Jez.

Jez Not since I've had this, Alex.

Indicates tape recorder.

(*into microphone*) The story of the fateful night of the real daddy's death as told by Alex Sawyer while sitting in the very flat where the deceased man lived and died. Wow! – Alex?

Alex Curtis's dad went down to the supermarket and –

Jez Set the scene. Come on, babe. Snow.

Slight pause.

Alex It was snowing. Winter. Curtis wasn't very well.

Jez Nor was his brother.

Link Jason.

Jez Who told you about Jason?

Link Curtis.

Jez Lordy, he must like you. What's ya secret?

Link I just ask a lot of questions.

Jez Curtis and Jason had been out playing in the snow. They caught a chill or something. Although, from what I can make out, Curtis was a sickly child generally. Hard to believe when you see him now.

Alex Oh, perr-leease.

Jez The murder!

Alex Curtis's mum asked his dad to go down to the chemist and get one of those lemon powder things.

Link To make a lemon drink?

Alex Exactly. So Dad walks down to the supermarket and gets the lemon powder and –

Jez A bit more 'oomph'.

Alex 'Oomph'?

Jez This *is* for posterity.

Slight pause.

Alex It's a blizzard. Howling wind! Icicles on every window sill. Who's that man making his way down the street?

Link It's Curtis's dad.

Alex He looks so cold. But his two sons are sickly and need medicine. Dad is clutching the medicine in his hands. His fingers are blue with cold.

441

Link I bet he can't wait to get back and have a hot bath.

Alex He can't.

Jez Only the facts, please.

Alex It's what I would do.

Link Me too.

Jez We can't assume *he* would. Only facts that can be verified. This is journalism, not movie of the week.

Link Go on, Alex. What happened?

Alex Muggers! They jump out of the dark. I can't see their faces. They're hitting and kicking Curtis's dad.

Link They want his money.

Alex Dad won't give it to them. They struggle. Dad falls to the ground. The muggers run off.

Link Did they get away with anything?

Alex They've got his wallet and wristwatch. Dad picks the medicine up from the snow. He starts to walk home.

Link Is he hurt?

Alex He's leaving a trail behind him.

Link Like a trail of breadcrumbs through a forest.

Alex Only this forest is a car park and the breadcrumbs are red.

Link Blood!

Alex Dad gets back to the tower block. The lifts ain't working. He walks up the stairs. All twenty-two floors.

Link Oh, God!

Alex Dad opens the front door. Dad walks down the hall. Dad walks into the room and –

Curtis steps into room.
  Slight pause.

Curtis Don't stop on my account.

Alex Dad is covered in blood. Mum screams. Jason screams. Curtis screams. And Dad falls dead. There! Right in front of his whole family.

442

Curtis Almost. He died in hospital the next day. He'd
been stabbed seven times.

Link I'm sorry.

Jez Were you with him when he died?

Curtis Yes.

Jez What were his last words?

Curtis He asked me if I was feeling better. Anything else?

Link Were they caught?

Curtis The killers? Course not. Black faces into the black
night.

Alex Or white faces into the white snow.

Curtis Dad knew the difference between black and –

Sees Jez holding microphone towards him.

Hang on! What's all this?

Alex It's for the magazine.

Jez *RYAP Monthly.*

Alex Rainbow Youth Against Prejudice.

Jez We meet at the library.

Alex Every Thursday evening.

Jez You're more than welcome.

Curtis Gimme that!

Grabs for tape recorder.

Jez Piss off!

Curtis You've got no right to be here and –

Jez On the contrary, *mein Führer*. I have every right. This
tower block is now a public space. Ergo, whatever
happens here is, in journalist terms, up for grabs so –
to coin a phrase – tough bloody titties.

*Has taken a camera from his bag and now takes a
photo of Curtis – Flash!*

Alex You're good.

Jez I know.

Slight pause.

Curtis That's it! The whole thing's off.
Alex What?
Curtis You heard!

Dials phone.

Jez takes photo – Flash!

Curtis I'm warning you!
Jez He's sexy when he's angry.

Takes another photo.

Curtis faces wall, his back to front door.

Curtis (*into mobile*) Me. I'm calling it off . . . Well,
Tommy's told you who's here, I suppose . . . And this
Jez pillock . . .
Alex Jez pillock?
Jez Sounds like a detergent.
Curtis No, Sarah . . . He's taking photos and – This is
supposed to be private! It was supposed to be me, you,
Tommy and – No! Go back downstairs. I'm sorry for
the trouble. Ask Tommy to give you the taxi money
home. I was stupid to organise something like this in
the first place. What was I thinking? I must have been
mad or something.

*Sarah has appeared, holding mobile to ear. She is
seventeen years old and wearing a simple and stylish
dress. She's obviously had her hair done and her make-
up is slight but very effective. She is carrying a bag.*

*Sarah gives a wave and smile to Alex and Jez, then
quickly indicates they should keep quiet as –*

Curtis Sarah? You there? Sarah, can you hear me?
Sarah Yes.

Curtis freezes.

Sarah Hello, Curtis.

Curtis keeps his back to her.

Curtis . . . Hello.

Slight pause.

Sarah You gonna look at me?
Curtis Yeah. Course.

Slowly – oh, so slowly – Curtis turns.

Slight pause.

Sarah This place . . . everything looks so small.
Curtis Yeah.
Sarah I remember it being . . . you know.
Curtis Yeah.

Jez takes photo – Flash!

Curtis There! *That's* what I'm talking about!
Sarah Thanks for coming, you two.
Jez Couldn't let Beauty go to the Beast's castle alone, could we?
Alex Especially in a dress like that.
Sarah I wore it for work, Al. We had the chief librarian round this afternoon.
Alex Really?
Sarah Really.
Nina (*off, calling*) Sarah! Coo-eee! Sar-rah?
Sarah Nina! – You okay, Neen?

Gavin and Tommy appear, carrying Nina in a wheelchair. She is nineteen years old and wearing a bright-green dress and lots of jewellery (mostly green and blue glass). Her hair has been tinted to suit her generally aquamarine appearance. She's one of those

445

people who seems to have gone from infancy to middle age with nothing in between.

Nina Careful! Stop jolting me! Talk about a life on the ocean waves.

Tommy Stop rocking her, Gav!

Gavin It's you!

Alex Out the way.

Nudges Gavin aside.

Nina Hello, my dear.

Alex Wotchya, gorgeous.

Nina They give me the giant from the beanstalk on this side and . . . one of the seven dwarfs on the other.

Link Dopey.

Link, Alex, Jez and Nina laugh.

Gavin Shut up! – (*at Curtis and Tommy*) Why don't you stick up for me?

Alex and Tommy bring Nina into room and put her down.

Tommy Careful.

Alex No? Really?

Nina Those stairs are truly an adventure! You see the dog crap on the fourth floor? It was sculptural, my dears, sculptural – Afternoon to you, Jez.

Jez Wotchya, sexy.

Tommy One of your wheels looks a bit wonky.

Nina I slipped down the curb this morning.

Tommy It just needs a – Hang on!

Pushes wheel into place.

Nina Oh, my!

Tommy That should do it!

Nina What aftershave you wearing, young man?

Tommy I . . . I dunno. It was a present.

Curtis Ocean Spray.

Nina Ocean Spray! May I have another whiff?

Tommy leans forward.

Nina Mmmm.

Tommy You . . . you want us to hunt out some chairs now, Curt.

Alex Don't bother.

Sarah It's off, apparently.

Nina Off?

Tommy Why?

Curtis This one's taking liberties.

Tommy Tell him to sod off.

Alex He goes, I go.

Sarah She goes, I go.

Nina She goes, I go.

Link Me too!

Curtis There you have it. Sarah, thanks for asking Nina to help. Nina, thanks for agreeing to help – Tom?

Heads for door.

Tommy Where's your car?

Curtis Round the corner.

Gavin Wicked.

Curtis You can walk.

Nina Ahhhh! There's something here . . . I feel it . . . Secrets . . . Terrible secrets . . . Suffocating secrets – Sarah, where's my refreshing libation?

Sarah gets a bottle from the bag she's carrying and gives it to Nina.
Nina drinks.

Sarah She's susceptible to atmospheres.

Nina When I was a child I heard voices. 'Nina,' they said, 'one day you'll be a ballet dancer.' What a sense of humour the spirit world has, eh?

447

Gavin That's gin!

Points at Nina's bottle.

Nina Slander! I'm a respectable children's librarian!

Tommy Curt . . . what d'ya wanna do?

Curtis I . . . don't know.

Alex Jez has a proposition for you, don't you, Jez?

Jez Thank you for that perfect cue, Alex. And, yes, indeed I do.

Curtis Well?

Jez I won't write about anything that happens here. No photos. Nothing. It remains off the record.

Curtis Oh, yeah, and I can trust you.

Alex Well, yes. You can actually.

Tommy What's the 'on condition that . . .' bit?

Jez On condition that . . . an interview. Exclusive. Me and you. 'How I Changed from Nice Boy To Nazi Boy.'

Curtis I'm not a Nazi.

Nina Your nose is growing.

Curtis I'm not!

Tommy None of us are!

Jez Okay. I won't say Nazi. You can describe your political beliefs in whatever way you like. I won't be judgemental.

Tommy Ha!

Alex He won't!

Tommy You know how I've been described? 'A henchman'. My mum was livid.

Jez Curtis can have approval of everything I quote from him.

Slight pause.

Alex Ashamed of your views, Curtis?

Curtis I'm not ashamed of anything.

Tommy All interviews have to be okayed by Mr Avalon.

Gavin Or Wayne.

Jez So phone 'em.

Gavin Wayne won't approve this. No way.

Slight pause.

Starts to hold out his hand to Jez.

Gavin What if they put you on the cover?

Curtis Eh?

Gavin You want everyone to think you bat for the other side?

Alex 'Bat for the other side'?

Jez It has a quaint charm.

Curtis You'll make it clear I'm . . . you know.

Jez Fascist but straight. You've got it.

Tommy Nationalist and heterosexual.

Jez Okay, whatever.

Curtis Deal!

Jez and Curtis shake hands.

Alex You've no idea where that hand was last night.

Curtis pulls hand away.

Sarah, Jez, Sarah and Link laugh.

Gavin It's disgusting – why's that funny, eh? Where's the bloody joke?

Alex Perhaps you're the joke.

Gavin Yeah? Ya think?

Tommy Okay! Chairs! How many we need?

Nina Everyone in the room needs to take part. No spectators allowed. I, as you see, have come fully equipped. One of the bonuses of breaking ya back when you're ten. You save a fortune on furniture for the rest of your life.

Tommy So that's . . . eight.

Curtis Not him.

449

Points at Link.

Alex Why?

Curtis What d'ya mean 'why'? He's sod-all to do with this.

Alex He goes, I go.

Jez She goes, I go.

Sarah Need we carry on?

Curtis Bloody hell, sell tickets, why don't ya!

Tommy Okay. Eight chairs.

Curtis Seven.

Tommy But I thought –

Curtis Gavin's waiting downstairs.

Gavin Eh? I'm *what*?

Curtis I want you to keep watch.

Gavin For what?

Tommy Just follow instructions, mate.

Gavin Nah, nah, hang on! Immigrants and perverts can be part of it but I've got to wait outside like a . . . a . . .

Alex Messy pup?

Gavin Shut up!

Tommy All he means is –

Gavin He can explain himself, I think.

Curtis I'm just . . . I'm just nervous Wayne might find out and –

Gavin How? He thinks we're canvassing the tube stations. 'Our mobiles'll be out of contact for a couple of hours, Wayne.' That's what I told him. Why me? 'Cos he trusts me. 'You tell him, Gav, he'll believe you.' Who said that? Eh?

Curtis Look, Gav –

Gavin Sod the lot of ya!

Heads for front door.

Tommy No! Gav!

Shoots Curtis a look.

Slight pause.

Gavin Well?

Curtis Mate. I'm sorry. Come here.

Gavin Why don't *you* come *here*?

Curtis goes to Gavin.

Curtis I wasn't thinking. I've been at my wits' end lately. You know that, don't ya? None of this would've been possible without you. Would it, Tom, eh?

Tommy No way.

Gavin I got a lot of votes pledged this afternoon. I bet Wayne'd be pleased if he knew how good I was getting on.

Curtis I'll tell him.

Gavin Perhaps a promotion.

Curtis Perhaps, yeah.

Gavin Chairs!

Curtis Tommy!

Tommy Pronto!

Tommy and Gavin rush out.

Nina Mmm . . . Ocean Spray!

Alex With a hint of pig.

Nina He can wrap his salty rashers round me any day.

Sarah Nina!

Nina I know. I despise myself – Curtis! Tell me about him!

Curtis Tom's my best mate.

Nina Not Mr Ocean Spray! Your dead brother. Jason. That's why we're all here. I need to get some image in my mind's eye – Sarah, where's my inspirational crystal?

Sarah Here, Neen?

Gets crystal from bag and gives it to Nina.

Link So it's your brother! Your *real* brother! Jason! He's the ghost!

Nina I prefer the word 'spirit', my dear.

Link And you're gonna . . . contact it!

Nina If I can, yes!

Sarah Nina made contact with a girl in the library.

Nina She'd died in a fire there about fifty years ago.

Sarah She wanted to know the end to a book she'd been reading.

Jez Did you tell her?

Nina Out of print, unfortunately.

Link (*at Curtis*) Was your real brother murdered like ya real dad?

Slight pause.

Curtis I . . . I don't think I can do this.

Nina Don't be silly. People's bodies stop working all the time. Don't get all wishy-washy about it.

Curtis But I –

Nina Listen, sweetie! I've just climbed an Everest of Dog Turds to get here. I did that because I thought you wanted a séance. Now stop farting about and spill the beans.

Jez Do you wanna rephrase that?

Nina No! I want information! Your dead brother! He died six years ago. That right?

Curtis . . . Yeah. Six years ago.

Slight pause.

Nina And? Come on!

Link He could paint.

Nina Eh? What's that?

Link There's pictures in the back bedroom.

Sarah My God! They still there?

Link They're brilliant.

Sarah rushes for bedroom, then reconsiders, hesitates.

Curtis I know. Me too.

Sarah You couldn't . . . ?
Curtis No.
Sarah Strange.
Curtis Yeah.
Sarah Too . . .
Curtis Real.
Sarah Yeah.
Jez (*at Alex*) You understanding any of this?
Alex Yeah. Flirt alert.
Sarah Shut up, Al!
Nina Dead brother!
Link Jason told him stories.
Jez From books?
Curtis No. Jason . . . he sort of made them up . . .
Nina Go on. I'm beginning to feel his karma.

    Caresses crystal.

Curtis When I was a kid – I mean, really young – I used
    to have trouble getting to sleep. Things used to scare
    me. Sound of next door's telly. Jason used to tell me
    stories to calm me down.
Jez About?
Link Kings and queens.
Curtis Fairy stories.

    A distant door gets kicked in.
      Dogs bark.

Sarah He used to mix them up with real stuff, didn't he,
    Curt. The stories.
Nina How d'you mean?
Curtis He used to put real places and people in them.
Sarah The Queen was your mum.
Curtis The Prince was Jason. Or me sometimes.
Jez Prince Curtis!
Nina Sarah says you couldn't find any photos of him.
Curtis We lost a lot of stuff in the move.

Alex You lost *every* photo of your brother?

Curtis Not *just* him! Lots. All the photos were in one box. We lost the box.

Sarah You can't blame Curt. He was only twelve at the time.

Nina It would have been so useful to have some . . . visual image.

Sarah That's why I've brought this.

Takes photo from bag.

Curtis Sarah?

Sarah The day we went to the fair. Remember?

Curtis I didn't know you had this.

Sarah I only found it recently.

Alex When she was chucking out everything to do with you probably!

Sarah hands photo to Nina.

Nina Oh, Sarah! Look at you!

Alex and Jez cluster round to look.

Sarah I was chubby then.

Jez You were gorgeous.

Alex *Are* gorgeous!

Nina (*at Curtis*) You were a midget.

Sarah He shot up all at once.

Jez Ooo, lordy.

Sarah It's funny . . . when I think of Jason, he's always so old. Like really grown-up. Like my dad or something. But look at him. He's young. Not much older than we are now.

Nina When was this taken?

Sarah The year he died.

Nina So Jason's . . . how old?

Sarah Nineteen. Curtis is twelve. I'm eleven.

Nina And . . . cut Jason's hair? Who is it?

Jez They could be twins.

Looks at Curtis.

Nina And where did you say it was taken?

Sarah Victoria Park. They used to have a fair there every spring.

Alex Still do.

Sarah But they were so much . . . *more*, then. Brighter. Louder.

Nina You're getting old, my dear.

Sarah Jason – he made friends with someone who worked there, didn't he, Curt?

Curtis . . . Yeah, that's right. He worked on the merry-go-round.

Sarah That's why we got all those rides for free.

Curtis Dolphins!

Sarah Yes! The merry-go-round was dolphins.

Curtis Blue dolphins!

Sarah And the moon, Curt. Remember? It had that big moon above.

Curtis A mirrorball.

Sarah Was it?

Curtis Yeah. It sparkled everywhere.

Sarah We tried to catch the sparkles – Moonbeams!

Curtis Moonbeams! That's what we called them!

Sarah If we catch enough we can turn them into jewels.

Curtis I've caught one!

Sarah Me too!

Alex Oh, lordy.

Curtis and Sarah have got carried away, lost in the bubble of their remembrance.
  Now the bubble bursts and they look round to see everyone staring at them.

Nina holds photo out to Curtis.
  Slight pause.

Curtis takes photo and looks at it.
  Slight pause.

Tommy and Gavin come in, holding two chairs each.

Tommy Okay. We struck lucky on the floor below.
Sarah Well done, Tommy.
Tommy I've wiped 'em down with a bit of old curtain, but double-check before you sit. We'll search another floor.
Sarah I don't mind standing.
Alex Nor do I.
Nina You have to sit. That's the rules. No spectators and everyone sitting and holding hands. The spirits get very stroppy if things ain't done properly. And it's me they'll take it out on. Believe me, I don't fancy an ancient aboriginal blowing his didgeridoo in my ear at three in the morning.

  Looks at Tommy.

You can blow your didgeridoo in my ear any time, darling.
Tommy Gav! (*Heads for door.*)
Gavin I'm bloody knackered!
Tommy You need to get fit!

  Tommy and Gavin leave.

Nina He wiped the chairs – Be still my heart!
Sarah Neen!
Nina Tell me about your brother's death.

  Pause.

Oh, for God's sake get on with it or we'll all be dead!
Curtis Gimme a second! I need to get it . . . into some kind of order. You don't live life as a story, do ya? You live it as life. The stories happen later.
Jez Oh, jeez.

Takes notebook from bag and scribbles in it.

Sarah That's off the record! Gimme!

Holds out hand.

Jez But it's a gem!
Sarah You gave your word!

Jez gives her notebook.

Sarah Curtis?
Curtis Jason had been looking after me since Dad died.
Nina Which was . . . ?
Jez It happened when Curtis was eleven. Must have been the year before that photo. Sorry.
Curtis My mum . . . she went off the rails a bit.
Sarah It was clinical depression, Curt.
Link My mate gets that. He says it's like falling into a dark pit. Once I touched his hand and he cried.
Curtis Mum started bringing stray dogs into the flat. Me and Jason were so scared for her.
Sarah But your mum got better as soon as she met Mr Avalon.
Curtis Oh, yeah.
Nina How long after your dad dying did she –?
Curtis Nine months.
Jez Where did they meet?
Curtis In the doctor's surgery. They were both waiting to see the same doctor. They started talking and – Wham! Love at first sight, I guess. Mum – she changed overnight. Her old self again. *Better* than her old self. It was brilliant. Jason was over the moon. He could get on with his life now. He'd put so much on hold for a year to look after me. He didn't apply for art school. And he could've done. Mr Avalon knew that Jason wanted to travel so he gave him some money to go anywhere in the world. Explore. It was a dream come

true for Jason. He couldn't stop talking about it.
Remember, Sarah?

Sarah Do I!? All those maps. The big compass.

Jez Where did he go?

Curtis The Colombian jungle. He wanted to see the Lost
City. God, he was excited. He was gonna hike it. More
of an adventure, he said. He talked me through the
route night after night. The Sierra Nevada Mountains.
We took him to the airport. Me, Mum, Mr Avalon and
Wayne. Jason was crying buckets. He kept saying, 'I've
got to do this, Curt. I'll miss ya. But I've gotta go.' I was
crying too. I'd never cried like that before. Not even
when Dad died. I hung on to Jason's jacket. I didn't
wanna let go. Mr Avalon said, 'Don't worry. You'll see
him again.' They had to pull me away from him. I was
screaming. Mr Avalon told Jason to run. Jason went
through the checkout.

A distant door is kicked in.
  Dogs bark.

Curtis – visibly distressed – goes to balcony.

Jez aims camera and takes photo of Curtis.

Sarah takes camera from Jez.
  She empties it of film.

Sarah gives camera back to Jez.

Nina (*at Sarah*) Get loverboy back. I need to know more.

Sarah *I* can tell you. And he's *not* loverboy.

Alex No?

Sarah No!

  Slight pause.

There were a few postcards from Jason. Fantastic
pictures on them. Flowers big as . . . that armchair.
Monkeys. Sunsets you wouldn't believe. The last

458

postcard said not to worry if it goes quiet for a while as he's about to enter the jungle and, as far as he knew, there weren't many post offices along the way. We all laughed at that.

Link And *did* it go quiet?

Sarah Yeah. A few weeks went by. A month. Two months. No one worried. All Curtis talked about was Jason coming back. 'I hope he's back for the wedding. He's gotta be here for the wedding.'

Nina That's Mr Avalon and Curtis's mum?

Sarah She'd moved in with him.

Nina In sin! What fun!

Sarah They'd started moving everyone out of this place by then so I suppose it was the obvious thing to do. And . . . well, Mr Avalon's politics weren't so . . . focused as they are now. I remember he talked about the Blitz spirit and land of hope and glory and all that. We all thought he was a bit of a joke. But I do remember one time . . . I forget when exactly. But it was early on. I was sitting in the living room with Curtis. Mr Avalon was spouting off about how his wife had had to wait ages for hospital treatment. 'It's the immigrants sapping the National Health,' he kept saying. 'They killed my wife.'

Nina Oh?

Sarah She'd died of . . . oh, what was it?

Jez Leukaemia.

Sarah Yeah, that's right. Wayne once told me his dad hardly ever visited her. Mr Avalon hated hospitals. It was all left up to Wayne. Must've been terrible for him. She died in the same month as Curtis's dad. It's what bonded Mr Avalon and Curtis's mum so quick. They kept talking about fate and stuff. You know? Both mourning the death of a spouse.

Jez Both blossoming Fascists.

Sarah No! Not Curtis's mum.

Jez But she is!

Sarah You didn't see her after the murder.

Alex So?

Sarah She was a wreck, Alex. Neighbours pointing at her. Kids calling names. I don't blame her for clinging on to anything that could save her. I'm not saying I agree with it. But if you ask me if I'd prefer to see her like she is now or after the murder I'd take now any day. I grew up with her. I lived three floors below. This was like a second home to me.

Alex Perhaps you see it different after you've dated a Fascist.

Sarah I did *not* date a Fascist!

Alex You forgotten that speech?

Sarah And that's when it ended! But until then . . . it all crept up slowly.

Alex I saw it coming a mile off.

Sarah You saw a boy! That's all! Politics had nothing to do with it!

Alex What's that supposed to mean?

Sarah You know!

Alex No! *You* tell *me*!

Nina Let's get back to the task in hand, shall we?

Slight pause.

Sarah, my dear?

Sarah . . . There was a telegram. Saying Jason had gone missing. He'd fallen down a steep hill or something.

Nina And then?

Sarah It's hard to . . . remember the order of things.

Jez They found a skull, didn't they?

Sarah That's right. Thanks, Jez. Mr Avalon received a letter saying a skull had been found by the edge of a river.

Link Did they carry out tests?

Sarah Yeah. Mr Avalon showed us everything.

Jez Jason was toast.
Nina Cause of death?
Sarah No one was sure. Boat propeller. Crocodiles. I just hope it was quick, that's all.

Tommy comes in with two chairs.

Tommy Okay. Nearly there. Gav's searching the lower floors for some more.
Nina Look at those arms. Let me feel . . . I don't bite.

Feels Tommy's arms.

Let's skip the small talk. How'd ya fancy a date with a mermaid? If you kiss me – who knows? I might wiggle my hips and dance the rumba.

Slight pause.

Tommy . . . Where's Curtis?

Sarah indicates balcony.

Tommy Should I . . . ?

Sarah shakes head.

Sarah Perhaps you can tell Nina about the ghost, Tom. The first time Curtis saw it.
Nina Were you there, darling?
Tommy Yeah. I'd been at the –
Sarah Hang on. Jez?

Holds out hands for tape recorder.

Jez But . . .

Slight pause.

Jez gives tape recorder to Sarah.

Sarah Tom?
Tommy I'd been boxing at the York Hall. Curtis came. Never misses.

461

Nina I bet you look gorgeous in your shorts.

Sarah You win, Tom?

Tommy A knockout!

Sarah (*with Nina*) Yesss!

Nina (*with Sarah*) Yesss!

Tommy We went for an Indian afterwards.

> *Jez snorts.*
> *They look at him.*

Jez I haven't said a word.

Tommy We got back to Curtis's place about midnight. We went up to his room. We were playing some music. Curtis got up to pull the curtains and – I heard him gasp! I looked up at him. I thought he was going to faint. I said, 'What's up, mate? You look like you've seen a ghost.'

Jez Oops.

Tommy He said, 'Tom! Look, mate!' He pointed to the other side of the road. I looked out the window.

Nina What did you see?

Tommy The other side of the road.

Alex What about the ghost?

Tommy That's what I mean. All I saw was the other side of the road. No ghost.

Nina But Curtis was convinced.

Tommy Oh, yeah. You should've seen him. He kept saying, 'I've just seen Jason! I've just seen Jason.' He wanted me to stay the night. I said, 'Sure.' I've got my own Zed bed there. I kept awake and made sure he was safe.

Sarah Oh, Tom.

Nina How far away is the other side of the road?

Jez Twenty yards.

Nina And is it well lit?

Tommy Not really.

Nina So why's Curtis so sure?

Gavin enters – breathless and sweating – with two chairs.

Tommy Well done, Gav.
Gavin Yeah, yeah.
Nina Can you smell – oh, Dopey's walked something in.
Gavin Eh? What?
Tommy Check ya shoes, mate.

Gavin checks his shoes.

Jez Ugh.
Alex You smell like your politics.
Gavin Shut up!
Nina Sarah, where's my *eau de toilette*?
Sarah Here, Neen.

Get it from Nina's bag.

Nina sprays herself.

The others are all laughing at Gavin.

Alex Messy pup!
Jez You should stay outside.
Gavin Shut up! Shut up!
Link It's supposed to be lucky.

Gavin punches Link hard.
Link stumbles back and falls.

Tommy Oi!
Sarah Curt!
Nina Look what you've done.
Alex Pig! Pig!

Slaps at Gavin.

Curtis has rushed in.

Curtis Gavin!
Gavin He was laughing at me.

Link is on his feet.
  His nose is bleeding.

Sarah We were *all* laughing at you! Wanna hit me too?
  Eh?
Nina What about me? I'm more your size!

  Goes to help Link.

Link I'm gonna get my mate. You'll be sorry.
Gavin Yeah?

  Link runs out of flat.

Alex Link!
Sarah Link!
Gavin Bloody vagrant. Should've cleared off in the first
  place.

  Wipes muck from shoe.

Alex Pig.
Curtis Get out!
Gavin (*at Alex*) You heard!
Curtis Not her! *You!*
Gavin Wh – what?
Tommy Curt?
Curtis I know what I'm doing! – You've been warned,
  Gav. Out!
Gavin Warned? Me?

  Steps towards Curtis.

  Tommy stands in front of Gavin.

Tommy Careful, Gavin.
Gavin Oh, yeah. Your true colours are out now, ain't
  they? I've told Wayne about you. Both of you. I've
  heard you in the gym. You don't see me. I'm just there
  to collect ya spit in a bucket. You ain't one of us.
  Neither of ya. It ain't in ya blood.

Curtis Get. Out!

Slight pause.

Gavin leaves.

Pause.

Curtis Come on. Let's get on with it. Quick!

Nina Why were you sure it was Jason's ghost?

Curtis The jacket.

Nina The jacket?

Sarah The sparkle jacket.

Curtis That's what we called it.

Sarah Jason was given a jacket.

Curtis A present.

Sarah I forget who gave it to him.

Curtis Don't think we ever knew.

Nina There's lots of jackets.

Sarah Not like this.

Curtis It'd been covered in those silver stud things.

Sarah It was beautiful.

Curtis Weighed a ton.

Sarah There was painting on it too.

Curtis Round the collar.

Sarah Bits on the back.

Curtis All done by hand.

Sarah Unique, Nina, unique.

Curtis It was my brother's ghost, Nina. I know it. And I've seen him three times since then. Twice more outside the house. And once outside the community hall after Wayne's speech. The ghost was standing in the estate opposite. I chased after it. Some people got pushed to the floor. Local press took photos. Wayne and Stacey did their nut.

Nina Did you tell them about the ghost?

Curtis Wayne and Stacey? God, no. Tommy's the only one.

465

Nina And the turd-foot dwarf.

Tommy That was an accident.

Jez Spit-buckets have ears.

Curtis I . . . didn't know what to do. My hands wouldn't stop shaking.

Sarah They still are.

Tommy That's why I phoned you.

Alex Yeah. Why *her* exactly?

Tommy 'Cos he's my mate.

Alex Well, *she's* my mate and I don't appreciate *you* digging up –

Tommy I don't give a toss! I'd do anything for him.

Alex Well, I'd do anything for her and she don't need you coming along and –

Sarah Stop it! Stop it! I wanted to come! I didn't want to turn a corner one day and see him when I wasn't ready! Okay? Now, put a sock in it, Alex!

Nina Cover the windows! Chairs round the table! We're going to talk to the dead!

They start to find ways of covering the windows.
Most of the boards can be put back in place.
A blanket is used for the balcony window.

Nina Hang it over the curtain rail! . . . That's it! Just lean that board against the – Yes! Good! There's still light there! . . . That'll have to do . . . The chairs! Come on!

The chairs have been put in place.
They are gathering round the table.

Nina Sit!

Curtis sits in between Nina and Sarah.
Alex swops places with Jez so she can be on the other side of Sarah.
This means Tommy is now sitting next to Jez.

Nina Hands!

Tommy hesitates at holding Jez's hand.
  The others watch.
  Slight pause.

Tommy holds Jez's hand.

Nina Spirits! Hear our cry! We are in search of the troubled spirit of Jason. Brother to Curtis. He passed into the spirit world six years ago. Please help us, O, spirits. Something is troubling Jason. I have sensed secrets. Please, spirits. Guide Jason to us.

Slight pause.

Nina I . . . feel something. Yes . . . oh, yes. Something is getting closer . . . closer . . .

Zak has appeared in the doorway. He is eighteen years old and wearing jeans, boots, T-shirt and a jacket decorated with silver studs and paint (exactly as described by Curtis and Sarah). He is breathing hard.

Nina Jason!

Sarah sees Zak and –

Sarah Ahhhhhh!

Jumps to her feet.

Alex Babe!
Tommy What's going on?

Sees Zak and –

Ahhhhh!

Now the others and –

Jez Ahhhhh!
Alex Ahhhhh!
Nina Blimey! It worked!

Sarah N-Nina?
Nina It's alright! Keep calm!

Wheels towards the figure.

Oh, spirit of Jason! Why are you here?

They stare at Zak.
  Zak stares back.

Link runs in, breathless.

Link Zak! It's . . . okay. It's . . . it's not any . . . of these.

Goes to Tommy.

Where's ya mate?

Tommy cannot answer.

Link Where?
Nina There . . . there was an argument, my dear.
Sarah He's not here, Link.
Link Lucky for him. My mate was gonna smash his skull
to bits then feed it to the birds. Weren't ya, Zak, eh?

Notices the way everyone is staring at Zak.

What's up?
Sarah Curt?

Slight pause.
  Then –

Curtis hurriedly knocks boards from windows etc.

Slight pause.

Zak is gazing at Curtis as if in a trance.

Jez It's not Jason?
Sarah No, no.
Link It's Zak.
Sarah But the jacket . . . Curt?

468

Curtis (*at Zak*) Where did you get that jacket?
Link He's had it ages. Since I met him.

Slowly, Curtis approaches Zak.

Zak reaches out to touch Curtis's cheek.
    Curtis slaps his hand away.

The slap brings Zak out of his 'trance'.
    Zak looks around at others.
    Slight pause.

Zak clicks into action and starts packing bags.

Link Zak?

Zak indicates Link should start packing.

Link We going? I thought we liked it here.

Zak continues packing.

Link But . . . we blew out lots of places to end up here!

Zak indicates Link should start packing.
    Zak starts packing.
    Others watch.
    Slight pause.

Nina Jason gave you that jacket, didn't he?

Zak freezes.

Alex Oh, lordy.
Link Zak?

Zak resumes packing.
    Slight pause.

Sarah Did you . . . did you meet him in the jungle?
Link Zak ain't been to no jungle. He's never been abroad.

Zak continues packing.

Nina Do you know how he died?

Zak freezes.

Alex Oh, lordy.
Sarah You do, don't you – Oh, Curt.

Zak picks up bag and heads for front door.

Link Hang on! We ain't packed everything yet!

Zak puts his arm round Link.
Zak and Link head for door –

Curtis No! Don't go!

Zak hesitates.

Curtis You can't go and not tell me! Don't think you'll
upset me. You won't. I've imagined so many things
about how Jason died. Each one worse than the last.
No matter how bad it was I'd rather : . . I'd rather just
know. Please.

Zak turns to face Curtis.

Zak I . . . can't.
Jez Why?
Zak I made a promise.
Sarah To who?

Slight pause.

Nina To Jason?

Zak turns to leave again.

Jez Jason didn't die in the jungle, did he?

Zak freezes.

Alex Oh, lordy.
Sarah Jez?
Curtis Of course he died in the jungle.

Jez Your brother went to the jungle with that jacket, you said. Now it's here on this bloke and he's never been abroad. *You* work it out.

Curtis Jason went to the airport. I waved goodbye to him.

Sarah The jacket!

Curtis It could've . . . it could've . . .

Slight pause.

Sarah *Where* did Jason die, Zak?

Jez *When*'s more the question.

Curtis Okay. Enough. 'When?' Jesus. Six years ago.

Jez How old are you, Zak?

Link He's eighteen.

Jez So he was – what? Twelve when he met Jason? In a jungle? I don't think so.

Curtis The authorities sent photos of where my brother went missing. Sarah, you saw them. My dad showed us.

Sarah Not your dad! Avalon!

Curtis They sent cremated remains, for chrissakes. We threw them from the roof of this place. Jason's dead! Six years ago. In the Colombian jungle . . . Perhaps that ain't his jacket.

Sarah You *know* it is.

Link Zak?

Slight pause.

Jez Did Jason . . . did he fake his own death?

Zak No!

Sarah Then *what*, Zak?

Nina You've got to tell us, my dear. We'll keep on guessing and guessing.

Sarah What is it, Zak?

Jez Tell us.

Sarah Please!

471

Alex Please, Zak.

Nina You *want* to tell us, don't you!

Zak Of course I bloody want to! It's eating me up.

Link No ugly pit, Zak.

Holds Zak.

Slight pause.

Alex Why did you come here, Zak?

Zak Because . . . I wanted to feel close to . . . someone
again. To see the things they grew up with . . . To see
the people they spoke about and . . . I can't explain it.
Not to you. You have to . . . love someone . . . and lose
them. Lose someone so special it's like . . . gravity
going. Nothing to hold you on the planet any more.
You won't understand that.

Sarah I do.

Curtis Me too.

Slight pause.

Nina wheels closer to Zak.

Nina Listen, my dear. The thing that's eating you up. It's
like a . . . a piranha in your belly. And piranhas are
ravenous things. Their little jaws keep nibbling and
nibbling and nibbling. In the end, they'll eat so much
of you there'll be nothing left. What's the cure? To spit
it out. Here! Now!

Slight pause.

Zak tries to say something.
   The words stick in his throat.
   He wants to speak but can't.

Sarah Do what Jason used to do. Tell us a . . . fairy story.

Link Yeah!

Nina Oh, very good.

Jez A fairy story ain't real, is it?

Alex Course not.

Nina And if we . . . deduce things from that story . . .

Sarah Well, that ain't Zak's fault.

Nina He wouldn't've broke any promise.

Sarah None at all.

Alex No way.

Link Show them what you can do, Zak. What *we* can do! Street entertainers supreme! Come on! Showtime!

He has climbed up on table.

Ladies and gentleman! Roll up, roll up. Spare us a few minutes of your time and enter a world of enchantment and wonder.

Nina Very good!

Wheels closer to table.

Link We bring you stories! Fantasy. Thriller. Thriller-fantasy. Comedy-weepie-fantasy! Zak here will spin a tale of surprise and magic before your very eyes. Nothing is prepared. Just call out three things and Zak will spin a web of a story to take your breath away. Come on! Don't be shy. This is an experience not to be missed. Three things. Anything you like . . . Who'll gimme the first?

Others are gathering round.

Nina A Prince called Jason!

Slight pause.

Link . . . Okay. First thing! A Prince called Jason! Next?

Sarah A jacket that sparkles.

Link Second thing! A jacket that sparkles – Oh, this is gonna be a challenge, O Storyteller. One more!

Curtis . . . A death!

Link . . . Okay! Zak, O Great Storyteller! Your story-telling challenge has been set. A story with a Prince

473

called Jason. A jacket that sparkles. And death. Tell us this story, O plot-weaving wizard. Our lives will be forever incomplete without it!

Jumps off table.

Slight pause.

Slowly, Zak gets up onto table.

Others are sitting round table like an audience.

For a while Zak does nothing.
      Then, abruptly, it's showtime –

Zak There was once a King and Queen.

Link We're off!

Zak The King and Queen had a son. Prince Jason!

Link The first thing! Well done, O Storyteller.

Zak One day Prince Jason looked out of the window and saw everything had turned white. Snow. He'd never seen it before. He rushed outside to play.

Link Where did he go, Storyteller?

Zak Prince Jason went to the forest, my inquisitive Apprentice. He climbed trees and knocked icicles from branches. He made snowmen. He made snow angels. He played all day. When he got home his lips were bright blue and he lay on his bed as motionless as a statue. A layer of frost covered his skin. The King and Queen started a big log fire in his room but, no matter how hot the room got, the layer of frost remained on Prince Jason and his lips remained bright blue.

Link Something is wrong with the Prince! Oh, what a twist! We're captivated already! What happens next! Tell us, O Storyteller!

Zak A Witch!

Link Of course! Why?

Zak The King went to a Witch and asked her to cure whatever was ailing the Prince. The Witch said, 'Prince Jason has snow in the bones. There is only one cure

I know of. You must go to the Wild Orchard at the edge of the Kingdom and pick five lemons from the tallest tree.'

Link Lemons? To make a . . . lemon drink?

The others are beginning visibly to react now.
They recognise the death of Curtis's dad in the story.
They glance at Curtis.

Zak But there was one thing the Witch forgot to warn the King about – Come on, Apprentice!

Link What did the Witch forget to warn the King about?

Zak The Dragon, my ever-inquisitive Apprentice. The Dragon that lived in the nearby mountain. The Dragon that protected the Orchard. And when this Dragon saw the King it swooped down on the King and stabbed him in the chest.

Link Did the King die, Storyteller?

Zak Eventually. But first he walked all the way back to the castle and gave the five magic lemons to Prince Jason.

Link And Prince Jason was cured?

Zak Yes. But – oh, the guilt Prince Jason felt, my Apprentice. The King is dead all because Prince Jason got snow in the bones. And now – oh, more guilt for the Prince.

Link What, O Storyteller?

Zak The King's death sent the Queen mad. She started to bring wolves into the castle. She cried, 'My precious wolves. They are all I need.'

The others are beginning to react more and more:
Lots of glances, tiny gasps, nods.
Lots of looks towards Curtis.
Curtis is looking increasingly agitated.

Zak Prince Jason couldn't bear to see the Queen so distressed. He went on long walks. He walked to parts

475

of the Kingdom he'd never been to before. One day he
found himself by the edge of a – oh, my!

Link What?

Zak A lagoon. The water was smooth as glass and blue
as cornflowers.

Link I see it!

Zak The Prince sits beside it. A young man comes up
and sits beside the Prince and says, 'You know, there's
a legend about this lagoon. It says that dolphins will
appear whenever two people who are in love with each
other are reflected in the water.'

Link What's this young man called, O Storyteller?

Zak He's called . . . Dolphin Boy. Prince Jason and
Dolphin Boy sit by the edge of the lagoon and talk.
They talk all day and into the night. They talk like
they have never talked to anyone before. Like they've
known each other all their lives. Then they hold each
other. Then they kiss each other. They look at their
reflections on the surface of the lagoon. And . . .
dolphins appear.

The reaction from the others intensifies.
Curtis's agitation is increasing.

Zak Back to the Queen!

Link Wolves!

Zak No!

Link No?

Zak The Queen has met a New King. From another
Kingdom. The Queen is in love with this New King.
The New King is in love with the Queen. They plan to
get married.

Link Stop press! Queen to marry New King!

Zak But there's a problem.

Link Tell us!

Zak Prince Jason says to Dolphin Boy, 'I've never felt
like this towards . . . another boy. You've made me

feel lots of new things. Up until now my life has been in neat boxes. All of them ordered and labelled. But you . . . you have come along and blown all the boxes apart. I want us to get as close as possible in all possible ways.' And Dolphin Boy says, 'I feel the same. That's why I have made you a gift to celebrate what we have created together . . .'

Link What is it, O Storyteller?

Zak 'Once a month the dolphins collect moonlight from the surface of the lagoon. This moonlight it the most precious thing in the whole world. I have woven it into this garment, my Prince. Please put on. It is called Moonfleece!'

Link The second thing! Well done, Storyteller!

Zak Many thanks, sweet Apprentice – But aren't you missing something?

Link What?

Zak I mentioned a problem.

Link Forgive me, O Storyteller. What is this problem you mentioned?

Zak The New King says to the Queen, 'There must be a reason our lives went so wrong.' The Queen says, 'I agree, but what could it have been?' The New King says, 'Well, my wife died when the moon was full.' The Queen says, 'I think the moon was full when my husband was killed too.' The New King says, 'That's it! Don't you see? The moon is to blame for everything.' The Queen says, 'Goodness! I've been so blind.' The New King says, 'We'll create a new Kingdom without anything to do with the moon! People who like the moon will be banished. All references to the moon will be taken out of the books. If the moon shines at night people must close their windows. If they happen to catch sight of it they must abuse it. And we will name this new kingdom after me. We will call it Avalon!' – You see the problem, sweet Apprentice?

Slight pause.

Apprentice!?

Link Storyteller! Yes. I see the problem.

Zak Prince Jason is wearing Moonfleece in a Kingdom called Avalon where the moon is despised.

Curtis is very agitated, very distraught.
Sarah is trying to calm him.

Zak Ahhhhh!!

Link Who are you now?

Zak The Queen.

Link What's happened?

Zak I've just seen Prince Jason.

Link And he's wearing Moonfleece!

Zak 'What are you wearing, my son?' 'Moonfleece.'
'Moon! Haven't you heard anything King Avalon has
been saying?' 'That's crazy talk, Mum.' 'Shhh! Avalon
will hear you.' 'Too late, my love.' 'I'm sure he didn't
mean it.' 'I do, Mum!' 'Take it off, Jason!' 'No,
Avalon! Dad! I like it!' 'It's disgusting!' 'It's not!' 'Then
you can't be part of this new family.' 'Please, son. Do
it for me!' 'I'd do anything for you, Mum! You know
I would! But I must wear Moonfleece! Moonfleece is
what I am!' 'Listen, you pervert! I have ambitions!
Plans for my future kingdom are taking shape. Someone
like you could ruin everything for me. I can't have you
around. I will give you a chest of gold to start a new
life elsewhere. We will tell everyone here that you were
killed in an accident. A fatal accident. I will fake all
the necessary documents. You will never show your
face in this Kingdom again. You must never make
contact with your mum. Or your younger brother.'

Link Younger brother?

Zak There's a younger brother. Ain't I mentioned that?
What a bloody oversight. His name's Prince Curtis.

And Curtis adores Jason. You remember when their dad had been killed? Jason looked after Curtis. And now their new dad, this Avalon, is telling Jason he must go away and never see his mum or Curtis again. And Jason says, 'If that's what my mum wants, I'll do it. But *only* if it's what *she* wants. Do you want me to go, Mum? Do you?'

Curtis is murmuring 'No . . . no . . .' now.
    His distress and agitation are becoming uncontrollable.
    Others are trying to restrain and calm him.

Zak Ask me what the mum replies, Apprentice.

Slight pause.

Zak Ask me!
Link What . . . what does Mum reply?

Zak jumps off table and faces Curtis.

Zak . . . 'Yes.'
Curtis No!
Zak Jason couldn't bear to see your mum upset again! He'd seen it after your real dad died. Jason wanted her to be happy!
Curtis I waved him off at the airport!
Zak And he went to the jungle. He sent you cards. But he came back.
Curtis I'm not listening!
Zak Avalon faked the whole thing. Documents. Human remains.
Curtis Shut up!
Zak Jason was back in this country all the time, Curtis. Travelling from place to place.
Curtis I don't believe you!
Zak I met him two years ago. In Cornwall. We lived together.

Curtis No!

Zak I was happy. But Jason wasn't. He wanted to come to you and tell you the whole story.

Curtis Then why didn't he?

Zak Because he couldn't upset your mum. He didn't want you feeling bad things about her. That's why he made me promise. No matter what happened to him. I must *never* find you. *Never* tell you the truth.

Curtis Shut up! Shut up!

Zak But now I have! And I'm glad!

Curtis Shut up!

Zak Everything your mum told is a lie, Curtis! A lie!

Curtis launches himself at Zak.
Zak and Curtis struggle.
Others pull Curtis off.

Curtis I don't believe it . . . Sarah? You hear what he's saying? Jason wouldn't leave me . . . My mum – she wouldn't agree . . . You *know* my mum, Sarah . . . Tom? You know her! . . . My mum wouldn't . . . my mum wouldn't . . . I know her . . . I know . . . I know . . . my mum . . . my mum . . . my mum . . .

Slowly, Curtis's anger is spent.
He is like a clockwork toy running down.
Slight pause.

Wayne rushes in. He is twenty years old and wearing a dove-grey suit. He is immaculately groomed and immaculately mannered. All smiles and calculated charisma.

Wayne Phew! Those stairs! . . . Dark and smelly or what, eh? Hello, everyone. Wayne. Wayne Avalon. Nice to see you all. Hello . . . Pleasure . . . Sarah! Luv! You look well. Hair's different. Suits you.

Points at Nina.

Library! Right? Like ya dress. Green's your colour. Tom,
I'm a bit out of condition, mate. I need a Tom-special
work out.

Goes to Curtis.

Wayne Bruv! What is all this? You're worrying us sick,
buddy.

*Stacey rushes in. She is twenty years and wearing a
dove-grey skirt and white blouse. Like Wayne, she is
immaculately groomed and immaculately mannered.
All smiles and calculated charisma. She is holding
Gavin's lighter.*

Stacey Oh, those stairs! Could barely see a thing!
Where's that Gavin got to – Gav?!
Wayne Leave him!
Stacey But I've got his lighter.
Wayne Then he should've kept up with ya! – Stace! Look
who's had her hair done!
Stacey Sarah! Oh, sweetheart! You look brilliant. And
that dress! You've lost weight. I hate you. Only joking.
Hello, everyone . . . Pleasure . . . Hi . . . You can really
feel autumn coming in now, can't ya, eh?

Points at Nina.

Library! Right? Green's really your colour. I think it's
wonderful the way you make the most of yourself.
Wayne Stace?

Indicates Curtis.

Stacey Oh, sweetheart. We've been worried sick.
Wayne I told him.

Stacey goes to Curtis and holds his hand.

Stacey You're trembling, sweetheart. Wayne, he's burning
up.

Wayne Let's get you home, buddy.

Wayne heads for door.
Stacey tugs at Curtis's hand.
Curtis doesn't move.

Stacey Oh, sweetheart.

Wayne What's up, buddy?

Stacey Those stairs are getting gloomier by the second, sweetheart. If you wait much longer the sun will be gone and –

Nina He hasn't heard the end of the story.

Wayne Eh? What story's this?

Nina These two handsome boys here. They're street entertainers. They've been telling us a story.

Sarah With three things in.

Nina Things we chose.

Stacey Oh, how cute!

Sarah So far we've only had two of the three things.

Tommy That's right, yeah.

Nina I'm sure when we've heard the whole story all of us will want to go.

Stacey Oh, you *must* hear the end. It'll drive ya crazy if you don't. Remember when your mum recorded that murder mystery for us, Wayne? And we sat up late one night to watch it. And just as we were about to find out who done it the screen went all fuzzy and the snooker came on? Ooo, we could've killed your mum, couldn't we.

Wayne Do you mind if we listen in?

Stacey Oh, I'm sure they wouldn't.

Nina The more the merrier.

Slight pause.

Link O Storyteller . . .

Stacey Ooo! Goosebumps. Look!

Link One thing remains to be woven into the fabric of your tale. Please put us out of our misery and tell us . . .

Slight pause.

Zak goes to speak but can't.
  He shakes his head.

Wayne Something wrong?
Nina Sore throat.
Stacey You need a good gargle with lemon juice and honey. You put it in hot water as hot as you can bear and –

Makes gargling noise.

Slight pause.

Link I think . . . *I* can.
Nina *You* know the end?
Link I . . . I think I do, yeah. Zak? It's the mate you had in Land's End, ain't it? Eh? The mate you mentioned who . . .

Zak nods.

Nina Go on, then, brave Apprentice.
Link The Prince . . . travels for many years. Until he reaches a place where land ends and sea begins. The Prince sits on the beach and thinks of his old Kingdom. He misses it so much but knows he can never go back. But he made a promise to the Queen – is this right, Zak?

Zak nods.

Link He made a promise to the Queen, and the Prince would never do anything to upset the Queen. He saw the Queen very upset once before, you see. And he couldn't bear to see her like that again.
Stacey Question! Why can't he go back exactly?

Link The Prince loves moonlight.

Nina And moonlight has been banished from the Kingdom.

Wayne How can you banish moonlight?

Stacey It's a fairy tale, silly.

Link And then the Prince sees dolphins swimming out in the ocean. They seem to be calling his name. The Prince walks into the water. The dolphins call him further and further out. The Prince swims until he can swim no more. He floats on his back and looks up at the sky. The moon is full and very bright.

Slight pause.

Stacey So . . . the Prince drowns. Is that it?

Link Yeah.

Wayne And that's . . . the end?

Nina Yes.

Stacey Well, I don't think you'll have Walt Disney knocking at your door for that one. But very good, though. Very entertaining. Weren't it, Wayne?

Wayne Very.

Sarah When did this happen? I mean . . . what time of year?

Zak The middle of summer.

Sarah Like the summer . . . just gone.

Zak Yes.

Nina Does the Queen know of the Prince's death?

Zak Not yet she doesn't.

Picks up his bags.

Link finishes packing the last few things.
Zak and Link head for door.

Curtis Zak?

Zak looks at Curtis.
Slight pause.

484

Zak goes over to Curtis.
  Slight pause.

Zak strokes Curtis's cheek.
  Curtis reaches out and touches the jacket.
  Slight pause.

Stacey Wayne?
Wayne Don't panic.

Zak and Link leave.

Nina Time to go, my dearies – Alex? Your muscles up to it, big boy?
Alex Yeah.
Nina (*at Tommy*) What about you, Ocean Spray?

Tommy looks at Curtis.
  Curtis nods.

Tommy A pleasure.
Nina Ooo! I feel a dance coming on.

Alex and Tommy pick Nina up.

Jez (*at Curtis*) Bye.

Curtis stares.

Alex Sarah?
Sarah Yeah.

Nina, Alex, Tommy, followed by Jez, leave.

Sarah looks at Curtis.
  Slight pause.

Gavin rushes in, breathless, holding his eye.

Gavin That . . . that bloke hit me!
Wayne What bloke?
Gavin In the jacket. Just 'cos I thumped his bum chum he – Oww! It's swelling!

Wayne Help show the others out. It's getting dark.
Gavin But I've only just got up here. I'm all out of puff.
Wayne Well, you should quit bloody smoking, then,
  shouldn't ya!
Gavin But –

Wayne growls at Gavin.

Gavin runs out.

Stacey Don't be a stranger, Sarah. Wayne's mum's always
  asking after you. Ain't she, Wayne?
Wayne Always.

Sarah leaves.

Stacey Oh, Curtis, my lovely, what's all this about?
Wayne I think I know. It's that beggar bloke.
Stacey What one?
Wayne The one in the jacket. He reminded you of your
  dead brother, didn't he?
Stacey Oh, sweetheart! We thought you were all over
  that.
Wayne We all lose people, buddy. You can't grieve all ya
  life.
Stacey It was awful what happened to Jason, sweetheart.
  I never had the pleasure of meeting him but, from
  what I hear, he was a charming young man with
  everything before him. But sometimes, you know,
  things happen for a reason. We don't know the reason.
  Only him upstairs knows that. Right, Wayne?
Wayne Right, Stace.
Stacey It's like when my sausage dog died. I loved that
  sausage dog. Banger its name was. And one day I
  looked in its little basket and Banger was as stiff as
  a board. I cried and cried. Dad wasn't much help.
  He said we should use it as a draft excluder. I got no
  sympathy at all. Dad wouldn't let me even bury Banger

in the back garden. So I wrapped Banger in some
kitchen foil and took him over to the park. They had
a flower garden there and I thought it would be nice
to bury Banger amongst all those daffodils. So I dug
a hole and put little Banger in. I was just covering
Banger up with earth when I heard the Park Keeper
yelling at me. Oh, the names he called me. The
language. I ran and ran. He chased me. I ran all the
way to the market. I was gasping. I went into this little
Paki shop to get a can of something. I took something
out the cooler and opened it and swigged a mouthful.
Ooo, it was delicious. It really was. I put my hand in
my pocket and – no money! Not a penny! I glanced up
at the Paki and he was serving someone else. So I
thought, I'll pop home and get the money and then I'll
come back and pay the Paki later. I'd only taken one
step out the bloody door when the Paki rushes over
and grabs me arm and accuses me of stealing. Me!
Well, I start screaming and shouting and giving the
bloody Paki a piece of my mind. And that's when this
man comes out the shop next door. A white man,
thank God! The man pays the Paki the money I owe
him and takes me into his own shop. And who's
answering the phone? Wayne. 'Cos the man who paid
the Paki was none other than Mr Avalon. So you see,
sweetheart, if it weren't for my dead Banger I'd never
have met Wayne.

Sarah appears in doorway, holding a packet of photos.

Sarah Oh. Sorry. I've . . . got something for Curtis.
Stacey Well, better give it to him now, sweetheart. We're
just on our way. Or you could come back with us and –
Sarah I don't think so, Stacey.

Slight pause.

Curtis I'm staying here a bit longer.

Wayne Not a good idea, buddy.

Stacey The light, sweetheart. The *light*!

Curtis I'm not bloody going yet!

Slight pause.

Stacey Let him have a last look round, Wayne. Get it out of his system. We don't want any more panic attacks, do we?

Wayne We're on the brink of a great victory, buddy. You know that.

Stacey We don't want anything to rock the boat, sweetheart.

Wayne Nothing *can* rock the boat. So long as people behave themselves.

Wayne and Stacey head for the door.
  At the door, Wayne stops and looks back at Curtis.

Wayne You know, buddy, sometimes we hear rumours about stuff and it . . . well, it confuses us. We wonder what's true, what's not true. It's happened to me. I've heard little whispers late at night. Did this happen? Did that happen? But you know what I do? I ask Dad. After all, he's there to look out for me, ain't he? He loves me. So I ask Dad and whatever he tells me . . . that's the truth. Life's simpler that way.

Wayne and Stacey walk out.
  Slight pause.

Sarah Zak wanted me to give you these.

Curtis What are they?

Sarah Photos. Taken of someone on a beach. Earlier this year.

Curtis Have you . . . ?

Sarah No.

Puts photos on table.

All those times we said, 'I wonder what Jason would've thought?' Remember? When I decided to go to art school. And now – when the leaves are turning brown. He loved this time of year, didn't he? And remember how we said how pleased he would've been when you . . . you and me . . .

Gently weeps.

Curtis steps towards her.

Sarah No!

Curtis stops.

Slight pause.

Sarah I don't feel young at all. Do you? I feel like I've lived a million years and . . . and gone through hundreds of wars and I can't tell anyone about them 'cos when they look at me all they see is this . . . young face. But it's not the face I should have. It's not my face.

Sarah goes to leave –

Curtis Sarah.

Sarah stops and looks at Curtis.

Sarah What?

Slight pause.

What do you wanna say, Curtis?

Slight pause.

Sarah leaves.

Curtis looks at the photos on the table.
   Slight pause.

Curtis approaches table.
  Slight pause.

Curtis picks photos up.
  Slight pause.

Curtis opens packet of photos.
  He hesitates before looking at them.

Curtis looks at first photo.
  He cries out.

The dogs start barking in response.

Curtis continues looking at photos.

The dogs bark louder and louder.

Blackout.

Love, Loss and Our True Skin

Philip Ridley interviewed by Jim Mulligan

Moonfleece is the third Philip Ridley play to be part of
the *Connections* programme. It is the central work in his
ongoing 'storyteller' sequence, which will, when complete,
consist of seven plays. Set in the East End of London,
the action takes place in a derelict tower block.

It is a very real tower block. It's at the back of the flats
where I live. Every time I walked past it I used to think
it was a fantastic place to set a drama. All that history.
All those memories. Peeling layers of wallpaper. Old
photos. Bits of furniture. And it was thinking about
this that helped create the world of the play. A play
about family and memory. The way we remember the
past as opposed to what really happened. The way,
as we grow up, we believe everything our parents tell
us without question. And why shouldn't we? After all,
they love us. They are there to protect us. And so their
version of the past becomes the accepted truth. But
what if the people that love us are not telling us the
truth? And so I hit on the idea of a family secret. And
it's this secret that's at the heart of the play.

The history in *Moonfleece* is that of Curtis and his family.
His grandmother was the first tenant to move into the
tower block, while the concrete in the basement was still
wet – her hand prints are still there. All significant family
moments took place there: children were born there, the
dead were buried from there and, finally, Curtis's father
staggered up the stairs, bleeding from a fatal stabbing,
and died there.

As the play starts, this old family flat is being squatted by Link and Zak. Two well-dressed intruders, Tommy and Gavin, members of the far-right Avalon Party, have knocked down the front door and are taking over the flat for what Link assumes to be a Fascist meeting. But the gathering that's being planned is not a political but a spiritual one. Curtis has been seeing the ghost of his long-dead brother, Jason, and is hoping that a séance will explain why.

Curtis had seen his mother go to pieces after the brutal death of his father. She was clinically depressed and only restored to good health when she met and married Mr Avalon, now the leader of the Avalon Party. It is implicit in the text that Curtis is going along with the racist rhetoric to keep his mother happy. As he says to Link, 'Dad's death ripped her to bloody pieces. You ever seen that happen to someone you love? Eh? It's shit. I'd rather kill myself than see that again.'

> Part of what *Moonfleece* is dealing with is the idea that we are what we make out we are. We have caught Curtis at the moment when he has to make a decision. If he carries on the way he's going he will end up becoming totally what he's been making out he is. If he's not going to become that, he's got to change now. Curtis has buried all his emotions and feelings to placate his mother. So he has an unspoken trauma. This is the loss of his brother. He now believes he has been seeing his brother's ghost, and all his grief and depression have caught up with him and he's on the brink of collapse. Loss is one thing that unites all the characters in the play. Everyone has lost something: a brother, a lover, their past, their home, their mobility.

The people who gather in the flat, some by accident, some by invitation, work a kind of magic to bring Curtis to the point where he understands the choice he must make. Link, on the surface a cocky street kid, is able to pick up on the pain of others and he feels an immediate affinity with Curtis. There is a real affection between Tommy and Curtis, and it is Tommy who sets up the gathering. The others come together to play their part and we hear two versions of the death of Curtis's father: one is the factual account, as related by Jez and Alex; the other is a reinterpretation of the events as a fairy story, as told by Zak and Link.

> The 'moonfleece' is a symbol, I guess. At least it has ended up being one. The moonfleece is like the real truth of who we are. It is a statement of our emotional landscape. In terms of love, it says: this is who I am. In terms of what I believe, it says: this is my truth, this is my real skin. The 'moonfleece' is who we really are. Sometimes we are born with it and sometimes it has to be given to us. Sometimes we wait years and years to be given it, and the person who gives it to us is the person we are destined to love. The question is, do we reveal the moonfleece or do we keep it hidden?

As the story is finally told we learn that, just as Curtis has shaped his life to protect his mother, so Jason has chosen exile rather than hurt her – an exile that will lead ultimately to his own suicide. Before he died, Jason had sworn Zak to secrecy. Jason had wanted to come and tell Curtis the whole story of how Mr Avalon had forced him out of the family because of his friendship with a man who ran the dolphin merry-go-round in the local park, and how Mr Avalon had faked Jason's death rather than have his political ambitions besmirched by Jason's dubious friendship. But Jason couldn't tell his brother all this, because he didn't want to upset his mum or have Curtis thinking bad things about her. When Curtis eventually realises the truth – that his mum has deliberately lied to him all these years – the revelation threatens to destroy him.

There are issues in the play, of course. But we shouldn't make too much of them. I think the play reveals itself through character, story, emotion, passion and truth. It is about a group of people trying to sort out the truth from the lies. It's about love, loss and our true skin. The play shows a moment in people's lives. That's all. And it leaves Curtis, in a strange way, at exactly the moment when the drama begins. He is looking at photographs proving conclusively that his brother had been alive all these years – that, in other words, everything he thought was true is a lie. So, is he going to go back home and confront everyone? Or is he going to keep it a secret? I think I know what he is going to do. But perhaps I'm wrong.

Production Notes

Moonfleece is an intense and thrilling exploration of
memory and identity. It also deals with themes that have
contemporary resonance: racism, homophobia, and how
those in authority distort both the truth and the past.
Written for eleven actors (seven male and four female),
it takes place in one location (a derelict flat) and plays in
real time. The design should be as realistic as possible.

The decrepit flat is a symbol of the lives of the people
in the play. Philip Ridley visited abandoned tower blocks
in East London when researching. He saw all that is
described – light patches on the wallpaper where pictures
had been hung, cracked mirrors, peeling wallpaper –
representing the layers of history and stories of the flat.
In amongst all this dereliction is revealed a pristine
political banner: what does that signify? Dogs are
barking, suggesting a threat and giving the place a wild
feel. The motif of the dogs barking is used at crucial
moments during the play to heighten the atmosphere.

The play is also about loss and identity. Curtis has lost
his father, brother, lover and history. Examine each
character to determine exactly what their loss has been.

The play might be described as an East End *Hamlet*, and
contains many references and parallels to Shakespeare's
play. There are also many references to fairy tales, a
reminder that *Moonfleece* is one of a sequence of plays by
Philip Ridley using fairy tales and storytelling as motifs.

Be as meticulous as possible in creating the 'back-
stories' of each character, geographically and historically
mapping their journeys to the beginning of the play.
Above all, the character of the missing older brother,

Jason. who never appears in the play, must be carefully constructed; it is essential that all the characters have a very clear image of Jason in their minds.

With one or two exeptions (most notably, some of the comments by Gavin) there is no overt racism in the play until Stacey enters. Stacey's 'Banger' story provides a context for the audience, who are shown the nature of the family in which Curtis has to live. This is designed to provide a volte-face for the audience, who should now feel sympathy for Curtis. Stacey's racism lampoons itself.

THE TEXT

The dialogue begins at pace and is quite confrontational. This shows us that Link is not afraid of or intimidated by authority: he is obviously streetwise and used to standing up for himself against this sort of threat. The smart suits, like the banner, are a contrast to the derelict flat, representing another world with other values. The British National Party (BNP) are concerned to appear as smart, respectable, clean-living and plausible representatives of the man on the street, not as the expected stereotype of skinhead thugs.

Look at the opening line of the play:

Link Who d'ya think you are?

And compare it with the last line of the play:

Sarah What do you wanna say, Curtis?

Both lines reinforce the theme of searching for identity.

From pages 420 to 428, the relationship between Tommy and Gavin is examined, along with the modus operandi of the BNP. Tommy plays things very much by the book, but Link has heard it all before and handles the intruders well: he is a clever, streetwise lad, familiar with the approach and arguments. His answers frustrate Gavin, who is intellectually impotent. Much later in the play Gavin punches Link for little apparent reason, but the build-up to this starts with the frustration that Gavin now feels. There is much exposition at this point, particularly about Curtis and how he and his family lived. The way Gavin delivers this information tells us a lot about his low intellectual capacity and about his relationship with Tommy, who is protective like a big brother. Link knows exactly how and when to wind Gavin up.

It is important to have clear photographs on the banner. This is the first introduction to the characters and it is important that the audience should have a clear picture in their minds of all of them.

Gavin and Tommy build up to a political frenzy which culminates in them chanting loudly; this sets off the dogs barking, and builds the atmosphere for the entrance of Curtis. This is crucial. Curtis, as well as seeing and hearing the boys chanting, is entering the flat for the first time since his brother vanished and his father died: the place is seething with memories. There is a lot going through Curtis's mind, and the audience should be aware of this. It is quite likely that Curtis arrived at the flats a while ago and has hung around until he is sure someone else is in there. The entrance is momentous for him.

On the following few pages more is revealed about relationships and relative status. Gavin is obviously bottom of the pecking order, and is constantly snubbed by Curtis. For all his apparent initial authority, Tommy is only marginally brighter than Gavin. This manifests itself in his use of very formal language. Tommy must think that this 'police-procedural' language elevates his status, whereas its pomposity is almost laughable.

The forgetting of the table and chairs not only highlights the intellectual limits of both Gavin and Tommy but also provides an opportunity to keep the actors moving in and out during the middle section of the play. The sound of doors being kicked in and the barking of disturbed dogs is used like musical punctuation, highlighting important moments in the play.

On pages 427–20 we are given a glimpse of the close nature of the relationship between Curtis and Tommy, and see a different side of Curtis when, speaking with Sarah on the phone, his harsh and authoritarian tone softens. But it is clear that Curtis is very tense because of the situation he finds himself in.

On pages 430–1 it becomes clear that a bond of under-standing is building between Curtis and Link, evidenced most obviously in this exchange on page 431:

Link It's like you're *in* the story. You know?
Curtis . . . Yeah.

At this point Curtis clearly remembers the stories Jason used to tell him and empathises with Link's description.

Link tells Curtis of Zak's technique of telling a story based on three given ideas from the audience. This prepares us for the story Zak is asked to tell towards the end of the play. Over pages 430–1 the dialogue quickens and the pace builds as Link tries to capitalise on his seeming acceptance by Curtis, whom he questions about his life and challenges over the ownership of the flat. This prompts Curtis's explosion of anger and passion on page 432 – a long, passionate speech which raises the emotional stakes of the play. He loses control, and as his smooth facade crumbles we see the angry, hurt twelve-year-old inside. The stakes are raised again when Alex enters: there is obviously an antipathy between Alex and Curtis and, clearly, Sarah is the cause of this.

Curtis She promised she wouldn't tell anyone.
Alex I'm not *anyone*, pal. (p. 435)

When Gavin and Tommy appear with a table, Gavin's moralistic reaction to Alex's innuendo – ' Don't be disgusting!' (p. 436) – starts to build an atmosphere of moralistic homophobia which is essential as the story develops.

On pages 436–7, Alex's long speech against Curtis and his treatment of Sarah further raises the emotional stakes, and begins to prepare the audience for the entrance of Sarah. It also gives Curtis more pressure to cope with.

Drama very often derives from the preventing of the protagonist achieving what he wants – in this case, getting on quietly with the séance. The lack of furniture, extra people arriving, and new and unsettling information are all working against him. Look carefully at how Curtis reacts, more strongly than you would expect, to these difficulties, and how he turns to Tommy when things are going badly. When Sarah arrives (p. 444), Tommy takes control, massages the tense Curtis and then goes down to meet her.

When Alex is telling the story of the murder of Curtis's real father, Curtis enters the flat at its climax and challenges Alex with the line 'Don't stop on my account' (p. 443). Alex rises to the challenge and finishes the story in a deliberately brutal manner. It is important that the detail and images of this passage are clearly delineated as they are the basis for Zak's final story and the audience need to be able to readily identify them.

The emotional stakes for Curtis clearly rise again. The challenging end to Alex's story, the arrival of Jez, and the constant flashing of the camera in his face all serve to aggravate his already tense feelings. Curtis feels pushed to the edge and phones Sarah to cancel the séance, but he is too late and Sarah arrives in the flat mid-conversation.

The meeting of Curtis and Sarah is a seminal moment in the play. We have heard a great deal about how this relationship came to an end, but we know that it remains unresolved as far as Sarah and Curtis are concerned. There is much subtext here to be sorted out and demonstrated by both actors.

The intensity of the moment is slowly reduced, first by the camera flash, then by the arrival of the irrepressible Nina. It is Nina who insists that the séance be reinstated when she 'senses an atmosphere' in the flat.

A power struggle occurs (pp. 450–1) when Gavin asserts himself and Curtis finally relents and accepts Gavin on more equal terms. Homophobic comments again serve to heighten the atmosphere of intolerance.

The details of the story about the dolphins and Jason's jacket (pp. 455–6) must be clearly enunciated, as they need to be recognised when they are taken up in Zak's final story. This section of the play also shows the closeness between Curtis and Sarah, who on two occasions are carried away by their memories of shared events.

On page 457 mention is made of Curtis's mum being depressed after the death of her husband and bringing stray dogs into the flats. This also needs highlighting as it becomes an important part of Zak's story, as does the blame Curtis's mum and Mr Avalon put on immigrants for the deaths of their respective partners.

The play is set in October 2003: construct a timeline of the plot working back from there.

When Gavin finally snaps and punches Link (p. 463), Curtis imposes his authority and throws Gavin out. Gavin, however, will tolerate no more of this and bites back. He tells Curtis and Tommy that he is suspicious of them and goes to seek out a new ally in Wayne.

The next few pages establish the nature of the jacket, preparing the audience for the imminent arrival of Zak. It also becomes clear that Wayne and Stacey are a couple to be wary of.

Curtis is anxious to get on with the séance, and Tommy is so anxious to help that he overcomes his aversion to holding Jez's hand.

Zak is making his way back to the flat having been fetched by Link to pay back Gavin for the punch.

From the start of the séance (p. 469) make every effort to avoid unintentional humour. Nina's invocation should be delivered perfectly seriously. When Zak appears and all scream, this *must* be carefully choreographed: the screams need to have variations and qualities appropriate to each character. Some might be just little gasps, tiny cries, or even silence – whatever works for the production.

On pages 468–9 none of the characters really knows what is going on. In order to show this, the questioning must have a light, breathy, uncertain quality to it.

When Curtis has torn down the window coverings he approaches Zak very carefully and with great difficulty, 'as if in a trance'. The tension must be built leading up to his question about the jacket: 'Where did you get that jacket?' (p. 469).

As Zak reaches to touch Curtis's face (because he is so like his elder brother – Zak's lover) Curtis slaps his hand away. This action immediately breaks the mood of the piece and ups the tempo of the action. Zak moves quickly to pack up and leave. It was found to have a powerful effect if Zak, with his back to the audience, froze his actions whenever some comment or question (like Nina's 'Jason gave you that jacket didn't he?') touched a nerve.

A very useful exercise would be to script the characters' thoughts and express them verbally during the running of this scene. Then lose the words and express them with looks, expression and gesture.

From page 470 onwards the characters move one by one from the table according to their thoughts and reactions. Slight movements have huge meaning. Everyone has a different agenda: what are these, and how are they manifested during this section?

There is a moment to be pointed on page 472 when Zak says they won't understand how terrible it is to lose someone they love. The response is:

Sarah I do.
Curtis Me too.

On pages 472–3 Zak is put under a lot of pressure to say what really happened. He cannot tell the true story, so reverts to fairy tale – at first glance a bizarre decision, but in fact so much preparation has been done in terms of descriptions and references to fairy tales and storytelling during the course of the play that this moment should seem a natural progression.

During Zak's fairy story each character should again have their thoughts and reactions carefully studied, scripted and then performed without the words, so that reactions can be created to these complex situations.

As Zak's story proceeds over page 476, the focus on Curtis intensifies. This can be achieved by making him the centre of attention on stage, and having the other characters watch him and his reactions carefully. On pages 478–9 Zak has a very difficult speech in which he must find three completely different voices – a trial of any young actor's skill.

On page 479, the pretence of the fairy tale begins to break down, and on page 480 Curtis is almost pushed over the edge by the revelations. As he slowly winds down, Wayne and Stacey enter. Their entrance freezes the moment. They are sickeningly polished and smooth as they 'work the crowd' with meaningless platitudes. Wayne is smooth and dangerous, Stacey completely insensitive.

Link has pieced together bits of information he has previously gleaned from Zak, and he continues the story to the point of Jason's suicide. Zak then (Hamlet-style) takes on the role of Claudius to allow Curtis to take the responsibility of telling his mother the truth about Jason.

On page 485, Zak again reaches and touches Curtis's cheek, echoing the earlier occasion; but this time the reaction and perhaps the motive is different. Again this is a moment requiring careful consideration and execution.

On page 487 we come across a seemingly banal story by Stacey about her pet sausage dog, Banger. This comes at a crucial phase of the story. It should be delivered very quickly, and the other characters should be completely thrown by it. At the end the racist references come as a shock from this seemingly ordinary girl. They hit home to Curtis: this is what he has to deal with, this is his family life and values. The speech seemed incongruous but in the context of the build-up of tension will be very effective.

On page 488, Sarah enters, Wayne and Stacey depart, and Wayne delivers an oblique threat to Curtis about not rocking the family boat. Curtis has a massive amount to deal with, and Wayne senses this could all go the wrong way. He effectively presents Curtis with the choice: either the family or Sarah.

You might try hot-seating your characters as a useful exercise and as an aid to the creation of convincing back-histories. In partiuclar, the the actor who plays Curtis needs to carry the whole weight of the back-history with him as he enters the tower block.

THE MUSICIANS

Patrick Marber

Characters

Alex

Roland

Second Flute

Cello

Second Trumpet

First Violin

Viola

Double Bass

Second Horn

First Horn

Timpani

Oboe

Clarinet

First Trumpet

Bassoon

First Flute

Except where obvious
the musicians can be male or female.

A larger company may perform the play
with a greater number of speaking roles by,
for example, judiciously allotting some of Violin's
lines to a new character called 'Second Violin', etc.
Alternatively, the company could keep the roles
as written and have a much larger orchestra
some of whom don't have speaking parts.
They will still have plenty to do.

SCENE ONE

The stage of a concert hall somewhere in Moscow.
   Chairs arranged for an orchestra to play.
   A young man in overalls, Alex, ambles on from the
wings with a broom and dustpan. He idles to the centre
of the stage and peers out at the auditorium.
   Suddenly, he raises his broom as if it's a guitar.

Alex (*In Russian*) Good evening, Moscow!

   He makes the sound of two thousand people
   applauding – they whoop and scream – he modestly
   acknowledges the applause.

(*in Russian*) Thank you, thank you!

   Fantasy over, he reaches into his pocket, turns on his
   Walkman and starts sweeping.
      He sings to himself as he works. He is Russian, but
   sings in English – though with a Russian accent.
      He is listening to 'Pinball Wizard' by The Who.
      He knows the song well and starts humming the
   opening guitar riff and then goes into Pete Townshend-
   style gyrations when the big chords come in.
      Once the vocals start, the broom becomes his
   microphone.

Alex (*singing*)
   Ever since I was a young boy,
   I played the silver ball,
   From Soho down to Brighton,
   I must have played 'em all,
   But I ain't seen nothin' like him

In any amusement hall,
That deaf, dumb and blind kid
Sure plays a mean pinball!

*Guitar break. He mimes with the broom. When the
vocals return he becomes the pinball wizard on his
machine.*

Alex (*singing*)
He stands like a statue,
Becomes part of the machine,
Feelin' all the bumpers,
Always playin' clean.
Plays by intuition,
The digit counters fall.
That deaf, dumb and blind kid
Sure plays a mean pinball!

Roland (*seventeen*) *appears in the wings. He is intense,
dedicated – but not without humour. He watches Alex,
somewhat embarrassed to be witnessing this private
display of insanity.*

Alex (*singing*)
He's a pinball wizard, there has to be a twist,
A pinball wizard's got such a supple wrist.
(*very high voice*)
How do you think he does it?
(*response*)
I don't know!
(*further response*)
What makes him so good?

*Alex is freaking out. A one-man concert with full
imaginary lasers and dry ice. Roland coughs but Alex
can't hear.*

Alex (*singing*)
Ain't got no distractions,

Can't hear no buzzes and bells,
Don't see no lights a-flashin',
Plays by sense of smell –

Roland strides onto the stage so Alex can see him.

Hey! Sorry! Hello!

Alex turns off the Walkman. Roland nods to him and carefully places his small, black leather case on a table.

'Pinball Wizard', The Who!

Roland gives him a 'thumbs-up' then surveys the stage and the auditorium.

You like The Who?

Roland considers what will best prevent further conversation.

Roland I have no opinion.
Alex Okay, I get message, shut cake-hole.

Alex resumes his sweeping but watches Roland with curiosity.

Are you in group?

Roland is lost in thought.

Hey! Britishman, are you make music?
Roland What?
Alex Speak English?
Roland Sometimes.
Alex You play music, la la la.
Roland Oh, yes.
Alex I like music! Alex.
Roland Roland.

They shake hands.

Alex You orchestra, yes? From UK.

Roland Correct.
Alex How is Queen?
Roland She was fine when I last spoke to her.
Alex That is joke?

Roland nods.

British jokes, I know all about. Very ho ho ho.

Alex gestures to Roland's small leather case.

Alex What instrument you have in box? Don't tell me,
    I'm guessing . . .

Alex goes up to the case and inspects it.

You have double bass! (*Beat.*) That is Russian joke.
Roland And most excellent it was.
Alex I play guitar.

He briefly demonstrates using his broom.

(*wistfully*) I don't have guitar really but can pretend . . .

Roland looks sympathetic.

I like all English music: The Who best, then also Beatles,
    Stones, Pistols, Davie Bowie, The Smith, Oasis,
    Coldplay, Radiohead –
Roland Sorry to stop you but is this list much longer?
    You see, I've got all day, so why don't I pull up a chair
    and you sing me every single song you've ever heard?
Alex You take piss?
Roland Just a bit.
Alex English humour: take piss, right?
Roland It's our national sport. Sorry.

Alex looks at the case again.

Alex So you play little erm . . . ?

He mimes a flute.

Roland Flute?

Alex nods.

No.

Alex Play what you play?

Roland I'm not playing anything today.

Alex You singer? *I* sing.

Roland No, I'm not a singer.

Alex What are you do?

> *Roland goes to the case, dramatically releases the*
> *catches and produces a conductor's baton.*

You wave stick?

Roland I'm the *conductor*!

Alex Duh, I *know*! Who you conduct, famous people?

Roland The Ridley Road School Orchestra.

> *Alex conceals his disappointment.*

Alex You are boss man?

Roland Well, kind of . . .

Alex Kind of what?

Roland Well, usually I play the cello, but I've been
conducting a few rehearsals recently. That's what I've
always wanted, to be a conductor. Our music teacher's
given me this one-off opportunity. So, if it goes well,
who knows . . .?

Alex This big break for you?

Roland Yeah.

Alex Big scary break, wake in middle of night in sweat
and screaming fear, yes?

Roland You could say that.

Alex Where from school?

Roland Croydon (or *wherever the company performing*
the play are based).

Alex I have been in Wolverhampton. You know? I live
Wolverhampton six week. On exchange. I stay with
family Henderson.

Roland Please don't ask me if I know them.

Alex Do you know them?

Roland No!

Alex Ken and Valerie Henderson. They have daughter, Donna. She love Rio Ferdinand, football player. She say he have good body, tall and slim.

Roland Have you finished your cleaning yet, your sweeping? I don't mean to be rude, it's just that I really need to prepare.

Alex Okay, I get. I bugger off.

Roland The stage looks perfect.

Alex I been sweep all day for you.

Roland Thank you.

Alex starts to exit.

By the way, where is everyone? The technicians, sound people, lights?

Alex All take break.

Roland What, tea break?

Alex Vodka break, take longer.

Roland (*worried*) They'll be back for the concert, tonight?

Beat.

Alex *Concert*? I thought you just practise?

Roland starts to panic.

Roland We're giving a concert *tonight*, right *here*!

Alex *Here*?? No one say nothing.

Roland It's for an invited audience of dignitaries and cultural luminaries.

Alex Huh?

Roland 'The European Festival of Youth' – there are posters all over town!

Alex I not see poster.

Roland We're representing our country, it's *incredibly* important!

Alex No one say about concert, you make wrong mistake?

Roland mops his brow, sweating with anxiety now.

Roland No! Look, here's the leaflet, it's *tonight*!

Alex (*reading*) Oh my God, *tonight*?!

Roland Yes, tonight!

Alex But it's impossible tonight!

Roland It's a catastrophe!

Alex starts laughing.

Alex I piss take! I take piss! They come back in half hour!

Roland (*relieved but angry*) Are you familiar with the word 'bastard'?

Alex And you with word 'tight-ass'?

Roland That's *two* words.

Alex Yeah, but only *one* tight-ass.

Roland shrugs, acknowledging the truth.

So you practise music now?

Roland Once the musicians arrive, we'll be *rehearsing*, yes.

Alex I stay watch? Please?

Roland looks wary.

Please, I silent. I never see orchestra before.

Roland Really?

Alex Only TV, not living.

Roland (*correcting him*) Live.

Alex Living, live, same thing?

Roland Not exactly. Now please, no more talking.

Alex I can see orchestra?

Roland If you *really* want to, yes – but you must be *quiet*, we desperately need this time to practise.

Alex (*confidentially*) Orchestra shit, need practice?

Roland *All* orchestras need practice – *rehearsal*. Now, *please*!

Alex I zip. (*He mimes zipping his mouth shut.*) Also zip other place of talking.

He mimes zipping his arse shut. He takes a chair and goes and sits near the wings with his broom and dustpan.

Roland takes up a position centre stage and practises with his baton. He silently goes through the opening section of the music.

Alex watches, fascinated, as Roland communes with the music. Eventually:

What is meaning of 'Pinball Wizard'?

Roland I don't know!

Alex Is he wizard who like to play pinball? Or is he very good pinball player so people call him wizard?

Roland The latter – the second one. Now, *please*.

He starts conducting again. As he's getting into it:

Alex Where is Brighton?

Roland (*furious*) On the South Coast of England!

He starts conducting again but Alex can't stop himself:

Alex Last question: what like please, Brighton?

Roland It's got a beach! Sad, middle-aged businessmen with dandruff take their equally sad menopausal secretaries there for dirty weekends.

Alex Huh?

Roland They go there to have sex!

Alex But not Pinball Wizard, he go there to play pinball only?

Roland So it seems.

Alex And there is amusement hall in Brighton, like in song?

Roland I believe there are many amusement halls in Brighton.

Alex I like go Brighton. Have sex, play pinball, meet wizard. Have sex with wizard, who knows!

Roland May your wish come true! Now I really *must* get on!

Alex But what is *meaning* of song?

Roland I DON'T KNOW! It's just a bloody song! It doesn't MEAN ANYTHING! There is no Pinball Wizard, he doesn't exist, he's like the Tooth Fairy or Father Christmas!

Alex (*very serious*) There *is* Pinball Wizard, he exist.

Roland NO THERE ISN'T! HE DOESN'T!

Alex YES HE DOES!

Roland NO HE DOES NOT!

Alex YES! TO *ME*, THERE IS PINBALL WIZARD!

Roland HE DOESN'T EXIST!

Alex I BELIEVE IN HIM!

Roland WELL YIPPEE FOR YOU – YOU BLOODY MUSCOVITE MORON!

Alex Okay, okay, no need get shitty shirty. Everyone in world hate British people. Wonder why.

Roland sighs, pinches his brow.

Roland Oh, help me, Lord. I'm very sorry, er . . . *Alex*. Forgive me? If you really want to know what the *meaning* of Pinball Wizard is, in my opinion, it is this: the song is metaphorical – symbolic, yes?

Alex nods.

The Pinball Wizard is deaf, dumb and blind. He is therefore wholly unsuitable for his chosen field of endeavour – i.e. pinball. And yet, against seemingly insurmountable odds, he succeeds to such an extent that he is anointed a 'Pinball Wizard'. The song is testament to that tedious but seductive cliché, 'the triumph of the human spirit in adversity'. Now will you please SHUT UP!

Alex takes in the information, satisfied.

Alex Thank you.

Roland continues to go through the music as Alex vaguely sweeps in the wings.

After a while thirty musicians (more is preferable, less is acceptable) approach from off stage. A rumble of voices and noise from all sides.
Roland looks panic-stricken as the sound intensifies. He rushes for the safety of his lectern.
The musicians enter, talking and shouting in high spirits. Some of them acknowledge Roland but most of them are too preoccupied to notice him.
They wear winter coats and stamp the snow from their shoes. It's freezing outside.
Entrance dialogue to be improvised. It lasts twenty seconds maximum.
Roland shouts above the hubbub:

Roland Members of the orchestra, welcome! Welcome! Quickly, please! Please take your seats!

The musicians do so, knowing exactly where to sit.
During this the Second Flautist – a very keen young girl – has staggered in with Roland's score – a big, heavy book. She positions it on the lectern in front of him.
Then she hovers in readiness. By now, the orchestra are seated.

Second Flute Anything else, maestro?

Roland hands her his baton which she cleans with a special cloth. The Cellist observes her:

Cello What a creep!
Second Flute (*to Cello*) What a loser!

She goes to sit with her fellow flautists.
  The musicians are now all seated, facing Roland. He taps his baton and after a while they pipe down.

Roland Is everyone alright?

General murmurs of assent until Second Trumpet stands up.

Second Trumpet Yeah, we're all marvellous, 'cept for one tiny thing: where's our *instruments*?!
Roland Ah, yes, apparently there was a bit of a mix-up at the airport. Mr Carmichael is in a van collecting the instruments as we speak.
First Violin What mix-up?
Roland Something to do with the hauliers, no need to panic
Cello Who's panicking?
Roland Sorry?
Cello You said 'no need to panic', implying that we were panicking. Who's panicking? I don't see anyone panicking.
Roland My apologies, I meant in a manner of speaking.
Viola (*to Cello*) Stop having a go, arsehole.

Murmurs of agreement from fellow viola players.

All the way from Gatwick to Moscow, whinge, whinge, whinge.
Cello I'm only making a point.
Viola Your point is pointless.
Roland Well, no harm done. Now, is everyone happy with their accommodation?

Double Bass My shower doesn't work.

Second Horn So what, he never had a wash in his life!

First Trumpet Only soap he knows is *Emmerdale*!

Double Bass Sod off!

First Horn We're whiffing you from here!

Timpani And here! It mings like a farm!

Roland Members of the orchestra! Please let's behave
like the ensemble we are! Now, while we're waiting
I thought we could use this time to discuss
Tchaikovsky's Fourth Symphony.

*Murmurs of dissent and mock yawning from Brass
section.*

Picture the scene: it's February 1878, the first performance
of the Fourth Symphony right here in Moscow – not
literally *here*, though it is in fact perfectly possible
that Tchaikovsky may have once stood on this very
stage. He might have actually stood where I'm standing
now . . .

*Roland can't speak, he stares at the floor, overcome by
the enormity of the thought. After a pause conversation
breaks out:*

Oboe My telly's bust.

Cello There's nothing to watch anyway, it's all in bloody
Russian.

Viola See! Always moaning, always got the hump.

Clarinet What I don't get is Chekhov. In *Three Sisters*,
they're all going, 'Ooo, if only we could get to
Moscow.' *Why??*

Murmurs of agreement.

First Trumpet At breakfast, they gave me black bread.
It wasn't burnt toast, it was black bread. What's that
all about?

Vociferous agreement.

Oboe You go outside, it's so cold your breath turns to snow. It like goes solid coming out your mouth.

Bassoon Snow's not solid.

Oboe What is it, then? It ain't liquid or gas, so it's gotta be solid. There aren't any other forms of matter – unless you've invented one, Einstein.

Bassoon For your information, snow is a liquid.

Timpani Only when you piss on it!

Roland As I was saying, it's 1878, Tchaikovsky's in *despair*; his marriage is a disaster, he's attempted suicide and, guess what, he doesn't even attend his own premiere! He's written this magnificent masterpiece and he's too distraught to hear it . . .

Once more Roland can't continue, too moved to speak.

Second Horn Anyone see those birds in the hotel lobby last night? I reckon they were prozzers.

Viola Did they talk to *you*?

Second Horn (*proudly*) Yeah!

Viola They must've been!

Second Trumpet Wonder how much they charge?

First Flute For *you* – about a billion roubles.

Timpani What's that then, ten p?

Roland Members of the orchestra! I must insist –

First Flute Anyone see those blokes with the big 'taches?

Viola Yeah, and the leather car coats – bet they were Mafia!

First Flute I wouldn't mind a bit of that!

Viola Yeah, you could end up owning a football club!

First Flute No, I'd make them buy me a castle like that Dr Zhivago.

Bassoon You what? He lived in a shack in the middle of nowhere!

First Flute Only at the end, not at the beginning *before* the Revolution.

Roland Can we please –

First Trumpet Anyone see that beggar?

First Horn What, the one passed out on the pavement?

First Trumpet D'you see all his snot and dribble had gone hard? If you gave him a little flick his whole head would shatter. It's sad really.

Second Trumpet When are the bloody instruments coming?

Clarinet Where's my clarinet?

First Violin Where's my violin?

Cello I want my cello!

Bassoon Where's my bassoon?

Second Trumpet Who's got my trumpet?

First Horn I want my horn!

Suddenly the whole orchestra stand and demand their instruments, like a many-headed beast. Pandemonium.

Roland SOON! SOON! SOON! The instruments will be here soon, *please* be patient! (*Beat.*) Now, please, let's discuss the music we're going to perform tonight.

First Violin *Murder* more like.

Roland I'm sorry?

First Violin You heard.

Roland Well, if we all adopt that kind of attitude we probably *will* murder it. So let's be positive.

First Violin Positive?! We spend so much time quarrelling and bickering and, quite frankly, listening to complete and utter garbage from 'certain persons', that we never actually get any proper rehearsal time. We need to practise, practise, practise!

A few sarcastic 'oohs' from the 'certain persons'.

Roland Actually, it's a fair point. Can I urge you all – just for today – to put aside your personal grievances and really commit yourselves to the music, just this once?

Clarinet I mean, how on earth did we ever *get* this booking? We're an absolute shambles.

Oboe It's obvious, there must've been a cancellation –

Second Horn And Carmichael wangled us in!

First Trumpet I bet he's taking a cut!

Second Trumpet And he's nicked our instruments!

First Horn He's pawning the lot in Vladivostock!

The Brass section start singing, softly at first and then getting louder as others begin to join in:

Brass Section We're shit and we know we are, we're shit and we know we are!

Woodwind We're shit and we know we are!

Strings We're shit and we know we are!

The entire orchestra are now at full volume, all pointing in unison at the beleaguered, cowering Roland.

All WE'RE SHIT AND WE KNOW WE ARE! WE'RE SHIT AND WE KNOW WE ARE!

Second Flute leaps up, screams with frustration:

Second Flute STOP IT! STOP IT! STOP IT!

The singing fades away. Second Flute speaks with great passion:

You're all horrible! Horrible, nasty, mean and unfair. *You* might be here for a jolly old piss-up at the British taxpayers' expense but *Roland's* here because he *lives* for music! This is supposed to be the greatest night of his life! Why can't you give him a chance? Why can't you behave like human beings instead of – of spoilt animals! There are people in Russia who would kill for the privileges we have, they *dream* of playing in an orchestra with proper instruments. You don't deserve Roland, he's too good for the whole mouldy lot of you!

Deathly silence. Second Flute sits down. Roland puts his head in his hands. He is, perhaps, the most embarrassed of them all.

Roland (*softly, to Second Flute*) Thank you.

She nods, unashamed.

Timpani (*murmurs*) We're still shit.

Others hush him up. Double Bass puts his hand up.

Roland Yes?

Double Bass 'Scuse me, but erm . . . (*whispering*) Who's he?

He points to Alex, who has been quietly observing throughout. As one, in perfect unison, the orchestra turn to look at him.

Roland Oh, this is Alex.

Alex waves, shyly, vaguely raises his broom.

He was sweeping up when I arrived. He's never seen an orchestra before, he asked me if he could watch us rehearse. I hoped you wouldn't mind . . .

Silence. They are all ashamed of themselves.

Alex (*amiably*) Hello, British orchestra!

Chastened murmurs of 'Hi', 'How ya doing', 'Hello', etc. Clarinet stands up, mortified.

Clarinet May I officially apologise for our wholly unreasonable criticisms of your beautiful city.

Others murmur similar apologies. Second Flute is triumphant.

Second Flute Well, it's a bit late now!

Oboe Better late than never.

Second Flute No, better to have never been so horribly rude!

Cello Why don't you button it for once in your life!

Viola (*to Cello*) Leave her alone, you big bully!

Second Flute (*to Viola*) Thank you, but I'm perfectly capable of defending myself against the rabble!

A row breaks out between the woodwind and strings. Roland's mobile rings. He shushes them to receive the call.

Roland (*in phone*) Mr Carmichael!

Roland crouches at the front of the stage, finger in his ear. The orchestra strains to earwig the conversation.

Yes, yes, all fine. Just in the middle of a fascinating debate about . . . Excuse me . . . ? (*Listens.*) Right . . . When? (*Listens.*) I *see* . . . *Right* . . . Yes. I will.

Roland rings off. He is ashen. Everyone looks at him. Without warning he lets out a huge wail – a primal scream of incredible and surprising volume.

AAAAAAAAGGGGGGHHHHHHH!!

The entire orchestra shrink back as one – in fear and astonishment.

You bastards! You shitting bloody bastards! Russian customs have impounded all your instruments! You're giving the most important concert of your lives in two hours time and you've got no instruments, you stupid, stupid bastards!

Consternation and panic break out in the orchestra.

Do you want to know *why*?

All Yes!

Roland Well *one* of you knows, don't you?
All No??

The entire orchestra turn to him:

A Russian sniffer dog found a *spliff* hidden in one of the instruments!

Gasps and shock. Everyone looks at everyone accusingly, improvised protests of innocence and denial ring out.

Cello Well, it wasn't me!
Viola We *know* that! You wouldn't know what a joint looks like!
Cello Oh, and I suppose you think it's cool to take drugs?
Viola In moderation, yes.
Oboe Who was it, Roland?
Second Trumpet Yeah, I'll kill him!
Clarinet It might be a *her*.

Clarinet glares at Viola.

Viola Wasn't bloody *me*!
Double Bass Yeah, she only does crack!

Second Flute begins to emit a high-pitched wail. A strange, sad sonic scream through her nose. All eyes gradually turn to her . . .

Second Horn No!
Second Trumpet No way!
Oboe It's impossible!
Bassoon Still waters run deep . . .
First Flute Leave her alone, it wasn't her!
Second Flute It was! It was! It was *me*! (*She rushes for the exit.*) I'm going to kill myself!

Various musicians prevent her leaving.

Roland Why, *why*?

Second Flute I did it for *you*. It was for *you*!

Roland *Me*?? I don't even smoke!

Second Flute But you get so anxious before a concert, I've seen you pacing around backstage, wearing a sad little strip in the carpet. And that's when you're only going to *play*. Now you're *conducting* I was scared you'd die of nerves. I thought a few quick puffs might relax you. I stole it from my sister. (*sobbing*) I didn't think anyone would check a flute.

Roland crumples into a chair, head in hands. Everyone else is in shock.

Is Mr Carmichael going to expel me from the orchestra? He will, I know he will, my life is over!

Roland You're one of the top two flautists in Croydon (*or wherever*). No one's kicking you out.

Double Bass What are we going to do?

Everyone turns to Roland hoping he's got the answer.

Roland (*gutted*) No other option. We'll have to cancel.

They are devastated.

First Violin Can't we borrow some instruments, from another orchestra?

Bassoon There aren't any others playing here tonight.

Oboe And who'd risk lending us lot?

Second Flute I'll never forgive myself!

First Violin We could play tomorrow instead . . .

First Trumpet We're flying home tomorrow, it's all booked.

Second Flute Please, someone, kill me now!

String Section We will if you don't shut up!!

Suddenly, Alex raises his hand.

Alex Erm . . . hello? Can speak?

527

Roland nods.

My father works in airport.

The entire orchestra turn to him as one – full of hope. Freeze.

Maybe he can speak to . . . how say . . . ?
Roland Customs?
Alex Yes.
Roland What does he do, in the airport?

Alex raises his broom.

Alex He's cleaner.

As one, the entire orchestra sighs, downcast.

He know lots people, maybe he explain . . . er . . . ?
Roland The situation?
Alex Yeah . . . who knows?
First Violin (*to Roland*) It's worth a go, isn't it?

Roland nods, hands his mobile to Alex.

Roland Thanks, mate.

Alex dials, gets through and has a quick murmured conversation in Russian. The orchestra strain to hear.

Alex They find him.

He waits, listens and then speaks into the phone in Russian. A fairly brief but animated conversation with his father. Everyone watches him intently, trying to discern what's happening. Finally Alex rings off and hands the phone to Roland.

He say he scared make fuss, might lose job. Sorry.
Roland (*to Alex*) Thanks for trying. (*to orchestra*) I'd better wait here for Mr Carmichael. I think you should all go back to the hotel.

He nods to the flautists consoling Second Flute.

First Flute Yeah, come on, we'll walk back with you.

They help her up.

Second Flute (*sniffling*) So sorry, everyone.

They lead her out. The other musicians slowly troop out.

First Trumpet Sorry, Roles.
Oboe Bad luck, mate.
Viola Maybe you'll get your chance another time.
Cello (*quietly sarcastic*) Yeah, right.
First Violin I didn't mean what I said. I mean, I did, but we do all appreciate you.
Double Bass (*to Alex*) See you, mate.

*Others shake Roland's hand as they exit disconsolately.
Eventually the stage is empty. Alex begins to tidy up.
Roland picks up his baton and then places it back in its case.*

Alex In situation like this, have to ask very important question: what would Pinball Wizard do?

Roland manages a slight smile. He stares at his score for a few moments then closes it.

Roland I really wanted you to hear this.
Alex Tchaikovsky?
Roland Mmm. Shall I send you the CD?
Alex Or maybe we meet in Brighton and you give to me?
Roland It's a deal.

*Roland paces and stands where Tchaikovsky might have stood.
He raises his face to the heavens.*

Pyotr Il'yich . . . I only wanted to honour you. I'm sorry. (*to Alex*) The irony is that old Tchaikovsky was condemned to death by his own schoolmates.

Alex They kill him?

Roland There was this sort of committee and they kind of forced him to kill himself.

Alex Why?

Roland Oh, he'd been having an affair with the son of some posh bloke.

Alex Tchaikovsky is poof?

Roland Er . . . yeah . . .

Alex Hmm. My brother is poof.

Roland Right . . .

Alex Are *you* poof?

Roland (*embarrassed*) Erm . . . I haven't decided yet. You?

Alex I think maybe *everyone* is bit of poof.

Pause. Roland sits in abject misery.

Roland You were right. I'm not a conductor. I never will be. I'm just a schoolboy waving a stick.

Pause.

Alex What is word? *Describe* this music you were to play?

Roland Oh, well, you're asking me to describe the indescribable.

Alex Please, if can.

Roland thinks for a while. He speaks softly, slowly formulating his thoughts.

Roland Well, it's beautiful. Really beautiful . . . (*Beat.*) It's joy. And passion. And hope and despair . . . it's *life*. It's like silk and velvet and slate and fire. (*Pause.*) When we play – and we're really pretty awful – but just occasionally, almost by accident, we hit it right and everyone plays *together*. Just for one bar. And it's incredible. Everyone knows they did something wonderful. It's our secret, for a moment. And then

it's gone. (*Beat.*) It makes you forget who you are
And it reminds you you're alive.

Silence. They listen.

Alex I can hear . . .
Roland (*quietly*) Me too . . .

They listen some more, both lost in thought.

Alex And I think maybe I have idea . . .

Roland turns to him, curious. They look at each other.

Blackout.

SCENE TWO

That night. The concert.
    *Same configuration of seats. Roland's score on its
lectern.*
    *The house lights are up, the stage lights dim, just
picking out the empty chairs. Murmur and buzz of the
waiting audience. The house lights go down and the stage
lights come up to concert state.*
    *Roland walks on stage holding his baton. He is now
wearing tails and a white bow tie.*
    *The audience applaud. Roland bows nervously and
gestures for silence.*

Roland (*in Russian*) Good evening, ladies and gentlemen.
    (*in English*) I'm afraid that's the full extent of my
    Russian. But a friend has very kindly offered to
    translate. (*Gestures to the wings.*) Alex!

*Alex strides on in a hastily improvised, ill-fitting dinner
suit and bow tie.*

Alex (*in Russian*) Good evening, Moscow!

He takes the applause, blinking in the bright lights,
enjoying himself.
Roland shoots him a look – Enough!

Roland You might have heard a rumour . . .

Alex translates into Russian.

That tonight's concert was to be cancelled.

Alex translates.

This was due to the unfortunate loss of our instruments.

Alex translates.
But his speech is considerably longer than Roland's.
It becomes obvious that he's decided to tell the
audience about the incident of the smuggled spliff.
Interspersed with his words, he mimes the custom
dog sniffing the instruments, the joint in the Second
Flute and Roland taking the call from Mr Carmichael.
Then he imitates Second Flute screaming and
weeping her confession, the orchestra's shock and their
sad acceptance that all was lost.
Roland conceals his fury as best he can.

However, due to a last-minute piece of inspiration . . .

Alex translates but inserts a reference to the Pinball
Wizard – Roland gives him a dirty look.

We are able – I hope – to give you our 'version' of the
Second Movement of Tchaikovsky's Symphony No. 4
in F Minor.

Alex translates.

May we humbly request your indulgence . . . and your
imagination.

Alex translates.

The Ridley Road School Orchestra!

Applause. As the orchestra take the stage Alex shakes Roland's hand, wishing him luck, and then exits.

The musicians are now wearing the appropriate dress for an orchestra. Evening wear/black and white, budget permitting. They enter with surprising grace and ease and stand at their seats.

Second Flute is the last to come on.

Roland hands her his baton, she gives it a good luck wipe with her special cloth and then goes to her seat.

The orchestra have no instruments. But they will act as if they do.

Roland turns to them and with one neat movement directs them to sit. Which they do. In perfect unison. On Roland's cue – after the third tap of his baton on the lectern – as one – they mime their instruments into life.

Brass section have brass. Strings have bows. Timpani has sticks. Woodwind have instruments at their mouths, their fingers at the ready. They hold their positions, poised to commence playing, focused, concentrating – as one.

Audience – hush of expectation.

Roland turns to the auditorium, holds up his baton and very seriously and symbolically places it in his inside pocket. He too will mime. He turns back to the orchestra, nods to the First Violin, who nods back. All is ready.

And Roland begins to conduct. The music begins with a slow oboe melody and plucked strings. The oboist plays, the strings pluck and Roland conducts.

IN COMPLETE SILENCE.

But gradually, imperceptibly, the actual music begins to flood the auditorium – as if the audience are really hearing it.

By the time the strings bring in their melody (around forty seconds in) the sound level is approaching concert volume and fairly soon the orchestra are in full flight. They mime as the music plays. And they must mime as if they know the music well.

The 'concert' miming need not be wholly naturalistic. The 'instruments' might be larger than life. The orchestra might even stand during the climactic sections. They might even dance. But whatever they do, they must do it as one.

After five minutes the movement reaches a climax and over the next twenty seconds the sound dips under and out as we start to hear the musicians inner thoughts. It may seem like they're talking to each other but they're not. The 'tone' is not dialogue but rather, interior monologue.

During this they continue to 'play'.

Second Horn Hey, it's sounding quite good!
Cello Eh?! It's not *sounding* like anything!
Second Trumpet All I can hear is my own breath.
First Horn My fingers are sweating.
First Violin Concentrate!
Bassoon They're listening! The audience are listening!
Clarinet They can *hear* it!
Double Bass They're not walking out!
Cello Only 'cos it's sub-zero out there!
First Flute They can hear it!
Viola It's a miracle!
Oboe Shit! I made a mistake!
First Trumpet Did Roland hear it?
Oboe Oh God, he's scowling at me!
Bassoon No, he's smiling, he's encouraging us!
Timpani I've never seen him smile before, he looks insane!
Second Flute He looks lovely, he's an angel!

Second Horn I never thought this would work.

Timpani That Alex bloke's a genius!

Second Trumpet How can we thank him?

Double Bass We did a collection, weren't you there?

First Trumpet I think I was in the bogs, throwing up.

First Flute Nerves?

First Trumpet No, that black toast.

Second Horn Roland's going to get him a present tomorrow.

First Violin Concentrate everyone, it's nearly the end . . .

Viola Gently – remember what Roland says . . .

Second Flute Play each note as if it's your last . . .

And now we hear the last two minutes of the movement. Roland brings the piece to its slow, beautiful conclusion.

The audience applaud.

Roland gestures the orchestra to stand. They rise as one and bow together.

Alex rushes on with a bouquet and presents it to Roland.

Roland plucks a single stem and motions Second Flute forward. He presents her with the flower and she immediately swoons with the emotion of it all. Alex catches her as she falls backwards into his arms, he slaps her back to consciousness.

Alex, Roland, Second Flute and the orchestra bow together one last time.

Blackout.

SCENE THREE

The following morning.
Empty stage. Just the chairs.
Alex wanders on in his cleaning overalls with his broom and dustpan. He comes to the centre of the stage and looks out at the auditorium. He half-raises his broom in a desultory fashion. He is in strangely low spirits.

Alex (*in Russian*) Good morning, Moscow.

He makes the vague sound of his own voice echoing in the empty auditorium:

Moscow – Moscow – Moscow . . .

He shrugs and starts to slowly sweep the stage, murmuring listlessly to himself:

Ever since I was a young boy,
I played the silver ball,
From Soho down to Brighton,
I must've played 'em all,
But I ain't seen nothin' like him,
In any amusement hall –
Roland (*singing loudly*)
That deaf, dumb and blind kid
Sure plays a mean pinball!

Roland strides on stage, full of beans, a changed man. He leaps in the air and does a few Townshend-style rock gyrations as he grinds through the chords.

(*singing*) Duh, duh, duh, duh, duh!

Alex nods to him.

Alex Hello.
Roland Hey! How are you?! Great party last night!
Alex Excuse. Have to clean stage and stick chairs.

Roland *Stack* chairs?

Alex Stick, stack, who cares?

Roland Alright, let me help you . . . ?

Alex shrugs, Roland starts to stack the chairs with him.

God, I'm totally wrecked!

Alex doesn't respond.

Hey, what's up with you? It was a triumph!

Alex For *you*, yes. I pleased for you. But I clean, sweep, slave. You come, you go, I stay. Never change.

Roland Ah, the famous Russian temperament.

Alex Huh?

Roland It might change, what about your trip to Brighton?

Alex No money. And can't leave, have family here. This home.

Roland Okay, but what about your music?

Alex Yeah, I write songs on broom. Stupid. All make-believe.

Roland But you're the Pinball Wizard of Moscow!

Alex (*despairingly*) No! I am *cleaner*! My father clean, my mother clean, I clean. My kids will clean!

Roland glances off stage and nods. The orchestra come on quickly and stand together in a tight group.

Second Flute is carrying a black instrument case.
    The shape is unmistakable – a guitar case.
    She gives it to Roland who goes on one knee and presents it to Alex.

Roland Alex, in recognition of your contribution to our concert and for helping me to be less of a tight-ass and for helping us to be an orchestra and not just a bunch of bickering musicians –

Cello It'll never happen again!

Viola Shh!

Roland We'd like you to have this. We wish you all the best with your music. And please don't forget to come and visit us when you're a huge rock star touring the world.

The orchestra applaud. Alex is beside himself with joy and excitement.

Alex Thank you! Thank you! I love British people!

He snaps the catches open and excitedly lifts the lid of the case . . .
His joy turns to abject sorrow as he takes out . . . a broom.
The lads of the Brass section all laugh. Alex is devastated.

British piss-take! Very shit funny. Bastards! British bastards!

Roland looks very apologetic – and furious. He turns on the orchestra:

Roland How could you?!

A huge improvised row breaks out between Brass section and Woodwind and Strings – the new-found unity is rapidly disintegrating . . .

(*pleading*) Orchestra! Orchestra! *Please!*

The argument is reaching a climax when Second Flute shrieks:

Second Flute QUIET, EVERYONE! LOOK!

She points to the wings, Double Bass runs on with the real present: a brand new electric guitar.
The orchestra applaud. Alex is overcome. He holds the guitar aloft and then quickly straps it on in case he's dreaming.

538

*Roland takes out his baton and with a grand gesture,
like a wizard, he points to the heavens. Immediately,
the lights snap to a single spot on Alex.*

*Roland conducts, readying the orchestra. On his cue
they start to hum the opening riff of The Who's
'Pinball Wizard' loud and clear – in perfect a cappella
unison. Different sections of the orchestra make the
sound of each instrument.*

*And on the first big guitar chord Alex thrashes along,
the full Pete Townshend whirling motion.*

*The stage lights start to come up so we can see the
orchestra clearly again. And once more they're in
unison. The vocal starts and their voices join in with
Alex:*

Orchestra (*singing*)
Ever since I was a young boy,
I played the silver ball,
From Soho down to Brighton,
I must have played 'em all,
But I ain't seen nothin' like him
In any amusement hall,
That deaf, dumb and blind kid
Sure plays a mean pinball!

*Guitar break. Alex does his stuff. When the vocals
return he mimes the Pinball Wizard on his machine.*

He stands like a statue,
Becomes part of the machine,
Feelin' all the bumpers,
Always playin' clean,
Plays by intuition,
The digit counters fall,
That deaf, dumb and blind kid
Sure plays a mean pinball!

He's a pinball wizard,
There has to be a twist,
A pinball wizard's got such a supple wrist.
Half the Orchestra (*high voice*)
How do you think he does it?
The Other Half (*response*)
I don't know!
Whole Orchestra
What makes him so good?

*Alex continues to freak out as Roland jubilantly
conducts.*
A final round of vocals:

Whole Orchestra
Ain't got no distractions,
Can't hear no buzzes and bells,
Don't see no lights a-flashin',
Plays by sense of smell,
Always gets a replay,
Never seen him fall,
THAT DEAF, DUMB AND BLIND KID
SURE PLAYS A MEAN PINBALL!

Suddenly – the whole company freeze as one.
Tableau. Everyone. Still. Silent. Together.

Blackout.

Obsessed by the Passion to Perform

Patrick Marber interviewed by Jim Mulligan

From the age of about thirteen Patrick Marber knew that he wanted to be a playwright – not an actor or director but the one who had the vision and wrote the words. In reality his theatrical career took off when he went to university and started doing stand-up comedy.

> I now think of my comedy years as being a fantastic training to be a playwright in terms of sharpening my material, being able to improvise, getting to the point fairly quickly, learning about audiences and learning about myself. It was a great education. That period informs my general writing style. I like the dialogue to be speedy and precise and to have a little comedic edge to it.

Patrick Marber's secondary education was not successful in a formal sense. 'I was a rebellious adolescent and wouldn't have liked any school. I didn't like anything I saw as being a system.' The alternative education he provided for himself included hanging out at the National Theatre to see shows on stand-by, obsessive listening to the *John Peel Show*, avid reading of *New Musical Express* and lots of gigs.

It is no surprise then that *The Musicians* is about two young people who are obsessed by music. Roland is clearly a talented musician, a conductor with a passion to perform at least one work and to coerce his youth orchestra into working as a team so that they can achieve one moment of perfection. Alex is a guitarist without a guitar but with a dream.

Alex and Roland are the protagonists and the play is about how, in their different ways, they both achieve something real, how they learn about themselves and how they grow. Alex hasn't even got a guitar, but he's got an active imagination. I think the play is saying that before you've got an instrument you need a passion to play one. There's no point in having an instrument if you don't have the passion, commitment and desire to play the damn thing.

By extension, the orchestra is a collection of Alexes, musicians without instruments. It is Roland's job to give them the passion.

Patrick Marber says that there is always desperation in his work, with people aspiring to do things that they can never achieve. The situation the actors find themselves in here is desperate: booked into a Moscow hotel, freezing cold, showers that don't work and a foyer which their imaginations people with prostitutes and gangsters. They turn up for rehearsal to find their instruments have been impounded by customs because of the foolishness of Second Flute. Roland is desperate. This is his moment of homage to Tchaikovsky and he is to be denied it by (as it turns out) the person who worships him, his acolyte, the Second Flute. 'I remember, doing plays as a kid, there was always someone who wasn't necessarily the most talented but who was often the most enthusiastic. Second Flute is one of those.'

It is left to Alex, inspired by the Pinball Wizard, to come up with a surreal solution: the orchestra will play without instruments and will convince the audience that they are actually hearing the music. This is the great challenge for the director and actors.

This is a very demanding play. The actors have to learn the piece of music they are supposed to be playing. They are required to mime and know when their

THE MUSICIANS

instruments come in. They've got to work collectively
in all the ensemble areas and the play asks them to
improvise dialogue at times. I don't think they have to
be musicians, but they have to learn about music just
to pull off that technical trick. They certainly have to
be able to sing when they accompany Alex at the end.

The school in *The Musicians* is not the school Patrick
Marber went to. It is a state school that could be anywhere
and one of the reasons why the characters have no names
is so that the play will be accessible to groups of young
people anywhere.

The whole of *The Musicians* is make-believe. There is
no such thing as a European Festival of Youth, and it is
unlikely, although not impossible, that a gifted young
musician would conduct a touring youth orchestra. But,
if the audience can be made to believe in silent music,
they can believe in this fantasy. It is obvious that Alex is
never going to be a rock star and Roland probably will
not become a conductor, but for this one night the
bantering, mixed group of young people come together in
order to achieve the impossible through the inspiration of
the wannabe Moscow cleaner. The Brass section is
laddish, the Strings are intense and the Woodwind is
somewhere in the middle, but they achieve one night of
collective glory. And, despite their jocular cynicism, they
can be generous – to Roland so that he can conduct on
the very spot where Tchaikovsky might have stood; to
Second Flute by forgiving her for her stupid mistake and
supporting her; and to Alex by having a whip-round to
buy him a guitar.

In the end it's about how, by working together, being a
collective, being involved in an enterprise is meaningful
if you all do it together – whether it's a sports team, or
being in a play, or dancing together.

Production Notes

STAGING SCENE ONE

Interrupting the naturalism of this scene on occasions
will help prepare for the stylised nature of Scene Two.
The orchestra need to react collectively (unconsciously)
in this first scene, so we can see the seeds are there for
them to emerge as a collective whole by Scene Three.

Much of the time, Roland has his back to the audience –
he's talking to the whole orchestra. Look at the staging of
this so it works. Find ways to 'cheat' him out so he can
be properly seen. This will be part of the challenge.

Clear the space: stack chairs at the back of the concert-
hall stage. There would possibly be a conductor's music
stand at the front preset – a wooden-topped stand, with a
lip at the bottom, tilted at a slight angle on an adjustable
leg. Other than this, it's an empty space.

Alex is sweeping centre stage. Roland enters from upstage
left so that the audience can see him watching Alex.
(Ideally you'll need more entrances for the orchestra, or
it'll take an eternity.)

Keep space between them at first . . . this scene is about
non-communication. Roland takes in the lie of the land.
Alex keeps his distance at the start, through respect – he
doesn't know who Roland is at first: he could be Nigel
Kennedy! Roland is excited to be in the space and should
not be depressed straight away – it's not immediately
combative, though he's a bit irritated at not being alone.

Alex's guitar impression is a big moment – the actor will
need to isolate himself and get some space so we see him

in all his glory – move him away from Roland when he says 'That is a Russian joke,' as if he is chuckling at his own wit.

It's quite a big space for just two actors – use it. Avoid having two people just standing still downstage. Look at how to move them around. Later it becomes smaller when the orchestra arrive.

Alex is virtually off the stage when he says, 'I've been sweeping all day,' and Roland calls him back. Roland needs to get upstage to call after Alex, 'Stage looks perfect, by the way.'

The wind-up. Roland could maybe start pacing and panicking. Perhaps Alex could follow him around. See how far you can push this. At the end of the dialogue, Roland sweeps his way to sit at the side, almost in the wing. Roland then moves to his lectern.

When Roland practises his conducting – facing forward – it's to himself, in his head. On 'No need to get shitty,' Alex goes for a sulk upstage. Roland has to try to win him back round. End of first section – Alex sweeps himself off and reappears later when we've forgotten about him.

As Roland heads upstage we hear the orchestra coming – hubbub from the wings. We see a moment of Roland's panic as he hears them and moves to the lectern in readiness.

Entrance of the orchestra. Let the sounds of their arrival gradually emanate from all four corners of the stage towards the audience. Some people should acknowledge Roland when they enter – he is their conductor.

Go straight to chairs and set them as you would at the start of every rehearsal. While this should appear compeletely routine, there's a 'newness' to this occasion.

It's cold outside, and this is a comparatively warm space. The chairs aren't laid out. Make it clear they've not been in this space before.

When the orchestra sit, they immediately stop talking. The conductor might shut pockets of noise up. Ideally they will be in and sat within twenty seconds, for Roland's 'Thank you.'

You could experiment with a more non-naturalistic entrance, letting the hubbub rise to a climax over fifteen to twenty seconds, then having the entrance in silence. They look at the space . . . then start talking again.

Entrance of Second Flute. Second Flautist enters from downstage left with the score and a cloth. It's her 'special cloth'. This tedious ritual happens at the beginning of every rehearsal. She's hovering by Roland's side. Roland doesn't even look at her – it's routine. Second Flute puts the score down, wipes baton, Roland says 'Thank you' and she scuttles back to her place. Once the baton is cleaned, Roland can move downstage right to provide space for the audience to see the 'creep'–'loser' exchange between Cello and Flute – the first indication that there's conflict within the orchestra.

Consider how to get Roland out of the middle at times so others are more visible. During the moment where he talks of Tchaikovsky he could move to the side and be 'lost in the moment'. Also look at finding ways for speakers to be seen: perhaps at times they can stand, especially those at the back. With rostra, you could put your orchestra on tiered sections. Strings would usually be seated on the floor at the front.

First Violin is anxious – perhaps her violin is a precious one. Maybe she's so concerned she stands and tries to engage the others. Keep it speedy. Cellists would support

Cello, the violas support Viola – when support is needed, look round to your section of the orchestra. Most of the instruments would belong to the school, but the keener kids such as Second Flute might own their own. Levels of anxiety will be higher to some degree here, but they do trust Roland so they're not over-panicky.

After 'mings like a farm', build to a general outpouring of abuse so that Roland has to control it. Enjoy abusing Double Bass over the top of others in the orchestra. As Roland walks off talking about Tchaikovsky the orchestra watch him collectively – 'he's going off on one' – *then* start their own conversation about the black bread, etc.

Allow five to ten seconds of impro with various members of the orchestra popping up demanding, 'Where's my Violin?', ' I want my Horn!' etc. Have an order to this at first, then everyone kicks in. Roland can move in among them to answer 'Soon, soon.' Orchestra can remain standing once they've made their demands.

Embrace the stupidity of Flute – she thinks she's smart with her *Dr Zhivago* reference. Let Second Horn first be proud with 'They talked to me,' then deflated by the response. Second Trumpet needs to stand for 'I wonder how much they charge.'

First Violin – frumpy, prudish – stands when she makes her speech. She's the Leader of the Orchestra, the second most important person after Roland. Decide who the rebellious people she refers to actually are – they need to react. Make the interplay specific, not general. There is a sense of an unstated challenge to Roland's authority ('*if I was running this orchestra*'). His response re-establishes his status – he takes back charge.

'*We're shit and we know we are.*' This is started by the Brass, then Woodwind join in, then Strings, so the sound

comes progressively towards the audience. Even First
Violin joins in eventually. It starts as fun but turns into
an attempt to torture Roland. They can point at him,
persecute him. Motivate Second Flute as much as possible
for her outburst. Roland needs almost to crumple when
he crouches. When she says 'Stop it!' everyone does stop.
She's impassioned at this moment, and they're almost too
embarrassed to respond. Make the following speech even
more embarrassing. Second Flute might move amongst
them and confront them individually, but they can't look
her in the eye. When she's getting angrier, the orchestra
members need to shift away from her slightly as she
passes, look at her differently once she's sat back down.

The audience need to think they've been suitably
chastened, and that order has been restored. But then
Second Horn speaks for all and they start laughing.

When Double Bass says 'Who's he?' and points to Alex,
everyone turns at once. Define and stylise this moment.
Freeze as they realise there's a witness. Unfreeze as
Double Bass says 'Alright mate?' There should be a
dynamic sense of an intruder – a fixed moment. Follow
Double Bass's hand as he points. Some can show their
shame – dropping their heads when they realise they've
been behaving so discourteously. They need to show
they're ashamed of themselves, maybe shift awkwardly.

Look for moments when members of the orchestra can
come out of their chairs. For example, Clarinet could
come forward into a more formal space for her apology.

Roland makes them feel guilty for their behaviour during
'He was sweeping up . . .' It's his revenge. We should see
the conductor coming out . . . the leader in him.

When the call from the airport comes through, Roland
should move downstage away from the orchestra – it's a

private call – and respond quietly. The orchestra crane forward to hear what he's saying. He screams out front, then turns to face them, still screaming – they shrink back.

There should be lots of pace in reaction to Roland's revelation about the 'spliff'. Second Flute's wail should last four to five seconds, then be interrupted. She stays standing, comes down centre stage – Roland can help her make this journey. She tries to exit through Second Violins and Horns, who stop her, improvising lines here. She faces Roland and confesses, tries to explain. They are face to face downstage, in profile to the audience. Roland should gesture kindly to her – she's his acolyte. He's kind to her despite the revelation.

When Alex asks 'Can speak?' don't wait for a nod from Roland. Alex is slightly heroic here. As soon as he mentions the airport, all turn to him in chorus.

When everyone turns to Alex, turn from the base of the spine to show your optimism, then the collapse can be more exaggerated. *It needs to be read across the space.* You could try leaning forward to take yourself off the seat and towards him in these moments – people at the back of the orchestra might even stand.

It is a great visual image to see forty people all straining one way. Alex reacts to the moment of tension when they all turn to him – he suddenly feels the pressure of leadership.

Speaking Russian. Minimise speaking Russian for the actor – this can be gobbledegook. He's having a conversation that we can't entirely hear. The orchestra crane in to hear what is being said. Alex makes a sad retreat back to the wings after the call ends.

On 'We should go back to the hotel,' we need to hear a small sob from Second Flute. Her wail speaks for the group. They make a sad way to any of the exits. Some acknowledge Roland as they leave. The overall style should be expressive and slightly heightened.

Alex and Roland alone. Find ways of using the space again. Roland moves upstage, a lonely man in an empty space. Alex moves about collecting detritus, tidying. Create some distance between them. We need to feel the sadness of two people in a room with empty chairs. By the end of the scene ideally they need to be at opposite sides of the stage, for when they both turn out. Roland could even sit at points during this section if it feels right, as if he's almost inconsolable.

There needs to be a definite moment to end the scene – a beat, a sense of energy between the two of them.

STAGING SCENE TWO

The orchestra needs to get on stage via the shortest route, quickly, cleanly and formally – front people first and so on. No bumping into people or furniture. Very different from their earlier entrance. Costume will help – also formal, at least black and white, contrasting with the colour of the rehearsal.

Settle. Pause. Conductor gives the cue to start. Second Flute enters as before from downstage left to baton-wipe. The physical quality needs to lift the temperature and energy. There should be a suspended quality to the body: walk with a sense of waiting for something to happen, almost floating, no sounds of feet. When Roland does the upbeat, the orchestra slightly rise in their bodies and then sit on a definite downbeat.

Roland comes from the upstage entrance, Alex from downstage left as before. He and Roland stand either side of the conductor's podium. In the translation, Alex gets physical to gesture his explanation. It's essential we hear key words – 'Pinball Wizard', 'spliff', etc. Alex give fast-forward edited highlights of the events: the sniffer dog, the spliff, the wail . . . Use actual translations for formal moments, such as 'Good evening, Moscow,' but gobble-degook for the rest. When Roland says 'The Ridley Road School Orchestra' he makes it an announcement and gestures for them to take their places.

See the later section (pages 553–5) for the miming of the instruments.

While Roland is still conducting, we hear the inner thoughts of the orchestra. They're still playing during the dialogue, they have to have their eyes on the conductor and keep to the beat/rhythm. This is a sort of collective consciousness. They should keep focused on Roland, and though it may appear that they are talking to each other, they're not. Get the tone and texture of this.

It's quite a simple extract. The First Violins play the tune, The rest of the strings are *pizzicato* (plucking). Wind have bits of melody over the top. trumpets, horns and timpani are not playing, but horns come back in later. There are some wind solo sections. It's quite thin music, so pick up cues, or it'll get too loud to hear the dialogue above it. There is a lot of detail towards the end. The conductor ends – ties a knot in the final note. Holds hands in a freeze . . . savours the moment. Then slowly he brings hands down – the instruments dissolve. Then he smiles, brings the orchestra to their feet, turns and bows to the audience. The orchestra take their bow from Roland: bow from the waist, hands by side, head down. Hold the bow for two to three seconds, then come up.

Alex rushes on with bouquet from downstage left. Roland takes one stem, turns and makes eye-contact with

Second Flute, she runs forward and receives it. She faints into Alex's arms.

STAGING SCENE THREE

An empty stage. Alex and Roland 'stick-stack' quite a lot of chairs in order to clear the stage ready for 'Pinball Wizard'. Alex enters sweeping, but then puts his broom to one side when he starts singing to himself and stacking chairs. He doesn't stop stacking when Roland comes on. Alex is a broken spirit, but Roland is a new man. He has far more confidence now. We see something comically different about him. This is the reverse of the first meeting between them. Alex is a little embarrassed by Roland's outburst of 'Pinball Wizard' and Roland needs to push this and enjoy it. Roland approaches him – 'But you're the Pinball Wizard of Moscow' – and at this moment they stop stacking chairs. Alex goes back to stacking chairs with his line, 'My kids will clean . . .'

Presenting the gift to Alex. Orchestra enter rapidly from various sides and congregate tightly – they are as one. Second Flute enters from downstage left and gives the guitar case to Roland. He moves to Alex and kneels before him to present the gift. Some of the orchestra will be aware of the practical joke, others aren't. It's likely to be a Brass section gag. Roland certainly doesn't know – he's furious. Others perhaps turn on the Brass section and there is momentary bickering again. Double Bass then runs on. Roland quietens the orchestra and presents the guitar to Alex.

Pinball Wizard. The orchestra spread out and perform. Lots of energy and movement. Freeze on the end beat in a tableau. It needs to be dynamic and energised.

THE ORCHESTRA

Start by arranging everyone in orchestra positions. No
music stands are required because there are no instruments,
and it would break the mime convention if they were
present (but it would be fun to have the orchestra mime
turning the pages of the music). The First Violin, as
Leader of the Orchestra, will be particularly attentive to
the conductor. Cello and Double Bass need bowing space.

You can't afford to have floppy fingers when miming the
instruments – there must be energy in the hands and the
fingers. The audience needs to believe you are holding the
instrument, so it needs real and imaginative energy. Make
it clean – almost a beat when you are making the shape
of the instrument. *Know* what you are doing. Exaggerate
the shape slightly. *Feel* the instrument between your hands.

Here are some notes on how each instrument is played (a
video of an orchestra playing would be vauable to
accompany these). Your aim is to make the audience gasp
at the technical precision of the orchestra.

VIOLIN AND VIOLA are similar, but the viola is larger
Both instruments are held under the chin. On the left-
hand side of the instrument is a chin-rest with a shoulder
pad on the underside: this sits on the shoulder. There is
tension involved in the neck. The instrument is gripped
by leaning the head to one side to hold it in place. Left-
hand fingers go down on the strings: there are no frets to
tell you where the notes are, so it is quite a demanding
instrument. You rest the instrument between your thumb
and forefingers. There should be a straight line between
the left-hand side of your chin and the end of the
instrument. The right hand uses the bow, which is held
with the thumb on one side, the other fingers coming

across to balance. The bowing is across the space above the bridge. The bow has to move straight across, so that the wrist needs to change position to accommodate this. High notes are closest to the body, and this requires the player to lean forward slightly. Both feet are planted on the floor, right foot slightly forward. Sitting bones should be right in the centre of the body.

CELLO There is a spike in the bottom of the instrument which rests on the floor. The left hand moves up and down the strings to create the notes. The thumb comes around the back of the neck of the instrument, fingers over the top.

DOUBLE BASS The fingers move up and down frantically because the notes are spread out on the fingerboard, the high notes being furthest from the body. The player needs space to allow bowing room. Have the player imagine something solid is there so the audience can read the shape.

FLUTE Playing is like blowing across a milk-bottle top. The flute needs to be held on the right-hand side, with the thumbs supporting the instrument.

CLARINET AND OBOE These are very similar, but the oboe has a double reed. The lips need to wrap around it. The pressure of the lips and the wind from underneath make the sound. Wind players have to sit up really well to access the muscles in their navel. The instrument is supported by the thumbs: left hand at top; right hand underneath. Fingers move around to play the keys. The instrument comes straight down in front of the body. Clarinets are single-reed. They are held up slightly more than the oboe. The player appears to bite the bottom lip.

BASSOON is a double tube folded back on itself. The sound comes out of the top. There is a spike on the floor, like the cello's. Another double-reeded instrument, to be bitten with the lips, but not so much wind pressure is required because the sound is lower. Left hand on top, right hand at bottom. The bassoon is a fat instrument, so the player wears a sling support around the neck, with the instrument leaning away slightly. The player needs to sit well up and slightly forward into the instrument. The basoon is usually played to the right-hand side of body.

TRUMPETS The mouthpiece is round-shaped. With the left hand on the keys, the other hand supporting the instrument, the player needs to blow a raspberry into it, slightly off-centre. The bell of the trumpet projects into the audience. During big moments, the instrument is often held up. Trumpets can produce a very loud sound.

HORNS These are curly-shaped with a big bell. The instrument rests on the lap of the player. The right hand goes into the bell and helps to support, the left hand goes onto the three valves – the fingers pressing down with definition. The valves are quite far towards the edge of the instrument. The player needs to tuck the elbows slightly behind on the bell end.

TIMPANI The sticks are held with a fairly loose grip. The player needs to hit the skin of the drum and let the top of the stick bounce away and take the momentum.

TASKS FOR THE ORCHESTRA

The conductor will have to learn how to conduct – not just say the lines. The main tool of the conductor is his/her eyes. The orchestra should be able to read the expression in them: is the conductor encouraging, asking for quietness, etc? Decide what mood the conductor is trying to create at any given point. Waving a stick about isn't communication. Usually the conductor would be raised about nine inches from the floor of the stage on a podium of some description.

The following tasks will encourage the orchestra to investigate the discipline and accuracy of playing the instruments. They can't be generalised.

1   Stand. Then be seated as an orchestra on a given cue, upright on the edge of the chairs. All the instruments take a lot of physical energy. There has to be a sense of purpose – a need to connect. Have the orchestra distinguish between the moments where they are less involved – they can be more relaxed when they're not required to play parts of the music.

2   The conductor should be linked with the orchestra. S/he needs to lead with energy. All eyes are on the conductor at all times. Practise standing/sitting on a visual up/down beat from the conductor. Get the orchestra practising and working as a group. Have them sit cleanly *on* the beat to create dramatic tension.

3   Practise making the shape of the allocated instruments on the conductor's upbeat. Try to avoid 'wobbling' – be precise and stick to the shape. Have players lead who have a good sense of physicality so the others can observe. The wind players must look strong in the body. Get them to use the muscles in the base of the spine, and have them plant their feet on the floor. Encourage the trumpets and horns to breathe! Find the breath for the movement.

Do these exercises one at a time, then combine Tasks 2 and 3. That is the start of the concert, essentially. The instruments all suddenly appear – as a fantasy. Don't worry about the reality of detail – picking them up, etc. It's not necessary within the conventions of the play.

Imagine there is a pole horizontally in front of you.

- Present the hands – hands out, face down, relaxed.
- Take the object – make a solid, definite movement to grasp the pole.

Tempo. The conductor beats in 4 to keep the tempo/beats in the same place. (But the piece in the play is actually in 2 *not* 4.)

1 Down beat (main beat).

2 Across to left-hand side.

3 Across to right-hand side.

4 Upbeat.

- Practise making notes on the instrument. Remember to breathe!
- Practise making notes in time to this beat.
- Practise making some sort of emphasis on the first beat.
- Perhaps do some sort of body movement on the first beat.
- Don't continue playing on 2, 3, 4 . . . just recover.
- Strings go *down* bow on the first beat. The bow should point up slightly. The elbow stays down. Try to follow the Leader so the bows move in the same direction within the sub-groups of the strings – be aware of the mini-chorus within the whole chorus.
- Hands should be taut and poised. For plucking, forget the bow and pluck the strings by hand.

PLAYING THE SYMPHONY Have the conductor conduct the group as a mimed orchestra to a CD recording of the piece. Bring in the instruments as detailed in the score. Have the conductor encourage shaping the instruments to the melody – for example, bringing them up when the music goes higher, down during lower, quieter moments. There should be a sense of animation for strings (with the bow). The conductor might want to shape the music –

adjust tempo, etc. Ask the conductor to anticipate what's coming; to think about it on the beat before.

This is not about drilling, but capturing the spirit of the music. The players can start dancing, literally and meta-phorically, with the instruments. They and the audience need to feel the music and see it – not just to play or hear it. The piece runs for about five and a half minutes before dialogue starts coming back in. It's watchable because the music is fantastic and we're present at a concert. Choreo-graph a five-minute sequence which starts naturalistically and develops into a more expressionistic piece.

SINGING AND PHYSICALISING Work on developing the movement by getting the players to stand up during their individual 'sections' in the music, with even the whole orchestra standing at 'big' moments, also coming forward/moving back to echo the shape of the piece.

Get the cast to sing the tune to get the 'feeling' of the piece inside them. Find the passionate moments and varied aspects to meaning – within the same tune even. Sing with the right energy, intensity, pitch, etc. Cello – warm sound; wind – delicate melodic lines . . . Connect the vocal mechanism with the diaphragm.

Music is about feeling – each phrase has a meaning. Tune in to that feeling – develop this into physical energy. Find an image to connect with it, sing it, physicalise it.

Look for information about Tchaikovsky's life which will help you discover some of the meanings in the piece.

1   Explore the tune – looking at rise and falls (high-low/loud-soft)

2   Then explore the marching section – as if there's hope in your heart. This adds energy, richness, vibration. The timpani is really important at these moments. Physicalise the energy of a march.

PINBALL WIZARD

It's essential to learn the guitar break as well as the song itself. Take a look at the rhythm of this 'thrashing'. It comes in 8-time when it gets going: there are 4 thrashes which are longer and 2 slightly shorter.

STRUCTURE OF THE SONG Look at sections which have the same tune and where the sections change tune, and mark this out in the script for the actors.

- Introduction – calm – *break*.
- Lead Guitar and Bass come in – *break*.
- Tune comes in for first time.
- Instrumental – *break*.
- Tune comes in for second time,
- *Break*.
- 'Pinball Wizard' tune – *short break*.
- Dialogue.
- Tune comes in for first time.

Split the orchestra in half for the 'How do you think he does it?' section.

Create a rock band for the split lines in the opening instrumental section: maybe four groups – lead guitar, bass, rhythm, percussion.

Standing up – sing through, mime like rock stars! Make sounds for instruments. Look at the physicality of this – it shouldn't be total chaos. It's at counterpoint with the orchestra in Act Two.

THE GUITAR The main body of the instrument should be over the pelvis. The weight should be on the back foot, then front – play around with this. Plant the feet wide apart. Bend the knees. The gravity is down.

Swing it side to side. Jump in the air . . . The music should be coming from the pelvis, not the upper body as in the orchestra sections. This has to be a lot more anarchic.

Keith Moon of The Who plays the drums quite erratically: up above, to sides, etc. The actor playing Alex might want to incorporate the other instruments played in 'Pinball Wizard' into his mime.

The introduction builds up, creating the tension as we anticipate the state of the song. Enjoy the energy of it. Alex needs to give the end-song everything – it's the moment we've been waiting for. If it's too difficult, then try with everyone singing everything rather than his/her own part.

The point of the singing of 'Pinball Wizard' is that the orchestra have learnt from their experience and now have an instinct for working together – it's collective, not rehearsed . . . just *instinctive*. They must 'freak out' together – *not* as individuals. It's *not* a performance.

THE CLIMAX In the play, the song ends halfway through. Bring it to a climax, find your own end. Like a reverb . . . a real concert ending. Build it up dramatically.

Try a tight whisper that builds from 'Ain't got no distractions' – pick out the key words in the whisper. There's an emphasis in the play on how much rehearsal is needed for the Tchaikovsky – by contrast, 'Pinball Wizard' must appear unrehearsed.

But the climax won't work if the orchestra seem to be just mucking around and enjoying themselves for a few minutes. The audience will be bored. It needs just as much work as the Tchaikovsky in rehearsal.

The group will need lots of eye-contact during the performance of the song. Connect the energy as a group, share it – this will bring some warmth to the song.

Alex is leading the group at the front during this section in the play. Think about playing around with: moving out around the stage; across and behind Alex; in and out towards him, etc.

SOME USEFUL WARM-UPS

- Stretch to the ceiling, feet planted.
  Clasp hands, reach up – stretch from side to side.
  Push the top of your body away from your pelvis.
  Rib cage up and out. Breathe.
  Release hands by your side.

- Stretch hands and fingers.
  Make a fist, then stretch fingers out, then shake hands.

- Open palms facing to ceiling. Bring in thumbs, then fingers one at a time to form a ball.
  Turn fists over and open out in reverse – start with little finger, end with thumbs.

Articulation of hands:

- Hold a shape in the mime with clarity and definition.
  Make a clawing gesture with hands.
  Create shape of instruments on 1, 2, 3, 4.
  Make instrument bigger and more solid.
  Give the impression you have something solid between your hands.

based on a workshop led by Patrick Marber,
Jane Gibson (movement direction)
and Andrew Charity (music direction)
transcribed by Lesley Turner

WHERE I COME FROM

SCENES FROM ABROAD
BY MIKE WILLIAMS

Richard Nelson

Characters

Young Man
our narrator, sixteen

Dan
the teacher's son, seventeen

Emily
his best friend, sixteen

Emma
her friend, seventeen

Richard
eighteen

Jane
his girlfriend, seventeen

Henry, sixteen

James, fifteen

Bill, sixteen

Kathy, sixteen

Libby, fifteen

Becca, sixteen

Cat
daughter of the owners of the B. & B.,
English, sixteen

PROLOGUE

The sitting room of a bed and breakfast, London.

Chairs, a sofa, end table, coffee table, lamps, etc. Off to one side is the entryway, and to the other the stairs to the bedrooms (neither need be seen). So anyone going from outside to upstairs must snake his way through this room.

To one side of the stage – a chair: this is not part of the sitting room.

Evening. The lamps are on. Emily sits alone, trying to read, her feet up. She has a box of tissues near her; she is a bit sick and has been sneezing and blowing her nose.

A Young Man stands and speaks to the audience. He is our narrator and he – like all but one of the characters – is American.

Young Man (*to us*) It's January 1987. And we're but a short walk from the Russell Square tube stop, on the crescent-shaped street, Cartwright Gardens, home to maybe five or six B. & B.s, this being the sitting room of one of them. (*He holds a paperback guidebook – Morton's* Americans in London.) There was – and is – much history in these grey streets for Americans. (*Holds up the book and opens it.*) Just around the corner, at 5 Woburn Walk, arrived the poet Ezra Pound with the fresh-off-the-boat and very young Robert Frost to a Monday night 'at home' at Mr William Butler Yeats'. It was at this gathering that Mr Frost asked the Irish poet, 'Do you really believe in fairies?' (*He turns a page.*) Guildford Street. (*He points it out.*) Where Mark Van Doren, while living in

the 'coldest room in London', got this published in the
agony column of *The Times*. (*Reads*.) 'Young American,
literary, but interested in everything, desires London
friends.' (*Turns to another page*.) Great Russell, from
where Hemingway wrote his father: 'Dear Pappy: I
can't think of any more appropriate place to write you
from than the Reading Room of the British Museum
with Englishmen as thick as Englishmen and a draft on
the back of my neck which I can feel in my balls.'
(*Turns pages*.) T. S. Eliot. Ralph Waldo Emerson. Fred
Astaire. (*Looks up, then closes the book*.) Unfortunately,
none of that has any bearing on our story. Instead, ours
is a tale of high-school students, from a Philadelphia
suburb – you'll meet many of them, the rest are staying
at the B. & B. next door – who are just completing
a long, hard, difficult week – of culture. With the
occasional break for shopping to keep their sanity.
Tomorrow they go home, so this is their last night.
(*He turns to Emily*.) Emily missed the play tonight.
She has a cold.

Emily sneezes.

Her best friend is Dan and he has promised to bring her
back a programme. Dan's father is Mr Williams, the
head teacher for this trip. He and the other two teachers,
for reasons unexplained, have rooms at the B. & B.
next door. Here Mr and Mrs Davis, the owners, rule
and keep the order. But tonight –

*Cat, sixteen enters with a cup of hot water and a
package of Lemsip for sick Emily.*

– they unexpectedly have been called away to the sick-
bed of Mrs Davis' mother, in Brighton, and so have
left their daughter, Caitlin, in charge.

Cat leaves.

Where I Come From: Scenes From Abroad. By – me.
  Scene One: 'Home Away From Home.'

*The Young Man steps aside as we begin to hear voices
  off – the students returning from the theatre. The
  Young Man will sit in the side chair and watch.*

SCENE ONE

Kathy, Libby and Becca enter, talking.

Kathy *What* did he say?

Libby Kathy –

Kathy (*over this*) What did he say?!

Libby (*to Becca*) I'm sorry I brought it up. I didn't –

Kathy (*over the end of this*) Tell me what he said, Libby.

Libby It was nothing. He thought she looked like you.

Kathy The girl in –

Becca In the play.

Kathy (*taking out cigarettes*) I don't even like him.

Emily (*over this*) How was the play –?

Kathy (*getting her cigarettes*) Which girl in the stupid
  play? Jesus Christ, the stuck-up one?

Becca (*over this to Emily*) How are you feeling?

Emily How was the –? (*Sneezes.*)

Libby (*to Emily*) Boring. Like every other one. Why
  would this be any different? Why couldn't I have
  gotten sick?

Kathy The girl in the knee-high socks?

Libby I don't know –

Kathy (*over this*) I hate those kind of socks. I'd rather die
  than – Who wears –?

Becca I don't think he meant –

Kathy (*a flush of excitement, she now has an excuse to
  go and confront this boy*) Where is he? Where's
  Henry? I want to talk to him.

She hurries back off. Becca follows.

Libby (*to Emily*) Did my mother call?

Emily About an hour ago, she said –

Libby I don't care what she said. I know all the shit that she says.

Dan enters carrying two programmes.

Emily Where's my programme?!

He holds it up.

How much did it cost?

Dan A pound fifty.

Libby They really rip you off here.

Dan They don't rip –

Libby (*to herself*) God, I sound like my mother.

Kathy and Becca are returning.

Becca He says every cute girl looks like you.

Kathy When does he –?

Emily Where's Henry?

Becca The boys are out front being lectured at by Mr Williams.

Dan I'm a boy and I'm not –

Emily What did they do now?

Becca I think they tried to sneak away –

Kathy And Dan's father caught them.

Dan What my father does has nothing to do with –

Becca Who's sensitive?

Kathy (*to Becca*) You got a light?

Becca looks through her purse and soon will pull out a lighter.

What did Henry really say about me?

Emily (*to Dan, over this, about the programme*) I'll pay you back when – It's nice.

Dan They are really nice.

Emily Where were they sneaking to this time? (*about the smoke*) I have a sore throat. Blow it over there.

Kathy Some club Henry knows or says he knows about.

Dan How does Henry know about –?

Becca A strip club.

Emily Really? Oh that would be right up his –

Kathy That's what I said. (*She laughs.*)

Becca He said he's already been there.

Emily When could he have –?

Becca He snuck out of the portrait museum and went.

Libby Maybe what he saw there reminded him of you too, Kathy.

Kathy (*smoking*) That – would be okay with me.

Laughter.

Maybe we should go with them. That would freak them out. Where are they, anyway? (*to Becca*) Go look.

Becca goes out. Short pause. Kathy smokes.

Emily (*to Kathy*) I like that skirt.

Libby It's mine. (*to Kathy*) Could I use your lip gloss?

Emily I know.

Kathy I think it should be shorter.

Pulls it up a little. Throws Libby her bag so she can find the lip gloss.

Libby (*holding up a little plastic bag*) I got something to – smoke.

Kathy Where did you –?

Libby (*over this*) A guy at the tube station, just came up to me. Five pounds.

Emily How do you know it's –?

Kathy Let's try it. Emily?

Emily Not tonight. My throat feels –

Kathy We won't even bother asking Dan. We know what he'd say.

Dan What would I say?

Over this, voices off as some of the boys are entering.

Henry Who the fuck does he think he is?

Henry, James and Bill enter, angry. Becca follows.

(*turns to Dan*) Your father, Dan, what is wrong with him?

Dan I don't know. I really don't know.

Kathy What did he –?

Henry He's screaming at us. What were we going to do? Ha has no idea what we were going to do. We hadn't done anything yet. He's guessing. He's an idiot.

Dan I know. I know.

James He threatened to call our parents. (*Sees the plastic bag.*) What's that?

Libby (*hiding it and flirting*) It's not for you. There's not enough. (*to Kathy*) We were on our way upstairs, weren't we? Becca?

Becca I'm coming.

Kathy (*to Henry*) I hear you thought someone looked like me?

Henry Who told you that? Yeah.

Kathy One of the actresses. She looked like –?

Henry Yeah. (*to others*) What was that play about anyway? I didn't get it.

Kathy Why did she look like me?

He shrugs.

Because she was ugly like me?

She smiles, can't resist a tickle and runs off up the stairs. Becca and Libby hurry after. Henry turns to James and hits him hard with his fist on the shoulder. James hits him back.

Henry (*to Dan*) Your dad's a moron.

Dan I know that. I do. He's an incredible moron.

James You know it's probably birdseed she bought. She thinks it's – But it's birdseed.

Bill Or oregano.

Richard and Jane enter.

(*to James*) Give me one of your cigarettes.

Richard (*over this*) What's got up Mr Williams's ass?

Jane He was out there shouting at us –

James (*at the same time*) He was screaming at us.

Richard (*at the same time*) We didn't do anything. Jane and I took a walk around the square. 'Where have you been? What have you been doing?' What has gotten into him?

They are all headed toward the stairs.

Henry What did *I* do? I watched every goddamn stupid play. I haven't complained much. Lay off me, man!

They are gone. Emily and Dan are alone.

Dan He gets this way sometimes. My father. What time is it where we come from?

Emily It's still the middle of the afternoon.

Dan So my mom's not home from work yet. So it couldn't be her. Sometimes when he talks to her . . .

Emily takes a sip of her Lemsip.

Emily This stuff really works. We should take some home.

Dan Yeah.

Emily Want a sip?

He starts to take one, then stops.

Dan Aren't you . . . (*sick*)

Emily Right. That was close.

Music is turned on upstairs.

They found a station that isn't just talk.

Emily (*fiddling with the programme*) So how was this
   play? (*Reads the title.*) *Misalliance.*

Dan It was okay.

Emily What does the title . . .

Dan I don't know. A plane flies into this house.

Emily They showed that?

Dan Yeah. It flew into a big picture window.

Emily Wow.

Dan Yeah.

He looks at the programme with her, then:

It didn't work tonight. It broke.

Emily What do you mean, it –?

Dan It started to fly into the – But it got stuck on
   something. Just sort of . . . They had to stop the show.
   When they started up again, the actors said some of the
   lines they'd already said – so they went back a little –
   it was weird. I don't know why they did that. But you
   could tell that it would have been neat. The plane.

Emily Yeah.

Dan My father loved it. The Royal Shakespeare Company.
   He loves all that stuff.

Emily He has to. He's a teacher.

Dan Right.

They look at the programme.

Emily Did you walk there or take the tube?

Dan We took the tube.

Emily I'm sorry I missed that. I love the tube.

Dan But the theatre's in a real strange place. Really –
   ugly. You think of England and you think – But this
   was – ugly. And confusing. The Barbican. It means
   something. I don't know what. And I don't care.
   (*Laughs to himself.*) We got lost like three times. Twice

getting there. And again coming home. Even my father. And he's been here . . .

Emily Did you walk behind him and make those faces? (*She mimics him making faces.*)

Dan I don't always do that.

Emily (*over the end of this*) You know that won't make them like you any more.

Dan That's not why I –

Emily And who cares what they think?

Dan That's not why I do that. And anyway, they like me. It's my dad they don't like.

Emily True.

Cat enters talking, wiping her hands on her apron. She has been doing the dishes.
 Lights begin to fade.

Cat And how is the patient –?

Emily It's already working, I think, Cat. My throat feels better. (*to Dan.*) It has something like aspirin in it too.

Cat (*to Dan*) It's what I always take.

Dan We should bring some home.

The music upstairs is suddenly louder. Dan starts to stand.

I can tell them to be quiet.

Cat It's fine. It's your last night. And you're the only guests. And – my parents aren't here. (*She smiles.*)

Dan Right.

Cat I'll go and make sure they're using the ashtrays.

Dan That's a good idea.

Emily I love your accent. It's so sweet.

Cat smiles and heads upstairs.

Emily (*to Dan*) Don't you love her accent? She sounds so smart.

Lights are out. Young Man turns to the audience.

575

Young Man The music got louder. They danced. Henry brought out the bottle of vodka he had hidden in his bag. The oregano or birdseed wasn't oregano or birdseed after all. Cat supplied potato chips, sold them beer and danced. And so at least an hour passed before Emily's room-mate suddenly appeared, her face red, her hands shaking, tears cascading down her cheeks.

Where I Come From. Scene Two:. 'Emma Upset.'

SCENE TWO

Emma (seventeen) stands before Emily and Dan; she is sobbing and trying to talk.

Emma I don't know what to do. I don't want . . . Oh God . . .

Emily (*taking her hands*) Emma, please. I can't answer. Tell us.

Dan Tell us, Emma. What happened.

She breaks down sobbing.

Emily Let's wash your face. (*to Dan*) I'll take her to the bathroom. (*helping her off*) Come on. You can tell us later. Let's get some cold water on that face . . .

They are gone. Dan turns and sees Richard and Jane, holding hands, having watched this.

Jane We heard . . . What's . . . ?

Dan shrugs. Lights fade.

Young Man Some time passed. News spread upstairs. Then finally the girls returned from the bathroom . . .

Lights up. Richard and Jane have been joined by Bęcca and James. Music continues loud off as the dancing continues. Emily tries to comfort Emma.

Jane I don't understand. Who's she talking about?
Richard (*to Jane*) Mr Alexander.
Jane Mr Alexander.
Young Man (*to us*) Mr Alexander was one of the teachers along on this trip.
Emma (*trying not to cry*) He . . . (*to Emily*) I told you –
Emily (*over this*) You don't have to –
Dan Maybe we should leave her alone.
Emily (*over this*) I'll tell them. (*to the others*) Mr Alexander and Emma, they were walking to the theatre – they were lost. Just the two of them?

Emma nods.

And they're crossing a little bridge and he puts his arm around her. And hugs her. Then asks for a bigger hug. And he holds her against him. Puts his face against her neck. She tried to push him . . . Right?
Emma I did.
Emily And he put his hand –? He tried to touch your breasts?
Emma (*shrugs*) I think so. It happened so . . . (*to the others*) But I pushed him away! And then he said: don't tell anyone about this. Forget it.
Emily And he walked off. They were lost and he walked off.
Jane I don't believe this. I like Mr Alexander.
Young Man (*to us*) He taught American History. He was nearly fifty. Two grown children. A wife.

Kathy, Libby and Henry enter.

Kathy What's –?
Richard Sh-sh. We'll tell you. (*to Dan*) She should talk to your father, Dan.
Dan I'll take her. He'll know what to –
Emily She's been to him.
Dan What??

Kathy (*whispers to Jane*) What's going –?

Jane whispers to Kathy as:

Emily That's where she's been. She went to Mr Williams right away. Like she thought she was supposed to do. This was during the play?

Emma At the intermission.

Emily I think that's why he's been so – angry tonight –

Richard Why be angry at us?

Emily I don't know. Anyway, you told him. He said not to tell anyone yet, right? To come to see him after, and you went.

Emma nods.

Kathy (*hearing what Jane has been whispering*) Oh my God. Shit.

Emily (*continuing*) And he tells her, 'Are you sure about this? Maybe there's been a misunderstanding. Maybe Mr Alexander was worried that you were cold, Emma. It's a cold night out.'

She looks at Dan, who shakes his head, he cannot believe this.

Then she says, she's sure, right?

Emma sniffles. Someone hands her a tissue from Emily's box. Richard hands her his beer.

Then he just stares at her and finally says:

Emma (*quietly*) 'Do you know how hard this is for me? Jack Alexander is a friend. Do you know what this could do to this man? You want to destroy his career?'

Kathy (*disgusted*) Oh my God.

Emma (*after a sip of beer*) 'Destroy – his family? His life?' And that's when I started crying and I couldn't stop. And he started yelling at me: 'Jack says you said you were cold, Emma!' 'You told him,' I said. 'I had to. What did you think?'

Emily And then he called Mr Alexander into the room with them. He was waiting right outside.

Dan suddenly walks away from everyone.

Libby It's not your fault, Dan. It isn't.

Bill is entering, followed by Cat. Kathy grabs them and whispers as:

Emily So Mr Williams says to Emma –

Emma 'Accuse him, Emma. There he is, accuse him to his face.' I look up and you can tell he's really angry at me. Then he says in a very dead voice, 'Emma you missed the first act of the play tonight. You knew you were going to be punished. To say things like this, that's not going to help you. It's wrong.' (*Pause.*) Then Mr Williams said, 'If you can't accuse him to his face, then I think you should get out of here.' So I started to leave, and he grabs my wrist and holds it and says, 'We all make mistakes. Let's forget this whole thing, okay? Let's even forget you were late for the play, okay?' And then I saw Mr Alexander wink at him and he let go and I went out into the hall. They closed the door and I could hear Mr Alexander say things about me. About what he says he's heard about me . . . The kind of person . . . (*She starts to sob.*) I don't know what to do . . . I don't know what . . .

Emily tries to hug her, she moves away. Looks at Dan, slowly goes to him, hits him on the shoulder and shouts:

Emma I hate your father! I hate him!

Others grab her and hold her.
  Lights fade out.

Young Man (*to us*) No one turned the music off upstairs. They let it play. At first no one knew what to say, then more beers were found, more potato chips. And they grouped themselves in front of the comforting warmth of the small gas fire and listened to each other talk. *Where I Come From*. Scene Three: 'Group Portrait.'

SCENE THREE

Music from upstairs. Everyone sits on the couch, chairs or floor in front of the gas fire (unseen). And they talk. Every now and then someone gets up to get another beer or go to the bathroom. One or two smoke, etc.

Libby Cat, I can't believe your parents just . . .

Cat Nothing's going to happen. No one's going to – hurt anything.

Libby I wasn't saying . . . (*She shrugs.*) They trust you.

Cat nods. Others nod at this thought. Libby sips her beer.

I don't think I'm ready to go home yet. (*Smiles to herself.*) Everyone's going to sleep on the plane. Coming over here, no one slept. That first day – like everything in slow motion. The whole day. (*another sip*) I miss my dog. I think that's all I miss. Becca here missed everything.

Becca That's not true. Stop that. Shut up.

Libby You cried –

Becca I said shut up.

Kathy She hugged her little stuffed rabbit –

Becca Go to hell.

Jane It's alright. What's the weather like at home. Snowing?

Libby No.

Becca She talks to her mother every day,

Jane So what? Leave her alone.

Emily I talk to my stepmother too. I've never been away from home before too.

Libby How did she know that I have never been –?

Emily It's okay.

Short pause. Music is heard.

Dan Anyone going to turn that (*the music*) off?

Emily It's a funny feeling, though, being so far away – thousands of miles away. You can't like just run home. (*She looks at Emma who is next to her, and strokes her arm.*) I think my dad was more worried that I was.

Kathy My dad was worried too. He kept giving me more money on the way to the airport. Sometimes I think he's the handsomest man in the world. And sometimes I think he's a pathetic jerk.

Other girls nod at this: their feeling about their fathers too.

Weird. He took me to look at his old college? Maybe for me to go there? (*Shakes her head, amazed: she'd never go there.*) He was like all nervous. We're walking outside – *outside* – and he's whispering. And I say, 'Dad, why are you whispering for God's sake?' I'll never go to his college. I'd never hear the end of it. Like I'm supposed to be him? He wanted to show me all the places – where he – whatever . . . (*Plays with the potato chips.*) I tried to explain to my mother but she can't hear it. She just defends him, so . . . (*Shrugs.*) Not defends, she wouldn't think that way – 'explains', as if you're two years old?

Libby I know what you –

Kathy He'll be five hours early at the airport. Sometimes he sits in the car, waiting for me to go somewhere, anywhere, and I purposely take longer, just to let him sit. He's not going to tell me what to do.

Becca No.

Jane My dad's always late. I don't think he listens. Mom
always has to tell him three times – anything. I don't
know where his mind is. You can snap your fingers in
his face and still . . .

James Thank God we have cars.

Jane What?

Kathy Why?

James (*on the spot*) So – we don't have to wait for our –
parents?

Kathy Jane doesn't have a car. Neither does –

James I know. I know. I meant – me.

Emma My mother says Kathy's dad's pretty cool. She
does.

Kathy Sometimes he is.

Emily (*over this*) What, she hitting on your dad?

Laughter.

Emma I don't think my mom is hitting on any guy.

Emily Right. Sorry. I –

Emma Don't be sorry. She just thinks he's cool. Thinks
he's funny.

Pause. They sip their beers, etc.

Libby My mother said – you may never get to Europe
again. So make the most of it, dear. Why did she have
to say that? Why does she say things like that? She's
never been to Europe. She loves to put pressure on –

James And they turn it around so it's about them.

Agreement.

Their thing or success or problem. Or how they will be
'seen'. They always do that.

Henry Ever catch your parents having sex? What about
you, Dan?

Emily Leave him alone –

Jane I have.
Bill I don't think Dan's father has sex –
Henry He must have had once –
Bill Maybe.

They laugh and are ignored by the others.

Jane (*continuing*) I caught mine once. I don't know what my dad was doing home. It was afternoon. We only had a half-day of school, so I . . . I was already home, in my room, when I heard them come in . . . I was about to say something when . . . you know, they went at it. Big time.
Richard In the bedroom?
Jane In the rec room. On the couch. From my room I could see them downstairs. It's not something a kid should see.

Others agree: 'No.'

Becca When I was maybe eight or nine. We were in a motel room. On some stupid trip. God knows where. I remember my father always wanting to show me a map and tell me this is where – we are or have been or something
Emily I know, I hate that.
Becca Anyway, some stupid 'family trip'.
Bill Those are the worst. I run like hell when I hear 'family trip' –
Becca (*continuing*) I have a bed and they have a bed. Actually my mom slept with me, cause I couldn't sleep – but then I realised later –
Jane To *get* you asleep.
Becca Right. So she must think I'm out and she slowly gets out of my bed, but I'm lying on my side, so I can see, Dad's looking at her, and from under the cover he is pulling off his pyjama bottoms, Mom's taking off her nightgown over her head, and I'm watching through a

583

slit in my eyes, then I can't move or anything or they'd notice, so . . . (*Sips her beer.*)
Yuch.

Richard They should have got another room.

Libby Yeah.

James That doesn't work, either. I was with my brothers and we were visiting my uncle in New York City. So we got two hotel rooms, one for my parents and the other for – us. To do what *we* want in. Jump on the beds, watch TV all night. I don't know what they thought, but you could hear everything through the wall.

He makes the sound of a bed banging against the wall. Then makes orgasm sounds that are gross.

Kathy Stop it!

James (*continuing*) I thought my brothers would pee in their pants. They didn't know what was going on. I told them Mom must have got a splinter and Dad was helping get it out. Parents are clueless. I thought they were supposed to protect us from . . .? I don't know. But Jesus Christ – (*Starts the sounds again.*)

Becca We said stop that!

Libby I caught my father once come home so completely drunk. He couldn't talk. Just looked away from me. Looked like he was angry at me.

Cat I've seen my father drunk many many times.

They glance at Cat, who has joined in for the first time, then back at each other.

Bill And when you catch *them* in a lie, they hate that, don't they? It's like it's your fault, that you should –

Emily My step-mom's pretty neat, I think. She should have been my mom. I don't know what she sees in my dad.

Bill She is neat.

Jane He thinks so because she wears jeans so tight you can see the crack in her pussy.

Bill That is one reason.

Laughter.

Emily I'm trying to get her to spend more time with me. I think she feels she doesn't want to – get in between or something. I don't understand.

Kathy I've never even seen my parents kiss.

This stops everyone.

Jane What?

Kathy On the lips. I haven't. Maybe they do. Maybe they don't.

Bill Maybe she just likes to suck him off.

Jane Shut up.

Libby My mother said to me – dear, you may never get this chance to go to Europe again, so –

Emma You already told us that.

Emily Talking about tongue-kissing –

Richard Who was talking about –?

Emily Anyone else have an Uncle who –?

Jane Tongue-kisses??

Emily Almost. It's what he wants to do. You feel that.

Libby How do you feel that?

Emily He'd wet his lips just before – And I think he wants me to see him wetting his lips . . . Then the look in his eyes as he kisses . . .

Jane I had an 'uncle' in quotes – a friend of my mom's. I think she'd dated him in college. I was maybe like twelve, just starting to get breasts –

Becca I'm still waiting for mine!

Laughter.

Jane And we're in the swimming pool, he like suddenly swims under me, then he pops up out of the water, and he like pressed against me and the side of the pool. He looked down and so I looked and you could tell he had this big hard-on in his trunks.

Kathy You were twelve and you knew what a 'hard-on' was –?

Jane I have an older sister.

Kathy Did you tell your mother?

Jane Tell her what? He didn't *do* anything. It was only a couple of years later that I realised . . . that he was seeing what I 'knew', where I – 'was'.

Becca Sometimes you think it's just you.

Emma I know. I know.

Others realise the more immediate meaning of Emma's agreement, but continue:

Henry I wanted to learn to swim. And there was a Y, but my father wouldn't take me, my mother told me it was because he didn't like taking his clothes off in front of men. For some reason I remember she found that really funny. Why?

Others shrug.

Bill I don't know.

Henry So she took me. Sent me into the dressing room by myself. I don't know. I don't remember any one thing that happened. But I never wanted to go back there.

Libby I think by law mothers should be made to wear only *one*-piece bathing suits.

Girls I agree!

Bill Not stepmothers!

Libby Not stepmothers. I went shopping once with my mother to buy me a new bathing suit –

Becca That – I would never do. I'd rather pull out my eyes –

Libby (*over this*) And she started trying on all these –
I said to her, you're not a kid, Mom. And that made
it worse.

Becca It would. Why didn't you know that?

Libby So she bought this bikini. (*She shakes her head.
Takes a big sip from her beer.*) She didn't even know
about shaving her hair . . .

Emily She must have known –

Libby If she did, she hadn't done it. Christ. I thought
I was going to throw up. I couldn't look at her. And
she was so happy with herself. Kept smiling at me.
Grinning.

Emily My mother once took me swimming in the reservoir.
She said she wanted a kind of 'mother–daughter'
memory.

Jane Uh-oh. That usually means trouble.

Becca True.

Emily So we're swimming in this sort of lake, we get out
to the middle and a little floating – dock, you know,
with a diving board on it, we're hanging on to it, and
she says – the sun's in my eyes now, so I can hardly see
her face – she has planned this. So she says – she hates
– my father. The things he's done to her, she won't go
into, because she knows I'll still have to see him, if I
wish. If I'm stupid enough is the implication. If I can
stomach it, which – she can't any more. But she
understands he's my – but he's fucking anything that
walks. Her words. So how much time will he really
have for me? So – she's leaving him. Actually he was
leaving her, but I only learn this later. Leaving him.
Now I'm in the middle of a lake. This is all a plan, so
I can't just walk away and slam my door. I hated her
for that. For doing that to me. From taking that away –
of just slamming my goddamn door. I didn't care that
she was crying. I just started swimming back. So we
drove home and I said shit to her. That's why I think

I stayed with my father for the first six months or so. Even though I hated that, I knew he didn't want me, he made that clear, but I wanted to punish my mother for telling me like that.

Pause.

Emma I got one of those.
Bill So do I –
Becca Let Emma . . .

Short pause, Emma takes her time to get settled, then:

Emma When Mom told me she and Dad – My dad wouldn't tell me anything. He just looked at me and shook his head. What does that mean? What did I do?
Bill I know I –
Emma So then she says – remember Barbara? And there's – Barbara, this woman who was part of our book club that Mom made us go to – so we could be – I don't know. She had something in mind. God, did I hate it. Barbara. She's a lawyer in town. She's going to be staying with us, Mom says. What does that mean? I don't say this, but . . .
Emily Sure.
Emma Yeah. Where's she going to sleep, Mom? There's only my room. This makes her laugh and she and Barbara now too I see in my bedroom doorway, and she is laughing and nodding and giving me a real 'sweet' look. Fuck her. Barbara, Mom says, will sleep on the pullout couch. But then – she didn't. They made up the couch for her that one night and no one slept on it. She and Mom . . . (*Sips her beer.*) Why do we have to guess at everything?

Pause. Music plays upstairs. Someone goes to get a few more beers. Then:

Barbara's okay. She's done nothing to me.

Becca Why can't they just talk to us?

Bill Right.

Kathy I don't want to talk to my parents.

Cat Me neither.

Richard Shit, no.

Bill When Dad got married the third time – they say the third wife and the first usually hit it off? I read that in a book. That didn't happen. I was trying to figure out what was going to happen. Anyway – every time they argue I now think – that's it. That's over. So I try to get it into my head, into my skin. So there'll be no – shock? Then in the morning – after the fight? – it's like nothing has happened? Well, something has happened to me. I just want to know – what I can feel.

Pause. New beers are brought. Music plays upstairs.

Henry We left the music –

Jane We'll go back.

Richard No one's going to sleep tonight.

Henry I don't think so.

Pause.

Kathy What time is it in Ardmore?

Henry Ten.

Pause.

Kathy I wonder if they're talking about us. Our parents.

Henry Some are and some aren't.

Becca I like my parents.

Bill Good for you. You're lucky.

Kathy I like her parents too. They're neat.

Bill Is everyone packed?

Jane Maybe we should dance?

Becca I'd like to be like my mom.

Libby I miss my parents too. I'm looking forward to going home. I hate being so far away.

589

There is a shift in tone, the conversation gets suddenly more lively.

Kathy I bought my dad a tie. It's the only thing I ever buy him. I think I looked for about two hours in that little tie store. I got one with the Queen. He likes ties.

Jane I got my parents these cute coasters from the Tate? Did you see them?

Others have.

Henry Who was the artist? I keep –

Emily Blake.

Jane I think they'll really like them. They always like what I give them.

James My parents too. They like whatever –

Jane I always used to make things –

Becca Me too.

Kathy Art stuff from school.

Richard Yeah.

Jane They keep everything, I think. Somewhere.

Short pause.

Richard I remember the first time I was away from my parents. I had like a babysitter or a friend of theirs or something. And they were going out – for dinner? Maybe they just told me this, but supposedly they say I could throw up whenever I . . . I could cry, make my face turn red and then throw up. So the last thing they'd see as they were closing the front door was me puking. That got them. That really got them.

Jane When was this – last summer?

Richard When I was like three or something. Shut up.

Kathy My dad cried at the airport.

Libby I cried at the airport.

Jane So did I.

Kathy It seems so far away.

Emily And everything here, it's so different. It is, Cat.
It really is.

Jane She'll have to come and visit –

Cat No, I don't think –

Becca You will. You have to.

Emily It's different, but then it's sort of similar, and that's
really confusing.

Emma I know what you mean.

Bill (*over this*) I remember playing cards with my dad
every night. Or some game. Then I beat him at chess
and he got really pissed at me. (*Laughs at this memory.*)

Jane I want my mother's chin. I love her chin. She's got a
little dimple . . .

Kathy What did you get your parents?

The lights start to fade as they all begin to talk at once:

Henry I got postcards from that portrait museum. My
dad likes real pictures – pictures of real things.

Becca (*over this*) A scarf for my mom, and for my dad
one of those magnets of the Tower Bridge –

Libby I got a little notebook with Princess Di on the –

Richard My mother wanted some biscuits, she said I can
get them at the airport –?

And the lights are out.

SCENE FOUR

Young Man (*to us*) After a while, they grew tired of
talking and, leaving Emma, Emily and Dan, once again
alone, they went upstairs – to dance.

*Upstairs: music and dancing is heard, kids shouting
with the music as they dance, etc.*
   *Emma, Emily and Dan sit. They eat chips, drink
both beer and vodka. All three are a bit drunk.*

Emma I've waited too long to call my mother. I'll have to wait until I get home to tell her . . .

Emily About Mr –?

Emma nods. Short pause.

Dan (*finally*) Maybe that's best.

Emily Why?

Dan What can her mother do now? It's – (*Looks at his watch and shows Emily.*) Wake up my father and scream at him? What's that going to achieve?

Short pause.

Emily I don't think that's the point – to achieve something. I think it'd be nice to know someone is fighting for you. So you're not alone.

Dan shrugs.

Dan I don't know. It's . . . (*Shows her his watch again. Turns to Emma.*) Do you feel alone?

She nods.

Emily See?

He takes a sip of his vodka. Music is suddenly loud upstairs.

Young Man (*to us*) *Where I Come From*. Scene Four: 'Sex.'

Emily suddenly stands.

Emily I've a couple of pictures I still have to take. What about one of Emma and me?

Emma No! Not like this, I must look –

Emily You look fine. Doesn't she?

Dan Sure –

Emily I'm the one who's sick.

Dan You seem a lot better, do you –?

Emily I'm fine. Take the two of us. Come on.

Dan takes the camera. Emily and Emma sit together on the couch.

Dan Sit still. A little closer. One. Two. Three.

Flash. Emma jumps up.

Emma One of the two of you. You're best friends.
Dan I don't need . . .
Emily You don't need what?
Dan Do *you* want –?
Emma Come on. Get closer. Put your arm around her, Dan. That's better. Emily, sit like that girl in the play.
Dan The one that Henry liked?
Emily I didn't see the play, remember. I'm –
Emma Put your legs – Dan, put her legs –

Dan takes Emily's legs and puts them across his legs.

Emma (*going up to Emily*) And pull up your skirt.
Emily Emma!

Dan playfully tickles her knee.

Emily Stop that! I'm sick.
Emma Shut up. One. Two. A little closer, Dan.

Suddenly Dan puts his face real close to Emily's and Emma takes the photo.

Three!

Flash.

Emily (*to Dan, moving her legs*) What are you doing?
Dan (*to Emma*) How many are left?
Emma One more. (*to Emily*) One more?
Dan Of me and Emma. Come on.

He takes Emma by the hand. She almost falls over.

Emma I tripped. Where should –?
Emily On the couch. Come on. And get real close.
Emma Like this?

She puts her arms around Dan and gives him a big kiss on the cheek.

Dan Emma –
Emily Do it again. Let me get that.

Emma aggressively takes his head and kisses him on the mouth.

Emily One. Two.

He pushes Emma off, she immediately goes for his ear with her mouth to kiss that. On the count of –

Three!

– flash. Emma starts to retch: she is going to be sick to her stomach.

Dan Shit!
Emma (*holding her mouth*) I'm going to be sick.
Emily Get to the bathroom. Come on, get up –

Emma starts to get up, she holds her stomach, and begins to dry-heave.

You'll be fine. Come on. I'll take you to the bathroom.

Emma and Emily are gone. Music is heard. Dan stands, not knowing what to do. After a few moments, Emily returns.

She made it.
Dan Shouldn't you –?
Emily No one wants company when . . .
Dan She drank too much.
Emily Yeah.

Short pause.

She won't be the only one. On the flight home, a lot of
people are . . . Listen.

The dancing upstairs. She rubs her face.

I should go to bed.
Dan Me too.
Emily We shouldn't leave her . . .
Dan No. You go and I'll –
Emily No. No. She's . . . She got it on her blouse. She
took off her blouse. I should stay.

Short pause.

I don't blame her one bit. Getting drunk.
Dan Me neither. (*He smiles.*)
Emily What are you smiling about?
Dan She had her tongue in my ear?
Emily What??
Dan She stuck her tongue in my ear. Just now. Then she
started . . . heaving. (*Laughs a little.*) Ever had a tongue
in your ear? It's weird.
Emily No. I haven't. (*Looks at him and smiles.*) She must
like you.
Dan I don't think –
Emily (*teasing*) I think she does.
Dan Come on. Leave her alone, she's gone through
enough today.
Emily You brought up the tongue – (*She straightens her
skirt.*) I have hips like a boy's.
Dan What are you talking about?
Emily I was just looking at my hips.
Dan You're thin. That's good, isn't it? Isn't that what
you want to be?
Emily I don't know.
Dan I like your hips.

Emily Forget it! I was talking to myself. I'm sorry I – (*new thought*) I should call my step-mom and tell her what time the flight gets in.

Dan Doesn't she know that? It was on the sheet the parents –

Emily I can tell her I forgot.

Dan It's really late. You could scare her. I know if I called my mom –

Emily I'll say I got the time wrong . . .

Dan looks at her and shrugs.

Do your parents know when you're lying? I can't tell about mine. Sometimes they seem to know everything. Then . . . I can tell them the biggest lie – They just accept. I don't get it.

Dan Maybe they just don't want to catch you. Sometimes I think they're more worried about catching you than what you're lying about.

Emily I don't understand.

Dan They don't want to know. Sometimes. They really don't. Least that's what I think. In my house we're never saying what we really are – thinking.

Emily I guess that's true with me too. (*Smiles at him.*) You know, it can't be easy for you – being the teacher's kid. Everyone watching . . . You handle it okay. You do.

Dan Thanks.

Emily I should check on . . . I'll be right back. (*She goes and returns in a moment.*) She's asleep. On the floor in there. Poor girl. I can't leave her, but I don't want to move her upstairs . . .

Dan You're right. You'll sleep on the plane.

Emily Yeah.

Pause.

Dan What are you thinking?

Emily I hate that question. My dad always asks me that. What are you supposed to say?

Dan I'm sorry.

Emily Why are you apologising?! Christ. (*She looks at him, then:*) Never mind. It was just that you suddenly reminded me of my father. Forget it. It's in my head. It's my problem. Put your arm around me.

He does.

And don't say anything.

Pause. Dan obviously wants to talk but feels like he shouldn't until:

Hand me some potato chips.

He does. One drops on her lap. He wipes it off, he allows his hand to linger, then removes it. She takes it and holds it.

Dan (*to say something*) Becca lost her passport today.

Emily Did she?

Young Man (*to us*) It would take another hour, but Dan would kiss Emily – on the lips. And she would immediately kiss him back.

Dan Yeah. It became this real big deal. My father went berserk. He went to the Embassy with her. He missed half the show. That's how Mr Alexander ended up – He wasn't with my father.

Emily So what happened with the passport? Did she get another one?

Young Man (*to us*) They danced here in the sitting room. They turned off the lamps. He slid his hand under her blouse and touched her. She pressed herself against him, and felt him.

Dan She found it in her raincoat. There's an inner pocket in her raincoat. She was wearing it. At the Embassy.

She just pulls it out, I'm told. I don't think she's going to get a very good grade for this course.

They laugh.

Young Man (*to us*) He unbuttoned two buttons of her blouse. She did the rest. She undid his belt and with her thumb and forefinger she pulled down the zipper of his pants.

Dan Becca tried to cry when she saw how angry Dad was. But Dad just walked away from her? And she stopped – like that. Amazing.

Emily That's Becca. I've seen her pull that with her parents.

He looks at her.

What?

Dan I've been wondering – if you brought a stuffed animal too, with you like Becca and her –

Emily Rabbit? (*pretending to be 'tough'*) And what if I did, buster? (*She touches his chest with her fingers.*) His name is Anthony. (*almost in baby-talk*) And he protects me. He's a koala bear. And I love him.

Young Man (*to us*) Once in the night, as she sat on him with him inside, they heard a noise. Someone coming through. It was Emma, sniffling as she shuffled up to bed. To keep him from speaking, Emily covered Dan's lips with her own.

Emily And the man I marry, he's going to have to just face it that Anthony's coming with me and he's sleeping in our bed.

Dan nods 'seriously', then:

Dan Exactly how big is he?

He smiles, she laughs and 'hits' him playfully.
Lights fade.

SCENE FIVE

Young Man (*to us*) Morning. *Where I Come From*. Scene
Five: 'Heading Home.'

*Morning light. The room is empty. No music plays off.
Then the students begin entering with their suitcases.
They are all tired, sleepy, even hung-over.*
Becca, Kathy, Libby enter with Cat.

Becca (*entering, to Cat*) You'll love it there. And we have
the room. My parents love guests. Especially when
they're from some place – exotic.
Cat I wouldn't call England –
Becca My parents would. I'll show you all the neat
places to hang out. Philadelphia isn't as bad as it first
seems.

Kathy makes a face.Becca pushes her.

Come on. If you know where to go. If you go to –
All Three Girls South Street.
Cat I'll ask my parents, but I'm not sure they'll –

*As they start to exit, Richard enters from the same
direction:*

Richard Mr Williams says to wait in here. Until the cabs
come. It's raining.
Libby What a surprise.
Becca (*continuing the conversation with Cat*) Tell them
it'll be educational. That always gets them.

Jane enters without a suitcase.

Jane (*to Richard*) What did you do with my bags?
Richard They're on the stoop.

She starts to go.

We're supposed to wait in here.

Jane, obviously exhausted, nods, and leans against a chair or couch.

Becca (*to Jane*) Cat's coming to visit. She's going to stay with me.
Cat I have to ask –
Jane Great. We can show her what a 'shower' is.

Laughs to herself at her 'joke'.

Cat What do you mean?
Kathy Ignore her. She's stupid.

Henry, James, Bill and Dan enter with their bags.

Jane (*making fun of the 'news'*) Cat's coming to America!
Bill Why?
James Now?
Cat No, maybe in the summer when school's out –
Libby You know how much vacation they get here? Like a week and a half.
Cat It's a little more than –
Jane We'll teach her about water pressure and vacations and –
Henry And hamburgers.
Cat We have –
Henry No you don't. You don't know. Trust me.

Richard takes a few of the girls' bags off.

Emily (*hurries in*) Has anyone seen my green scarf? I can't find it anywhere upstairs.
Bill (*obviously not listening*) What colour is it?

She looks at him.

Emily Green.
Bill No.

Emily What colour scarf have you seen?
Bill I haven't seen any scarf. What are you talking about?

She starts back upstairs.

Dan You want some help?

They share a look, then she shakes her head and goes, bumping into Emma.

Emma Is everyone as – as tired as I am?

Almost everyone groans in agreement.

Henry We're supposed to wait in –
Emma I don't care. Sh – sh. (*She drops her bags down and breathes deeply. Pause.*) What are we doing?
Libby (*shrugs*) Waiting.
Kathy (*quietly*) Goodbye little B. & B.! You are so – authentic!
Dan Shouldn't we pay Cat for some of the beer and food last night –?
Henry I thought we did –
Dan Not for everything.
Cat (*over this*) It's alright. It's fine. That's okay, I –
Henry Give me your change, Bill. What do you have left?

They start giving Cat their change.

Libby We don't pay for the taxi – or do we?
Dan It's part of the whole deal.
James Here's – fifty pence. That's fifty, right?
Bill I've got a – two. This big one.
Dan (*reading it*) It's two pence.
Bill Is that okay?

As Cat reluctantly collects their change:

Becca Goodbye, England. Goodbye, Cartwright Gardens. Goodbye –
Libby All those plays. Whatever they were called.

Becca (*to Emma*) Cat's going to visit.

Emma Good. Don't stay with her (*Becca*). You'll never see anything. Stay with us. We've got a pullout couch that no one uses.

Pause. Everyone waits.

Young Man (*to us*) And so – they went home. Where Jane and –

Richard comes in and grabs a few more bags and goes.

– Richard will soon split up. That will be big news. And Emma – she will never tell her mother what had happened with her and the teacher. There will never seem to be the right moment, until too much time will pass and she'll know that she'd have to explain that as well. Mr Alexander in school will treat her as he always had treated her – as if nothing had happened. She will cry herself to sleep many a night.

Kathy's father will be waiting at the airport when they arrive. He'll have been there about three hours early.

Jane's dad will be late. Mr Williams will be forced to wait with her until he shows up.

Richard hurries in.

Richard The taxis are here. Let's go.

Everyone (*to Cat*) Goodbye, goodbye.

Cat (*helping with the luggage*) We'll say our goodbyes outside.

As they all go:

Dan I'll wait for Emily. She'll be right down.

All go except for Dan.

Young Man (*to us*) And Dan and Emily? They will soon learn that they conceived a baby that night. In this room. On that couch – or one very much like it.

Emily enters holding up her scarf.

Emily It *was* under the bed. I'd looked three times. I would have been so upset if I . . .

She and Dan smile at each other. An awkward moment as he hesitantly kisses her on the cheek. She starts to put on her scarf as:

Young Man (*to us*) They will return to a storm of outrage by their parents. There will be a desperate attempt at self-abortion. There will be tears and screams and accusations made. And there will be cries and the almost continuous whispers of adults throughout the long and lonely nights.
Then nine months later a boy will be born. And they will name me Michael.

Emily (*as they go off*) We're coming. (*with a glance back*) Goodbye . . .

They are gone. The Young Man goes and sits on the couch.

End.

Portrait of a Rich and Complex World

Richard Nelson interviewed by Jim Mulligan

Richard Nelson started writing plays when he was fifteen years old, continued in college, and has been writing plays ever since. He has also worked in theatres as a dramaturg, director and associate director.

In 1988 Richard was commissioned by the Royal Shakespeare Company to write *Some Americans Abroad*, a play about a group of American college professors who are taking a group of students on a cultural tour to London and Stratford. *Where I Come From* is a companion piece.

> *Some Americans Abroad* was a story about adults. When I was asked to write a play for *Connections*, I thought a good way in would be to go back to that story, this time from the point of view of high-school students. This enabled me to write about a group of young people and the individuals within the group. My last three plays were about adolescents and because I was directing them I was talking to and observing a lot of young people. I felt I was prepared to write about adolescence one more time.

A good deal of Richard Nelson's work is about people who are out of time, out of place or in the wrong place. They have a sense of homelessness – not street homelessness but a general, larger sense of being cut off. The young people in *Where I Come From* are away from their families in a strange country and, on this particular night, away from adults. They are young, preparing to end an adventure and go back to family life with varying degrees of enthusiasm. In the course of a few hours they drink, take drugs, eddy around relationships and, above all, they talk.

When I started to write about adolescents I realised it is a time of life when we are homeless, in a sense. We don't fit our bodies. Our bodies don't fit us. We change daily. We have feelings of confusion and of being out of place. I love these kids. They are complicated and rich and just as complex as I am or any other adult and I think young people are not always portrayed that way.

It may be tempting to see someone who says, 'Plays are only to see pretty girls,' as uncultured, but Richard Nelson insists that they should not be criticised. It is not their fault if they have not been prepared for a cultural event like going to see a play at a London theatre. He describes a situation and does not make judgements. Nor does he judge what they do on their last night in London.

The fact is that kids of sixteen or seventeen smoke, drink, take drugs, have sex. Anyone who denies that is living on the moon. Then the argument might be, 'Let's not tell the truth. This may be the way things are but I don't want to know about it.' There's nothing you can do with people like that. I'm painting a portrait of what I observe. I'm a descriptive writer. I'm not trying to tell anyone to do anything. I want to present a world that is rich and complex and complicated in a way that the audience can see it. I'll never achieve that goal but that's what I'm trying to do.

The dramatic event in this play on which so much hangs is the reported incident between Mr Alexander and Emma. We have no way of knowing if she is telling the truth, but if the allegations she makes are true then they should be investigated. According to her, Dan's father, the teacher in charge of the visit, connives with his colleague. This gives the actors and audience an interesting exercise in interpretation.

Dan's father did not handle the situation well. He panicked, tried to get through it. From what we know, both teachers behaved badly, Mr Alexander for what he did and Dan's father for trying to sweep it under the carpet. But who knows? Mr Alexander's wink could be conniving or it could be saying, 'You handled that well. Good for you.'

Usually with a cast of thirteen only two characters will be talking, the other eleven watching. In *Where I Come From* there is one scene, almost half the play in length, where twelve people are on stage or walking through, interacting, conversing, commenting and contributing to a sharing of ideas about how they all relate to their parents.

It was hard to write that scene. It's one that I'm proud of and, when I had conceptualised it, I really thought I knew how to write the play. Sex is a big part of adolescence, and it is going to be on their minds all the time. We have one kid who says, 'I've never seen my parents kiss,' others who have seen their parents make love and one whose mother is in a lesbian relationship. There is a sense of not knowing how to talk about it, and yet sex is a constant question. There is anger at one moment, and at the next they are talking about the presents they have bought their parents.

Adults tempted to criticise the attitudes and behaviour of the characters in the play would do well to look carefully at the title and at the date when the play is set. They would then see that they are looking at themselves as they were when they were young and as they are perceived by the narrator.

It's quite a moving moment when at the end of the play the narrator says, 'A boy will be born and they will name me Michael.' And he then goes and sits down on the couch where he was conceived. That will make people think. That will provoke discussion. After all, a play is a whole event that goes from beginning to end and I have tried to make it so that the end makes people look at all the events in a different way.

Production Notes

Half-comedy, half-drama, *Where I Come From* is a play about adolescents forced to be older than their years. There are thirteen characters, six boys and seven girls. All but one are American, from Ardmore, Pennsylvania. This is in suburban Philadelphia on the 'Main Line', a region of generally wealthy towns. Yet, important to this play, Ardmore is a socio-economically diverse community. There is a greater range in terms of class and income than in surrounding towns – not just white-collar 'city' types but also craftsmen and blue-collar workers. Accents need only be suggested and should not get in the way. More than being American, these are young people. Start with cultural similarities as opposed to differences.

The single setting is a bed-and-breakfast sitting room, which need only be minimally represented. The focus must remain clearly on the action.

The play's main title, *Where I Come From*, evokes its themes more aptly than *Scenes From Abroad*. There is no 'message'. The play is about complexity, ambiguity, a richness of texture and the complicated circumstances of these characters' lives. The central theme is homelessness as in 'rootlessness', examined through the prism of adolescence. These kids are thousands of miles from home. Whom can they trust? Who will protect them? How are the circumstances 'extraordinary'?

Richard Nelson has two daughters, one teenage and one in college. He's fascinated by their struggles and perseverance, their curiosity. Adolescence itself is a kind of rootlessness. He wants you to avoid the easiest pitfall: don't make the kids victims. These kids are heroic, and, despite some jokes and teasing, they are also remarkably acceptant of other people. There is a healthy refusal to be judgemental.

Play around with the sound upstairs as a persistent bass thump suggesting the action – placing speakers high above the stage would be a nice effect. It all takes place in 1987, and all music should be culled from that era – *Breakfast Club* is a film that might provide hints to the flavour of the era. *Lord of the Flies*, by William Golding, was an indirect influence – also depicting a world without adults, its status games, treacheries and fears. But Richard's favourite writer is Chekhov, and with this play as with any by Chekhov you are encouraged to look for the many layers of subtext and meaning behind and beneath the lines. Constantly ask yourself: what are these characters trying to do?

As a writer, Richard neither 'sees' nor 'hears' his plays. They grow from a feeling, a 'dynamic', so as a director he is always open to unusual casting ideas – characteristics like height, hair colour, etc., are of little importance. He encourages you to follow a similar course when casting: to look for that which might not be obvious.

THE CHARACTERS

MIKE There are many ways to explore the playing of Mike, but it would be best to keep him onstage and engaged both as a listener and participant in the story. Experiment with him watching the scenes in different ways – have him sit or straddle a chair turned round, for instance. The dramatic tension between Mike's direct address and the naturalism of everything else empowers the narrator, so avoid breaking the fourth wall when Mike's not involved. Mike talks about famous Americans, but he's being playful and just reading from a guidebook.

His own history is much more important to him. Mike's obsession is the utterly human need to tell a story. Keep it simple, clear, passionate in that regard. Mike could be a girl – if you need to change this bit of casting, call her Susan.

EMMA Don't play Emma as a victim. She doesn't call her parents. She deals with her dilemma herself. Emma has an 'I'll cope' attitude – the resilience of youth . . . She tries to create through photographs 'happy memories'. Emma accepts and respects (ultimately) her mother's lesbianism: her mom is a role model. She is probably a flirt. Mr Alexander isn't a stalker by nature but . . . This play is very much about the vagaries and subtleties of teenage sexuality. There are no easy or pat answers. Also, sexual harassment laws and rules are different now. Richard tells us that 'the sex issue is the motor of the play'. He encourages actors to explore the bridge from 'the incident' to the kids talking about their parents. How and why does it play out like this? Richard encourages you to decide how sick Emma is, and whether she's exaggerating an illness to gain attention.

CAT is a responsible girl. Her challenge is to appear an authority figure for kids of her own age. She goes back and forth between being peer and authority figure. She exudes maturity.

THE TEXT

A dash (–) indicates an interruption, even within one's own thought pattern, whereas an ellipsis (. . .) indicates a trailing away of thought, an incompleteness to the idea expressed. The speech is *active*, and the characters must speak and think at the same time.

Richard's happy for the audience not to hear all his
dialogue so long as the feeling, the intention of the scene
gets across truthfully. Consequently, lines can be spoken
from off stage, or entering or exiting, if they evoke the
appropriate intention. There are universal truths at play
here, not necessarily 'American' ones.

SCENE ONE The kids enjoy winding Dan up, referring to
Mr Williams as 'Dan's father'. And he is once again
excluded during the marijuana episode. Yet Dan is happy
to be around girls and observe them. He is an 'honorary
girl'.

Kathy (sixteen), Libby (fifteen), and Becca (sixteen) form
a clique, work as a group. The girls discuss (and live out)
status roles through clothes (socks) and make up (lip gloss).

Look for places where the dialogue might overlap to
bring texture, life and spontaneity to the moments.

Henry punches his mate – hormones at work. When
words fail, physicality takes over.

Richard at eighteen is the oldest, and he and Jane seem
like a married couple, they have that status.

The 'fade-out' nature of the end of the scene is part of the
play's intrinsic rhythm. It doesn't end with a snappy
'button' tag.

SCENE TWO Emma cries, Emily intuits trouble. That
intuition is a girl thing. The scene starts in jarring
contrast to the end of Scene One. The most important
information of the play is delivered second hand. As
Emma relates the story of the unwanted sexual attention,
the lines. 'But I pushed him away' and 'And he walked
off' are significant for clarity of storytelling.

Pressure builds as more characters enter the scene; there's a natural momentum to the drama here. Teenagers are innately excited by a crisis, and, as here, have an acute sense of injustice.

At the end of the scene, Emma is not ready for comfort, refusing hugs. In her final confession/story, it's vital that the moment carries, as it is central to the play. The complexities, confusion, the grey areas of life are here.

Address the issue of Emma's mother's lesbianism. Does Emma need to act 'I'm not gay' much as Dan acts 'My dad's a jerk'? Audiences should not be picking apart the psychology of characters but rather *feel* their dilemmas.

SCENE THREE In this scene, ideas and topics pop out of nowhere – these are the ever-restless, wandering minds of adolescents, and expressive of teen angst.

Libby's line 'I miss my dog. I think that's all I miss' is a good example of subtext for actors. Explore it.

Teens struggle for independence. Kathy's dad takes her to his old school, and she feels: 'I'm supposed to be like him.'

Emily makes a joke about Emma's mom hitting on a guy. It's in good spirits There's no judgement about lesbianism here. There's a support network among them, and a real generosity of spirit.

James begins to tell the story of his parents having sex, a kind of showing-off, but when the language becomes too 'on the nose' he trails off. 'I thought they were supposed to protect us from . . . I don't know.' The conversation dwindles to grunts (a defence mechanism). It's too raw, too vulnerable for him.

As these stories about parents' sex lives mount, you can work to get a sense of 'I got a better story than that', of topping one another, as opposed to the characters' dwelling on their misery and pain. No one's asking for sympathy, it's the truth they want.

On page 586, when Becca says, 'Sometimes you think it's just you,' Emma responds, 'I know. I know.' It's a telling moment. The group tacitly acknowledge the deeper, more immediate truth she's speaking. Henry attempts to erase embarrassment by telling the swimming story, but that kind of peters out as conversations frequently do. These are the moments of Chekhovian realism that Richard cares about.

Emily's monologue about being trapped by her parents' hatred of each other (pp. 557–8) should be said simply. This is who she is. Soon afterwards, Emma says, 'Why do we have to guess at everything?' – one of the more significant lines in the play.

When Bill relates tales of his father's serial monogamy, we see the profundity of young people trying to make sense of their world. Richard's 'puke story' which follows is an example of a kind of victory for kids over their parents. As the lights fade, there's an emerging affection for their parents, the rituals and gifts . . .

SCENE FOUR Dan and Emily want sex more than they need sex. It's a more interesting choice.

Their playfulness builds. Emma has the freedom of drunkenness. Decide if theirs is a conscious attraction or something more innocent and so confusing – a tumbling forth of words and actions.

As the attraction becomes more evident, the question is asked, 'What are you thinking?' perhaps projecting, 'I'm afraid of what I'm thinking.'

There is a series of false starts: a non-spoken negotiation, not predatory.

SCENE FIVE The play is made up of five completely different scenes. The inspiration for Scene Five is Act Four of *The Cherry Orchard*: saying goodbye . . . They are on 'molasses time', morning-after behaviour, missed connections. Dead air . . . 'What are we doing?'

As they stumble through their leaving, Richard doesn't care if all the words can't be heard but would rather you go for the intentions, for the truth and reality of the situation.

RICHARD NELSON'S WORKSHOP

Richard Nelson gave a workshop during the Keswick retreat, and the following notes summarise some of the points that emerged.

Mike's opening monologue is right out of Morton's *Americans in London*, which can be purchased from Amazon for about five quid. Mike finishes reading, puts down the book, and then begins his story in earnest. He is mocking the book. He turns on the lights as he introduces everyone, perhaps setting the book down for Dan and Emily to leaf through later. But don't be too 'on the nose' with the book. It will get the audience thinking too much.

The last two kids enter the scene *fast* – it's consciously written that way in contrast to the lingering groups. Rhythm . . . Dan and Emily provide a moment of stillness after the whirlwind.

Mike is Mike Williams, so we know Dan has participated in his life, since he has his name. The 'storm of outrage

by parents', the 'desperate attempt to self-abort', the
'tears, screams and accusations' – all are healthy fodder
for discussion among your casts. Dan and Emily's fate?
Perhaps the loving, gentle kiss at the end gives us a clue.

Emily has been reaching out to Dan indirectly, through
talk of *Misalliance*, the tube. It's a tender friendship. She's
hunting for a way to help resolve Dan's problems.

The goodbyes are to the simplicity of life. Do they get
married? A good discussion to have. Make choices: a clue
to the healthiness of the relationship is Mike's ease in
talking about his conception. What has transpired is
healthy and is reflected in Mike's relationship to the story
and with the audience. Although he, too, is now an
adolescent of sixteen, our overall inpression is not of
an angst-ridden 'This is what fucked me up' but, 'Isn't
life amazing? I came from this . . . ?' This is a moral play
which is also life-affirming, putting life's ambiguities on
stage.

One of Richard's techniques in directing is putting things
to get in the actors' way – lamps, furniture, brochures,
magazines. Make life more complicated and more real.
But no TV here. Wouldn't it be on?

The 'rhythm of life' is made manifest through behaviour:
sneezing, wriggling, primping, the Lemsip, etc. Make the
entrances of the girls all about coming in and *not* settling
down – create 'the joy of constant movement'.

Can Mike wander into scenes? Sit on an arm of a sofa
during the action? Richard said, 'Experiment.' Could he
sit in the front row? 'Sure. It's an idea to explore . . .'

Kathy makes the story about the actress in the play all
about her. Again, a teen's self-obsession. These three girls
are *totally* self involved.

When is an Emily sneeze a 'notice me' sneeze?

Dan's stillness versus the hyperactivity of the girls. A nice dynamic. 'There's a sense that Dan is brooding.' From the moment Dan enters, his father is on his mind. The teasing that ensues is playful, not malicious. Dan's calm is inherited by Mike, his son.

Focus on the stop-start rhythm of the conversations in Scene One. This should contrast with the more settled, focused quality of Scene Three.

Where are people *going*? It is a transient setting. When people settle, it's a big deal. Ironically, at the end, when they are trying to leave, they are stuck there.

THE WILLOW PATTERN

Judith Johnson

Author's Note

In adapting the story of 'The Willow Pattern', I have been inspired by the cult TV series *Monkey*, taken from the ancient Chinese tale of the same name. The acting style of the TV series is larger-than-life caricature, done with tongue in cheek.

The staging of the play that follows is entirely up to each director, although I have made a few suggestions. 'The Willow Pattern' story became known in the West in the late eighteenth century, when the British began to import 'willow' plates from China. Although the story is of course uniquely Chinese, I do see it as a universal tale; hence the design of the piece doesn't necessarily need to follow Chinese traditions.

Characters

Narrator
keeps us posted

The Mandarin
a very important man

Knoon-She
his daughter

Min
her maid and confidante

Chang
the Mandarin's secretary

Ta-Jin
a warrior, Knoon-She's suitor

Ta-Jin's Mother
a wealthy woman

Two Doves
Knoon-She's pets

Ensemble
providing music, dancing,
scenery, and atmosphere

The Narrator explodes, jumps, rolls, runs, glides, skateboards, sky-dives, somersaults, trampolines or even apparates into the performing space (unless you can think of something even more spectacular). He/she is full of life and eager to tell his/her tale.

Narrator HOOOOOOOOOOOOOORAAAAAH! HOOPLAAH! AND GREETINGS, MY GOOD FRIENDS!

It is written, 'He that is angry is seldom at ease.' I myself know this to be true. And maybe you know this too. But never has there been a man so ruined by anger as the man whose story I'm about to tell. Long ago, in Ancient Times, long before any of you were born. (*S/he looks around.*) Well, most of you anyway. Way way back, when things were different. When things were clearer, when decisions were easier, when life was more definite. And so was death. Back then, there lived a Mandarin.

He was the most important man in the province. He was eminent, influential, powerful. He was the chief, the boss, the main man, the king. He was critical, crucial, focal. Of great consequence, of great magnitude, of great worth. You get the picture. Everyone bowed down before him. Everyone except his daughter.

There is a loud fanfare or other musical/vocal flourish and the Narrator steps back. The Mandarin, dressed in fine regalia, enters. He is flanked by other dignitaries. He sits on his throne. The dignitaries bow down, then

go to the sides of the space. There is another vocal/
musical flourish and Knoon-She, dressed up to the
nines, is carried in, possibly on a sedan chair, by a
retinue of bearers. She is followed on foot by Min.
Knoon-She is placed carefully down and the bearers
retreat. Silence.

Mandarin My daughter.
Knoon-She My father.
Mandarin I trust you are well.
Knoon-She I am well.
Mandarin I trust you are strong?
Knoon-She I am strong.
Mandarin You are chaste.
Knoon-She I am chaste.
Mandarin You are sweet, you are fragrant.
Knoon-She I am both.
Mandarin You are polite?
Knoon-She I am. Thank you so much for asking.
Mandarin You are respectful?
Knoon-She Indeed, sir, I am.
Mandarin You are dutiful?
Knoon-She If that is what you want of me.
Mandarin You are loyal.
Knoon-She Most loyal and true.

Beat.

Mandarin (*smiles*) Then all is well!

The dignitaries and bearers all smile, sigh happily.
Knoon-She beams at everyone. Min rolls her eyes. The
Mandarin abruptly stops smiling.

(*suddenly cross*) Come on. Chop chop. What are you
waiting for?! You may all leave now!

The dignitaries and bearers bow and leave
immediately, leaving Knoon-She, Min and the

*Mandarin alone. There is a moment's pause in which
the Mandarin and Knoon-She stare solemnly at each
other, then the Mandarin breaks into a big grin.*

My little apple dumpling.
Knoon-She Daddy!

*They run at each other. The Mandarin picks Knoon-
She up and spins her round. She giggles uncontrollably.
Min shakes her head. They spin faster and faster,
then fall down. Knoon-She gets up laughing but the
Mandarin lies on the floor holding his head. Knoon-
She realises something is wrong and stops laughing.*

Mandarin Oh!
Knoon-She Daddy? Are you alright? Min!
Min Yes, miss?
Knoon-She Daddy's fallen!
Min I expect he was rather dizzy.
Knoon-She Well, don't just stand there, help him up!

*Min gives Knoon-She a look, saunters over to where
the Mandarin is sitting, holding his head. Without
looking at him she offers him her hand, which he
takes. She pulls him to his feet with rather too much
force, then goes back to where she was standing. This
is all done with a deadpan attitude.*

Knoon-She Daddy, are you alright now?
Mandarin I'm fine, pumpkin.
Knoon-She Good, because you haven't given me a
present yet today.
Mandarin Ah!
Knoon-She (*wheedling*) I was wondering if you really
loved me.
Mandarin Of course I love you, my precious. You are the
most beloved, cherished item, I mean person, in my
life.

Knoon-She Oh goody, what have you got me?

Mandarin See if you can guess?

Knoon-She Is it a fine dress of the best silk in my favourite colours?

Mandarin No. For what dress could make *you* any prettier?

Knoon-She Is it a box of the most delicious hand-made chocolate delights?

Mandarin No. You are quite delicious enough already, my angel.

Min (*aside*) Is it a bowl in which to be sick?

Knoon-She Is it . . . a new story book? Oh please say yes, I want a new story book more than anything in the world.

Mandarin (*worried*) Oh.

Min It's not a new story book.

Mandarin It's better! A living thing . . .

Knoon-She A living thing?!

Mandarin Two living things!

He claps his hands and the two doves fly in (or are brought in). These could be puppets, or people, or projections or anything else you can think of. They fly round the space. Beautifully graceful. Then come to alight on Knoon-She's shoulders, or arms, or hold her hands or in some other way attach themselves fondly to her.

Knoon-She Oh Daddy! Daddy! They're beautiful!

Mandarin I *knew* you would like them!

Knoon-She (*kissing her father*) You're the best daddy in the whole wide world. Isn't he, Min?

Min (*sarky*) Oh yeah. The best.

Mandarin They will bless your life with the gift of peace.

Knoon-She How wonderful!

Mandarin They were your mother's favourite bird.

The Mandarin looks sad. Knoon-She goes to him and puts her arms round him.

Knoon-She Thank you so very much, Daddy. Mummy would have been proud of you.
Mandarin She would have been prouder of you.
Knoon-She I love you so much.
Mandarin And I you, my sweet sugarplum.

Min mimes putting her fingers down her throat. Knoon-She and the Mandarin part.

Mandarin Ah, but I must leave you. Duty calls.
Knoon-She Are you collecting taxes today, Daddy?
Mandarin No.
Knoon-She Admonishing peasants?
Mandarin No. Writing letters with Chang. Have you seen him today?
Knoon-She (*acting a bit shifty*) Who? Chang? No. I hardly ever see him.
Mandarin If you do see him, tell him I'm ready to start. I'll see you later, pumpkin. Enjoy your doves!
Knoon-She I will.

The Mandarin exits. Knoon-She stays on stage, playing with her doves. Min exits, but comes back on during the following with a basket of beautiful cloth, which she hangs up on a washing line during the Narrator's speech and the next scene. The Narrator bounds forwards.

Narrator It is said, 'A friend is one who knows everything about you, and yet still likes you.' Oh so true. And lucky Knoon-She had such a friend. Living in her father's palace was not easy for a young spirited girl like her. She had been without playmates all her life, imagine that. Only her old maid Min to keep her company, and she was hardly a barrel of laughs.

Min gives the Narrator a dirty look. The Narrator pulls tongues at her.

A girl like this – (*indicating Knoon-She*) – a girl full of life. A girl full of vivacity and energy, full of excitement. A girl with verve, with vitality, with vigour.

Min Get on with it.

Narrator (*louder, at Min*) A girl with dash, dynamism, daring. Such a girl needs a friend to soothe her soul, to calm her thoughts, to temper her flights of fancy.

Min Anything in it for the friend?

Narrator Such a friend was Chang. The Mandarin's secretary. A gentle, poetic soul, who loved the very ground that Knoon-She walked upon. It is written: 'Love is patient, love is kind. It does not envy, it does not boast, it is not proud.' The love that Chang had for Knoon-She was just like this. And Knoon-She, despite her headstrong ways, was wise enough to know when she was onto a good thing.

Enter Chang, carrying parchment and quills for writing. The Narrator steps back.

Knoon-She Chang! Look! Look at my doves!

Chang comes to look.

Chang They're beautiful, Knoon-She!

Knoon-She Daddy got them for me.

Chang I know. He had me write to every menagerie in the province in search of the perfect pair.

Knoon-She Really? Then it is you who chose them for me! Thank you, Chang!

She throws her arms round him and kisses him. Min steps forward, warningly. Chang disentangles himself, reluctantly.

Chang Be careful, your father might see us.

Knoon-She makes a face at Min and moves away. Beat.

Chang They . . . stay together all their lives. The doves.
Knoon-She Really?
Chang Yes. They are lifelong, devoted partners.
Knoon-She How romantic!
Min Do they poo as much as other pigeons?
Chang I am sure they'll keep away from your washing, Min.
Min They'd better. I'm rather partial to pigeon pie.
Knoon-She (*to the doves*) Don't you listen to her, mean old thing.

The doves fly to Min and alight on her shoulders or otherwise attach themselves fondly to her.

Min Bog off, before I bite your heads off.

The doves fly back sharpish to Knoon-She.

Knoon-She I have a gift for you too.
Min Knoon-She!
Knoon-She It's just a little thing!

She takes a bead out of her pocket. Gives it to Chang, who takes it, hesitantly.

Knoon-She It's my lucky bead. My mum gave it to me when I was really little.
Chang Your mother? I can't take this!
Min You can't give him Cressida's bead!
Knoon-She I want him to have it! (*to Chang*) You are always so kind to me.

She folds it in his hand, lingering a bit over the hand-holding. Min doesn't see. Chang moves away nervously.

Chang I . . . have a new poem for you, Knoon-She.
Knoon-She Oh. No story yet?

Chang No, I haven't had time for the story, your father has been keeping me very busy of late.

Knoon-She (*disappointed*) Oh. You know I love stories!

Chang But I do have the poem. They really don't take that long at all.

Knoon-She It is written, 'Poetry is something that heals oneself.'

Chang It certainly makes *me* feel better.

Knoon-She Read it to me and I'll tell you if it makes me feel better too.

Chang Okay.

Knoon-She lies down with her eyes closed. Chang unrolls one of his parchments. He clears his throat.

(*for Min's benefit*) It's the kind of poem that a lover would write to his sweetheart. If he had one. It's just an example.

Min (*knowingly*) Really.

Chang coughs, then reads.

Chang
When I awake my ears are open
Listening for you.
My heart is here. My soul is yours.
My love is strong and true.

While I sleep, my eyes are closed
Dreaming dreams of you.
My arms are waiting. Anticipating.
Are you dreaming too?

Chang looks to Knoon-She for reaction. Knoon-She lies still with her eyes closed, smiling. Min stares at Chang in disbelief. Beat.

Min It is written, 'He who wears his heart on his sleeve often looks stupid.'

Knoon-She sits up.

Knoon-She (*to Chang, fondly*) You're such an old softy.
Chang (*embarrassed*) I know.
Knoon-She Come and sit with me.

Chang does so. Knoon-She puts her arms round him.
He removes them immediately. Knoon-She pouts.

Knoon-She You shouldn't worry about Daddy. You
know I can wrap him round my little finger.
Chang If he ever thought that we . . .
Knoon-She That we what?
Chang That there was anything . . . wrong.
Knoon-She Nothing is 'wrong'.
Chang I would lose my job.
Min He'd chop your arms off if he thought you'd even
touched her.
Chang Not just my arms.
Min It would depend what you had touched her with.

Pause. They all look unhappy. Especially Chang.

Knoon-She (*to Chang*) Anyway. When I'm old enough
to do what I want, we'll have a house of our own,
won't we?
Chang It would be lovely if we did.
Knoon-She With a willow tree to watch over us.
Chang And a veranda with a swinging seat, where we
can both sit and watch the world go by.
Knoon-She Like two doves in a dovecote.
Chang Like two doves in a dovecote.

Pause. Chang and Knoon-She sit. They smile at each
other, very fondly. The doves hover contentedly
nearby. Min shakes her head. Chang sighs.

Chang You'd better go. Your father will be coming.
More letters demanding taxes.

Knoon-She He says you're ever so good at them.

Chang I'd rather finish your story.

Knoon-She Tell me a little of what it's about before you go!

Chang Well . . .

Knoon-She Please!

Chang It's about a girl who lives all alone in a castle, with no friends, who is very unhappy, until one day she is visited by a kind and handsome poet . . .

Min *Purrlease!*

Knoon-She (*going off*) I'll see you later, Chang.

Chang See you later, Knoon-She.

Short burst of music. Knoon-She, Min and the doves exit. Chang sits down with his pen and parchment, poised to write. The Mandarin enters, through the beautiful cloths. He paces.

Mandarin Dear Land Owner –

Chang (*writing*) Dear Land Owner –

Mandarin You haven't paid me for some time.

Chang You haven't paid me for some time.

Mandarin Pay me by Saturday, or I will have your head chopped off.

Chang frowns. The Mandarin stops pacing.

Mandarin What's the problem?

Chang Mm. May I make a suggestion?

Mandarin Yes, yes. Go on.

Chang I think the Land Owner may run away if you threaten to chop his head off.

Mandarin Then I'll have him caught, and when he's caught it won't be just his head that I chop off.

Chang flinches.

Chang But . . . the last five Land Owners that we wrote this letter to ran away and were *not* caught.

Mandarin Mm. I'll boil their eyeballs if we ever *do* catch
them.

Chang How about a bit of *gentle* persuasion?

Mandarin 'Dear Land Owner, please pay me by
Saturday, or I'll pull your finger nails out?'

Chang Well . . .

Mandarin That's not so bad.

Chang I was thinking more along the lines of 'Dear Land
Owner, your taxes have now been outstanding for
some time. Perhaps you would like to come to the
Palace, and we can discuss ways in which you can
repay your arrears.'

Pause. The Mandarin looks puzzled.

Mandarin Do you think that would do it?

Chang It would perhaps make him feel less threatened.

Mandarin *Less* threatened?

Chang In which case he would not run away.

Mandarin Mm. (*He still doesn't look very sure.*)

Chang And you could send a couple of your warriors to
fetch him, to make sure he kept his appointment.

Mandarin Ah! Yes. And while he was at the Palace
I could send more warriors to ransack his home and
bring me what he owes me!

Chang I didn't exactly mean . . .

Mandarin You are a clever old clerk, Chang. So! 'Dear
Land Owner –'

Chang (*sighs, writes*) 'Dear Land Owner –'

Mandarin And so on.

Chang And so on.

Chang writes. The Mandarin paces.

Mandarin Talking of warriors. We need to make some
arrangements.

Chang Arrangements?

Mandarin Yes. Next week, Ta-Jin, the great warrior, is coming to the Palace. And his mother.

Chang Ta-Jin and his mother? I see. And to what do we owe this honour?

Mandarin I'm going to present him to Knoon-She, as a possible suitor.

Beat.

Chang To Knoon-She?

Mandarin Yes. I think it's time we started looking at possible husbands for her, don't you? I'm not getting any younger.

Chang But Ta-Jin is stupid. His mum still gets him dressed every day. She still cleans his teeth for him. And wipes his . . .

Mandarin He is *said* to be stupid, although I'm not sure that's true, people always say things like that, it's often just envy. I *do* know he is very strong, and also very rich. His father left his mum fifteen donkeys when he died!

Chang But, surely, Knoon-Shee would be better off with someone more . . . intelligent. Someone she can talk to. Apparently Ta-Jin's mum does all his talking *for* him.

Mandarin Well. Knoon-She doesn't want someone who can outwit her, does she? (*fondly*) She's just like me, she likes to be in control.

Chang But I've heard Ta-Jin's mum is very bossy.

Mandarin She needs to be, a widow woman, a big strapping lad like that!

Beat.

Chang But Ta-Jin spends all his time just . . . fighting!

Mandarin He's a warrior. It's a noble pastime.

Chang But what if he fights with Knoon-She? You know how argumentative she can be.

Mandarin She'd make minced meat of him!

Chang But . . .

Mandarin Enough butting, it's only an introduction, for
goodness' sake, Chang! What is the matter with you?
Now, you need to order the food. And dancers too.
And fireworks possibly, what d'you think?

Chang Fireworks? Just for an introduction?

Mandarin Perhaps fireworks is pushing it a bit far.
Whatever. I'll leave it to you. But I *do* want to make a
good impression. Ta-Jin's mum does own those fifteen
donkeys, and with all these Land Owners running away
I'm a little down in the donkey stakes at the moment.
Let's give them a good welcome, if nothing else!

*The Mandarin waltzes off. Chang sits for a moment,
looking downcast, then rolls up his parchments and
exits. The Narrator bounds forward.*

Narrator It is written: 'To get used to something is
something terrible.' But that is exactly what Chang
had to do. He picked himself up, he dusted himself off,
and he started to make arrangements. He ordered the
finest food. Tender pigs roasted on open fires. Fish,
freshly caught from fast-flowing rivers. Cheese made
from the milk of wild goats, fed on fresh mountain
herbs. Honey from the bees who buzzed about the
exotic flowers of the Palace gardens. Sweet, newly
picked, crisp green vegetables and juicy ripe fruit,
tasting of summer. Wine of superlative quality. The
veritable nectar. He organised the best musicians in the
province to be there and the top singers. Really, he
kind of went a little overboard. But then again, it has
been said, 'Happiness is like a perfume: we cannot
sprinkle it on someone else, without a few drops
falling on ourselves.'

*During the above the ensemble (including Min and
directed by Chang) bring on a table and chairs. They*

cover the table with the fine cloth from Min's washing line. They lay fine food and wine upon the tables, hang decorations about the place (perhaps from Min's washing line), and finally sit at the table and eat. Musicians and singers enter. As the Narrator finishes, they begin to play and sing. Something pompous, celebratory. As they do so the Mandarin and a sulky-looking Knoon-She, accompanied by Ta-Jin and his mother, enter. Ta-Jin is puffed up and arrogant-looking, his Mother haughty and smug. Everyone stands up to bow to the two families, they bow down to each other, then everyone sits and eats. The song ends. The Mandarin stands up, with a goblet of wine in his hand.

Mandarin I would like to say a few words of welcome to Ta-Jin and his charming mother. What an honour it is to have such esteemed and wealthy, I mean healthy, visitors. I propose a toast: To Ta-Jin and family!

He raises his glass. The ensemble repeat: 'To Ta-Jin and family.' Everyone knocks back their wine. Ta-Jin's mother gets to her feet.

Ta-Jin's Mother Too kind, too kind. I would also like to say a few words. You have been the soul of hospitality, the food has been excellent, the entertainment top-notch and the company – (*She glances at Knoon-She.*) – very interesting. We would like to offer you some small gifts, to show our appreciation.

She claps her hands and a donkey is brought on. The Mandarin looks absolutely delighted.

Min That's small?
Mandarin Oh! How absolutely wonderful. Isn't it wonderful, Knoon-She?
Knoon-She (*monotone*) Yeah. Really wonderful.

Ta-Jin's Mother (*prompting Ta-Jin*) And a little something for your beautiful daughter?

Ta-Jin looks puzzled for a moment. His mum nods towards the table. Ta-Jin clicks. He leans under the table, pokes around underneath it for a while, then brings out a very ornate box, overflowing with jewels.

(*to Knoon-She*) For you.

Knoon-She takes the box. She is actually impressed, despite herself, but tries to be nonchalant.

Knoon-She Oh. Right. Ta.

Ta-Jin leans towards his mum and whispers something coyly in her ear.

Ta-Jin's Mother And now, my son would like to show you his form.

Beat.

Mandarin Pardon?

Ta-Jin's Mother His form. The movements of his art. The art of fighting.

Mandarin Oh! Right! Marvellous. Do go ahead.

Ta-Jin gets up from the table, moves solemnly into the space in front of the table, and goes through a collection of martial-arts-like movements, which involve use of a fighting stick or sword. He is very serious and very self-important. There is utter silence, and in some quarters disbelief, as they watch. At the end, he bows smugly to Knoon-She in the absolute conviction that she thinks he's great. She looks at him, aghast. A beat, then Ta-Jin's Mother starts to applaud. The Mandarin joins in and everyone else follows politely. Ta-Jin milks the applause.

Ta-Jin's Mother (*proudly*) He's been practising in his bedroom.

Mandarin I'm sure he has. So. Ta-Jin. You have fought many battles?

Ta-Jin goes to speak but his mum butts in.

Ta-Jin's Mother Oh yes.

Mandarin And won many victories?

Ta-Jin's Mother (*butting in again*) Yes indeed. He's very good.

Mandarin (*pointedly to Ta-Jin*) And tell me, do you, in your spare time, have any hobbies?

Ta-Jin's Mother Oh yes, he does.

Mandarin And what may they be?

Ta-Jin's Mother Fighting.

Beat.

Mandarin Fighting?

Ta-Jin's Mother Oh yes. Sparring. Practising moves. Perfecting his form.

Mandarin (*to Ta-Jin*) Anything else?

Ta-Jin goes to speak again but his Mother butts in.

Ta-Jin's Mother Oh yes.

Mandarin Good! And what might that be?

Ta-Jin's Mother Training.

Mandarin I see.

Ta-Jin's Mother Building muscles. Improving strength. Ready for the fight.

Mandarin Right.

Ta-Jin's Mother Always. Ready for the fight!

Ta-Jin flexes his muscles and smiles enticingly at Knoon-She. She looks away, astonished. A moment's awkward silence.

Mandarin Er, Knoon-She, do you have anything you'd like to ask Ta-Jin?

Everyone looks at Knoon-She.

Knoon-She (*incredulous*) Me?!
Mandarin Yes. Any questions? Any conversation?
Knoon-She No!

Beat. Very awkward pause. After a moment Ta-Jin takes a breath and looks as if he's about to say something. Everyone looks at him expectantly. He lets the breath out and looks worried. More awkward silence. Chang stands up.

Chang Perhaps we should repair to the gardens? We have some beautiful rhododendrons growing near the stream.
Mandarin Ah yes, the rhododendrons!
Ta-Jin's Mother (*getting up*) Rhododendrons, how lovely!

She takes the Mandarin's arm. The party exits, taking the food and table with them, chatting. Chang brings up the rear. Knoon-She, with Min, lingers until last. She grabs Chang's hand.

Knoon-She (*lowering voice, mimicking Ta-Jin's Mother*) 'Always. Ready for the fight.' I could *never* marry him!

Chang laughs, pulls his hand away.

Min Knoon-She, your guests are waiting. Come on!

Knoon-She kisses Chang quickly on the cheek and exits, with Min. Chang holds his cheek for a moment, happy, then exits too. Music. The ensemble transform the space into a beautiful palace garden, with a stream running through it. The Narrator dances among the flowers then speaks.

Narrator It goes without saying, Knoon-She said 'No' to Ta-Jin. Her heart was elsewhere, as we know. The Mandarin accepted his daughter's decision – he wasn't too worried, he'd got a donkey out of the deal and you can't say fairer than that! He decided to let things ride for a while. He was in no great hurry to marry his apple dumpling off. And so Chang and Knoon-She were able to continue seeing each other. They basked in each other's companionship when they could. They relaxed. No one disturbed them. Even Min let them be, for she had been young once herself. They started to think that things would stay like that for ever. But they were living in cloud cuckoo land. As the saying goes, 'Love, and a cough, cannot be hid.'

The Narrator steps back. Enter Knoon-She, with Chang. Chang is carrying a parchment. He sits down near the stream. Knoon-She sits opposite him, quite close, and stares at him in excited anticipation. Chang opens up the parchment.

Chang Ready?
Knoon-She Yes yes yes! I can't wait!

Chang coughs.

Chang Right. Here we go, then.

Pause. He coughs again.

Sorry. I'm ready now. Okay.

He takes a deep breath, lets it out.

Knoon-She Come on!
Chang I'm just preparing.
Knoon-She Are you nervous?
Chang Well.
Knoon-She You are, aren't you! Silly sausage.
Chang I've been working on this story for quite a long time. It's always frightening the first time you . . . share your work.
Knoon-She How many stories have you written?

Chang Just this one.

Knoon-She Oh Chang! And it's especially for me!

Chang Yes.

Chang gulps. Beat.

Knoon-She How about if I sit over there, with my back to you? So you can't see my face. Just in case it looks like I'm not enjoying it. (*quickly*) Although I'm sure I will.

Chang No no, that's okay. I'd rather know what you really feel. I think.

Knoon-She But what if I *don't* like it?

Chang Then you must tell me.

Knoon-She Right.

Beat. Chang thinks.

Chang Actually, I'd rather you pretended you like it even if you don't. To be honest.

Knoon-She Would you? Wouldn't that be like, lying, though? I don't want there to be any untruths between us, Chang.

Chang Then, perhaps if you don't like it, you could find one small thing in it that you did like, and praise me just for that.

Pause. Knoon-She considers this for a moment, then:

Knoon-She Yes! That's what we'll do.

Chang Okay!

Pause.

Knoon-She Come on then!

Chang Right.

He coughs, then sudddenly launches into it, reading very quickly.

'Many years ago, in ancient times, there lived a girl called Pnoon-Mee.'

Knoon-She Who?
Chang Pnoon-Mee.

Knoon-She beams.

Knoon-She Okay!
Chang (*still reading very fast*) 'Pnoon-Mee lived all alone with her father in a castle that stood at the very ends of the earth.'
Knoon-She Ends of the what?
Chang The earth.
Knoon-She Okay.
Chang (*still fast*) 'No one ever came to visit the castle, because Pnoon-Mee's father was said to be a mean and irascible old man who would not welcome visitors into his home.'
Knoon-She Chang?
Chang Yes? Is it terrible?
Knoon-She No! But you need to slow down a bit.
Chang Right. Slow down. Okay.

He takes another deep breath.

Chang 'Pnoon-Mee was very lonely. She spent her days staring out across the sea, longing for a ship to sail into view, but none ever came. She spent her nights dreaming of a world where many people lived in harmony together. Where there was music and songs and dancing. Her father didn't like too much noise.'
Knoon-She Poor Pnoon-Mee.
Chang Yes.

Pause.

Knoon-She And?
Chang And?
Knoon-She What happened next?
Chang Do you think the bit about the ship works?
Knoon-She Yes, yes. It's fine. Does the Poet come soon?

Chang You don't think it's a little extraneous to the plot?

Knoon-She What? Extraneous? No, yes, whatever . . .

Chang (*stricken*) Yes!

Knoon-She Whatever! Get on with the story.

Chang (*worried*) Alright.

Chang lifts up the parchment.

Chang 'One day, when Pnoon-Mee was walking in the gardens of the Castle, she heard a sound she had never heard before in her life. It was the voice of someone else, someone other than herself or her father.'

Knoon-She It was him, wasn't it? The Poet! I knew it!

Chang (*a bit cross*) Just a minute.

Knoon-She Was he handsome, was he kind?

Chang Just a minute!

Knoon-She Was he tall? Or short?

Chang 'It was the voice of a poet . . .'

Knoon-She I knew it!

Chang '. . . who had lost his way and wandered into the Castle gardens by mistake.'

Knoon-She Ooh! Can they keep him secret from her father?! Please, Chang, that would make the story more exciting, if they had to hide him somewhere in the Castle!

Chang More exciting? Isn't it exciting already?

Knoon-She (*carried away*) No, not quite enough yet, but I think if we added a bit where he had to hide, and her father knew, and he threatened to . . . to pull her fingernails out unless she told him where the Poet was, that would be brilliant!

Chang It would be a bit bloodthirsty.

Knoon-She Yes! It needs a bit of action, don't you think?

Chang It's not that kind of story.

Knoon-She Oh, but it would be great . . . if . . . it . . . was.

Knoon-She grinds to a halt. Chang is looking very miffed.

Knoon-She What's the matter?

Chang This is my story, not yours.

Knoon-She I was just saying.

Chang I've been writing it for a long time. It's all worked out. There's no room for a change in the plot now.

Beat.

Knoon-She Sorry.

No answer from Chang.

It's ever so good.

Still no answer.

Please don't fall out with me, Chang.

Knoon-She moves right next to Chang. She puts her arm round him.

I only got a bit carried away. If the story hadn't been so good in the first place I wouldn't have got so excited.

Chang You said it *wasn't* exciting.

Knoon-She It is. Really.

Chang You're not just saying that?

Knoon-She Of course not.

Beat. During the following exchange, Knoon-She and Chang get closer and closer until they are on the verge of kissing.

Knoon-She You were really cross with me then.

Chang I know.

Knoon-She You've never been cross with me before, it was horrible.

Chang I was only a little cross.

Knoon-She Really?

Chang Of course. I'm not cross any more.
Knoon-She Give me a kiss, to prove it.
Chang I . . . mustn't! Min isn't far away.
Knoon-She She won't tell.
Chang Won't she?
Knoon-She No.

Beat. Silence. They are millimetres from each other.

Knoon-She Are you going to kiss me?
Chang Okay.

*Chang kisses Knoon-She. Almost immediately, the
Mandarin enters.*

Mandarin Ah, Chang, there you . . . are.

*Chang and Knoon-She jump apart, but it is too late.
Silence.*

Mandarin What is going on here?
Knoon-She Daddy! How wonderful to see you!

*Knoon-She launches herself at the Mandarin, a
desperate hug. He pushes her off. Addresses Chang.*

Mandarin I asked you a question?
Knoon-She I had some dirt in my eye, Daddy! Isn't Chang
kind? He was trying to get it out.
Mandarin Knoon-She, be quiet.
Knoon-She But . . .
Mandarin (*shouting*) BE QUIET!!

*Silence. The Mandarin walks over to Chang and pulls
him up by his collar.*

Mandarin I am waiting for an explanation.

Min comes running on.

Min Is everything alright, I heard shouting?
Knoon-She Min!

Mandarin (*to Chang, shouting in his face*) I AM WAITING FOR AN EXPLANATION!!

Chang I . . . I was kissing Knoon-She.

Min What!?

Knoon-She No!

Chang She . . . she didn't ask me to. *She* hasn't done anything. It was my idea, I couldn't help myself. Your daughter is more beautiful and more dear to me than anyone or anything on this earth.

Silence. After a moment the Mandarin drops Chang down.

Knoon-She (*suddenly, to Chang. Shouting at the top of her voice*) RUNNNNNNNNNNNNNNNN!!

Chang gets up, and runs off stage.

Mandarin What?! Come back! Where's my warriors? Warriors!!

Knoon-She grabs her father to stop him going off in search of warriors. He struggles.

Mandarin Get off me! Warriors! Warriors!!

Knoon-She No! Let him go!

During the struggle, Min quietly exits after Chang. The Mandarin and Knoon-She don't see her. The Mandarin finally breaks free of Knoon-She, knocking her to the ground as he does so.

Mandarin (*to Knoon-She*) You disgust me.

He exits. Immediately, some warriors run across the space, and go in the direction that Chang and Min went. There is music or vocalistions, cacophonous sounds. The ensemble comes on and makes a fence round the garden and round Knoon-She. Knoon-She watches, horrified, as she is fenced in, then covers her face. During this the Narrator steps forward and speaks, while the doves come to join Knoon-She, flying round her, trying to comfort her.

Narrator What sadness! What sorrow and sadness and strain. The Mandarin was so angry with his daughter, he placed a high fence round the Palace and garden, and refused to let her see anyone! He sent out warriors, searching for Chang high and low, promising a reward of four donkeys to anyone who could bring back his dead body. And worst of all, he told Knoon-She he had decided something. He had decided she was to marry Ta-Jin after all. Knoon-She was heart-broken. She wandered the garden day after day, thinking about Chang. She wouldn't admit it to herself, but deep in her heart she felt he was dead.

Knoon-She wanders. The doves follow her.

Not even her old maid Min had been allowed to see her, so there was no one to tell her that Chang had not been found, and no one knew where he was. She was more unhappy than she had ever been in her life but, as it is said, 'The soul would have no rainbow if the eyes had no tears.' And then, anyway, one day something happened to wipe her tears away.

Music: light, hopeful. The Narrator steps back. Knoon-She sits by the stream. After a moment a small boat floats down it. Knoon-She is amazed, she looks around her to check no one is looking, picks up the boat. Inside is the bead she gave Chang earlier, and the parchment with his story. She holds the bead up to the light then clasps it to her heart. She picks up the story and the boat, then exits, quickly. The fence and gardens exit with her, as do the doves, leaving the space bare. Enter Chang, with a sleeping-mat. He puts the sleeping mat on the floor, then lies on it. He looks sad. After a moment, Min enters. She is carrying a bowl of water with a cloth to wash in it. The parchment with the story on it is stuck into the belt behind her back. Chang sits up.

Chang Any news from the Palace?

Min They still won't let me see her but apparently it's the same story. The Mandarin is not talking to the daughter. The daughter is not talking to the Mandarin. Both are in a foul frame of mind. No one in the Palace dares speak, let alone smile or laugh.

Chang Oh dear.

Min Another warrior has returned, finding no trace of you anywhere in the province. They have searched east and west, north and south. They have left very few stones unturned. Nobody has thought to look so close. It is as I said. All roads lead you astray. Stay home.

Chang You are very kind to keep me here.

Min I am an old fool and I will suffer for it.

Chang Your tongue is sharp but your heart is soft.

Min Your intention is good but your words are twaddle.

Chang I only meant to thank you for helping me.

Min Then say that. The best poetry is direct.

Chang You think so.

Min I know so. Direct. And unsentimental.

Chang I see.

Min I hope you do.

Chang sighs.

Chang (*sentimentally*) Is my beloved and most cherished Knoon-She truly unhappy?

Min (*shakes her head*) Unbelievable.

Min puts the bowl down and starts washing the cloth.

Chang I miss her with all my heart.

Min She's feeling a bit better.

Chang Is she?

Min She got your message.

Chang (*jumping to his feet*) You're kidding? The boat?

Min Yep, strange as it may seem, the plan worked.

Chang Did she return it back down the stream? With the story?

Min She . . . did.

Pause.

Chang Well. Do you have it?

Min (*stops washing*) I do have it.

Beat.

Chang And. So. Can you give it to me?

Min I can give it to you. But I have to warn you.

Chang Yes?

Min She's finished the story.

Chang What?

Min Try not to be cross. It has a happy ending.

Pause. Chang composes himself.

Chang The important thing is, she got it, she knows I'm alive.

Min (*giving over the parchment*) I hope you feel the same after you've read it.

Chang opens the parchment, sits down and reads. Min continues washing.

Chang (*after a bit, looking up, astounded*) The Poet is dead!

Min Good thing. He took himself far too seriously.

Chang But . . .

Min Read on.

Chang I thought you said it had a happy ending!

Min It does. But there are more surprises first.

649

Chang reads. Min washes.

Chang (*looks up*) She's killed the father!

Min Yes. The fight was terrific, I thought.

Chang But Pnoon-Mee would never have been able to wield an axe like that! Would she?

Min Hell hath no fury . . . And so on.

Chang (*reading*) Ah! Wait! The Poet has come back to life!

Min Yes. Cunning twist that. Giving him the paralysing powder.

Beat.

Chang (*happy*) And now they are married, and the Castle is full of people, 'Living in harmony together. With music and songs and dancing.'

Min I told you it was happy.

Chang Just like it's going to be for us. A happy ending!

Min Don't count your chickens.

Chang Min?

Min (*suspicious*) Mm?

Chang Are you sure I can't creep up to the fence? Catch a glimpse of her in the Palace gardens?

Min I'm sure.

Chang But I would so love just to see her dear dear face.

Min You would lose your own dear face if someone caught you.

Chang But . . .

Min We stick to the plan. It's the only way. 'If we do not change direction, we will probably get to where we are going,' as the saying goes.

Chang When is Ta-Jin arriving?

Min Next week. There isn't long to wait.

Chang So I'm stuck in here until then.

Min It's not so bad. Without going outside, you may know the whole world.

Chang You are a very wise person, Min.

Min I have my ignorance to thank for the few things I know.

Chang You know you are risking . . . everything by helping us.

Min I promised Knoon-She's mother I would always take care of her and that is what I am going to do.

Chang You are a genuinely good person.

Min And when you and Knoon-She set up your house together, far away from here, I will be with you and I will be free.

Chang Yes! We will all be free. I really believe we will.

Min finishes washing her cloth. Stands up.

Min I don't think we have an ice cream's chance in Hell. But, as the saying goes, 'You have only failed when you have failed to try.'

Min exits. Chang cradles his parchment in his arms. Then rolls up his sleeping mat and exits too. The Narrator steps forward.

Narrator The week passed faster than anyone could have imagined and soon it was the eve of Knoon-She and Ta-Jin's nuptials. The Mandarin threw a stag party and invited all the eminent men of the province, such was the local tradition. Knoon-She was cleaned and preened while Ta-Jin and the Mandarin caroused the night away. And, unbeknownst to anyone, Min and Chang set their plan into action.

Music. Wedding celebrations. The Mandarin, Ta-Jin, and other men come staggering onto the stage, roaring drunk, singing a drinking song at the tops of their voices. One of these men is Chang, in disguise.

Stag song (just the lyrics – make up your own tune).

1 He's old enough to vote,
   He's sowed his wild oats,
   He's brought a new coat
   For the wedding!

   She's got him bewitched
   So it's time they was hitched
   And lying on their newly stitched
   Bedding.

Chorus
   Man and wife!
   Man and wife!
   They're in it for life.
   He and she!
   He and she!
   For e-tern-it-tee.

   Boy and girl,
   Boy and girl,
   Oyster and pearl.
   Girl and boy,
   Girl and boy,
   A bundle of joy.

2 A man's life is short
   And he don't need much thought
   About how much he needs
   A dear spouse.

   To keep him indoors
   To lay down the law,
   To berate him and call him
   A louse.

Chorus
   Man and wife!
   Man and wife!
   Oh what a life.

He and she,
He and she,
Take pity on me!
Boy and girl,
Boy and girl,
Oh how she makes me hurl!

Girl and boy,
Girl and boy,
She does cloy and annoy!

Girl and boy,
Girl and boy,
She does cloy and annoy!

As they sing, on the other side of the stage, Knoon-She enters, wearing plain undergarments. During what follows, she is dressed up in her wedding outfit by two handmaids (not Min). Her outfit should be very ostentatious and made up of many pieces. Knoon-She stands very still and looks stoic throughout. The men finish their drunken song and go to sit down.

Mandarin (*his arm round Ta-Jin, drunk*) So, my boy, soon to be married eh?

Ta-Jin nods contentedly.

You and my girl, all done up, all fine and dandy and ready to go!

Ta-Jin nods.

D'you know, I remember my own wedding. I stood in the Pagoda, awaiting my bride. I'd never seen her before, we didn't in those days, so I was pretty nervous, I can tell you. Then suddenly, there she was, walking through the arbour towards me. My beautiful Cressida. Her face framed by lotus blossoms. A vision.

Beat. The Mandarin struggles against tears. Ta-Jin looks suitably sad.

She was a diamond. A diamond of a wife. Kind and sweet and joyful. She cheered me up, I can tell you. I never was a very happy person, I always had a terrible temper so people tended to keep away from me. But she didn't even seem to notice. Not a cross word between us. Ten years. And then she gave me a wonderful gift.

Ta-Jin looks questioningly at the Mandarin.

A daughter. A darling little bundle of enchantment. And just as my wife was gentle and kind, her daughter was vigorous and strong. Like a little firecracker, full of fizz. I loved her so much.

Ta-Jin nods happily.

And now my Cressida is dead and you are going to take my apple dumpling away from me.

The Mandarin starts to cry. Ta-Jin looks confused.

(*crying, patting Ta-Jin on the back*) Don't worry. It's my fault. I've brought it on myself yet again with that stinking temper of mine. It has always been my downfall. D'you know when my beloved spouse was taken away from me by that damned fever? I went into a rage the like of which has not been seen in this province before or since. Even I was amazed. I threw out all the people who lived in the Palace at the time. I kept only a few servants. I shouted the house down. I broke all the statues. I kept Knoon-Shee away from people, I didn't want her to catch something and die too, you see. And that's how come she fell in love with that insipid secretary of mine instead of a fine healthy fellow like yourself. And now I'm making her marry someone she despises, and again it's all my fault.

*Pause. Ta-Jin looks concerned. He knits his brow.
After a moment he takes a deep breath as if to say
something. The Mandarin looks at him expectantly.
Ta-Jin lets the breath out. The Mandarin looks away,
but then Ta-Jin breathes deep and speaks. When his
voice comes out it is very thin and weedy (David
Beckham springs to mind).*

Ta-Jin Can I say something?

*Beat. Everyone stares at Ta-Jin in amazement because
he's spoken.*

Mandarin Please do!

Ta-Jin If Knoon-She doesn't like me, maybe we shouldn't
be getting married at all.

Beat. All stare at him, aghast.

Mandarin (*after a moment. Heartily*) Nonsense, my boy.
Can't call off a good wedding at this late stage. What
would we tell the guests? Besides, the ten donkeys your
mother gave me have settled in beautifully. We wouldn't
want to disturb them, would we? (*The Mandarin leaps
to his feet.*) Come along, we can't sit moping on the
floor! We have drinking to do, we must make merry,
we must party and revel and whoop it up!

*The men all jump up and throw themselves into their
drunken song once again, this time with a choreographed
dance too. The maids have by now dressed Knoon-She
up and left. She is sitting alone, staring sadly into space.
Chang quietly slips away from the drunken revelry
towards Knoon-She. As he does so, his hat falls off. He
goes to Knoon-She. She looks confused, wonders who
he is. He takes off the rest of his disguise so she can
recognise him. Knoon-She gasps and throws her arms
around him. Chang undresses Knoon-She, taking off
her wedding clothes until she is in her undergarments*

*once more. This should be a tender moment, in contrast
to the drunken wedding song going on at the same
time. They embrace, then Chang shushes Knoon-She,
takes her hand. Knoon-She stops a moment to grab the
box of jewels given to her by Ta-Jin, then Chang leads
her off. As he does so, Ta-Jin notices Chang's hat on
the floor. He looks over to where Knoon-She was. He
looks puzzled, whispers something in the Mandarin's
ear. The Mandarin looks over to where Knoon-She
was, looks absolutely livid, then yells at the top of
his voice.*

Mandarin STOOOPPPPPPPPPPPPPPPPPPPPPPPPPPP!!

*Everyone stops dancing and singing. Silence. Then the
Mandarin takes a deep breath and shouts again.*

Mandarin
BRINNNNNNNNNNNNNNNNGGGGGGG!!
MEEEEEEEEEEEEEEEEEEEEEEEEEEEEEEE!!
MYYYYYYYYYYYYYYYYYYYYYYYYYYYY!!
WAAAAAAAAAARRIIIIIIORRRRRRRRRRS!!

*Everyone exits. Music: loud, cacophonous. The
ensemble comes on and makes a bridge. Min waits on
the other side of the bridge in a boat. After a moment
Knoon-She and Chang come running onto the bridge.
They are soon followed by Ta-Jin, the Mandarin and
some warriors. The warriors and Ta-Jin have fighting
sticks. Chang and Knoon-She turn to face them. It
looks like they've had it, but then Min springs forward
with fighting sticks for Chang, Knoon-She and herself.
A fierce fight follows which is finally won by Min,
Chang, and Knoon-She (Knoon-She and Min proving
to be the best fighters). At some point during the fight,
Knoon-She gives Chang the jewellery box to hold so
she can fight better. The Mandarin notices this. At the
end of the fight, the warriors and Ta-Jin lie strewn all*

*over the space, while Chang, Knoon-She and Min
escape in the boat.*

Mandarin (*as the boat draws away*) Do something! Do
something! Do something!

*No answer from the exhausted warriors and Ta-Jin.
The Mandarin runs to the end of the bridge and shouts
after his daughter.*

I'll find you, d'you hear me! I'll find you. And when I do,
you'll be sorry you did this to me!!

*The two doves come flying onto the bridge, about to
follow Knoon-She. The Mandarin grabs them. They
struggle but he holds them tight and exits with them.
Music stops. The warriors and Ta-Jin get slowly to
their feet, nursing their wounds, and leave the space.
After a moment, the Narrator bounds forward.*

Narrator Phew! Phewee, gadzooks, and gosh! What a
kerfuffle, What a to-do. What a turn up for the books.
Knoon-She and Chang sailed away until they found a
small island, protected by a beautiful willow tree.

*The bridge breaks up and exits, leaving a few people
behind to represent or make the willow tree. As the
Narrator speaks, Knoon-She, Chang and Min enter.
They start to build houses. One for Knoon-She and
Chang, one for Min. This can be done using the
ensemble, or blocks, or whatever you like. The houses
are simple, but elegant. There is a swing seat at the
front of Knoon-She and Chang's, which they sit on
when the building is finished.*

And here they made homes for themselves, and for Min,
too, because, as it is written, 'You can get everything
you want in life, if you help enough other people get
what they want.'

Min puts her thumb up, and smiles.

The lovers and their friend were happy. They were
contented, blissful, pleased. They were jovial, delighted,
cheery and glad.

Min Enough.

Narrator They were like doves in a dovecote. They were
on Cloud Nine.

Min Enough!!

Narrator Back home, in the province they had left behind,
it was a different story. The Mandarin went on the
rampage, breaking up the Palace and chucking out all
his wedding guests. It was like when his wife died,
only worse. Ta-Jin and his mum took back all their
donkeys and left the place in a huff. And the Mandarin,
alone in his Palace with no one to talk to, became
more and more vengeful.

*Enter Mandarin, looking wild and angry. He brings
with him the two doves, in a cage. Knoon-She and
Min's houses remain on.*

It is said, 'Those who think of revenge keep their wounds
open.' Oh so true. The Mandarin could not get past it.
All he could think about was the way his beloved
Knoon-She had betrayed him. He wanted to find his
daughter and Chang and have them thrown into prison.
But by the law of the province, he could not do so because, actually, they hadn't really done anything wrong.
By now they were both of age, they could marry who-
ever they liked. It was only tradition that saw the matter
differently. Tradition, and the Mandarin. He was livid,
but his hands were tied. So he brooded and brooded
and fretted and festered until, one day, he had a visitor.

*Enter Ta-Jin's Mother. Narrator steps back. The
Mandarin jumps up, shocked. Ta-Jin's Mother bows
to him, briefly.*

Ta-Jin's Mother Mandarin.

Mandarin Madam.

Ta-Jin's Mother Are you alright? You look a little . . . dishevelled.

Mandarin I . . . haven't been feeling too good.

Ta-Jin's Mother Yes. Well. I suppose that's understandable. You have been made a mockery of. The whole province is talking about you, how foolish you look, betrayed by your own daughter. You know she's living out of wedlock with that scribe, don't you? She was obviously bad from the start, thank goodness my Taji *didn't* get to marry her.

Mandarin Can I help you with anything or are you just here to exercise your mouth?

Ta-Jin's Mother (*pursing her lips*) The small matter of the jewellery box.

Mandarin The what?

Ta-Jin's Mother The box of jewels given to your daughter, by my son, as an introduction present. We want it back.

The Mandarin looks puzzled.

Mandarin I don't remember any jewellery box!

Ta-Jin's Mother Mandarin! Aren't you ashamed enough? Do not disgrace yourself further by lying now!

Mandarin How dare you accuse me of lying! I may be a fool, yes. I may be disgraced. I may be a silly, bad-tempered, irascible, surly old man but . . .

He grinds to a halt.

. . . just a minute! Was it blue?

Ta-Jin's Mother What?

Mandarin The box, woman, was it blue?!

Ta-Jin's Mother Yes, I think it was, but . . .

Mandarin (*over the moon*) I saw it in his hands the night they went away! Theft! Yes. Theft!

Ta-Jin's Mother What are you going on about?

Mandarin (*jubilant*) Madam, I am very sorry to have to tell you, your jewellery box has been stolen!

Ta-Jin's Mother Has it?

Mandarin Yes, by my erstwhile secretary, Chang. But don't you worry, I will do my utmost, believe me, to bring it, and the thief, and his accomplices, right back where they came from.

Ta-Jin's Mother And how are you going to do that? No one knows where they are.

Mandarin (*eyeing the doves, who flutter and beat their wings against the cage*) Oh, I think I know someone who could find them.

He goes over to the doves, and open the doors to the cage. The doves flutter then fly out.

Mandarin (*taking Ta-Jin's Mother's hand*) Don't worry, madam. You will have your jewellery box. And I will have my revenge.

The doves fly off, the Mandarin follows. Ta-Jin's Mother, looking confused, exits the other way. The Narrator springs forward. During the following, the doves fly round the hall and through the audience, followed by an intensely resolute Mandarin. Eventually they come back up into the performing space to where Knoon-She, Chang and Min have their houses.

Narrator (*urgently*) Vengeance. Retribution. Reprisal. Retaliation. Reckoning. Justice. Punishment. Comeback. The words ran round the Mandarin's head as he followed Knoon-She's doves closer and closer to his daughter. When a man grows angry his reason rides out. When wrath speaks, wisdom veils her face. When temper rises, reason drops. Night fell, and the Mandarin got nearer.

Knoon-She and Chang snuggle down to sleep in their houses. Min does the same.

And as he got nearer, his rage got bigger, until he had forgotten all about the jewellery box, he had forgotten all about throwing Chang in prison, all he could see was a big red mist and he just wanted to envelop them in it so they could feel exactly just how hurt, how hurt and full of rage he was.

Silence. The doves have arrived at the houses. They hover around and watch the sleeping Knoon-She and Chang. The Mandarin creeps over. The doves fly away in distress. The Mandarin stares in at his sleeping daughter and Chang. He is breathing very heavily, seething. Suddenly, he runs off. The doves come back and start beating their wings against the house but Chang and Knoon-She don't wake up. The Mandarin runs back on with a flaming torch and throws it into the house. The house begins to burn. The Mandarin hides at the side and watches. Knoon-She and Chang wake up. They scream, cry for help and try to get out of the house, but they are trapped. Min wakes up and tries to help them out, tries to put out the fire, but she can't. The doves flap about in distress. Finally the house is razed to the ground and Knoon-She and Chang lie dead on the floor. The doves settle beside their bodies. Min falls to her knees and sobs. The Mandarin stands up, in shock. He looks terrible. He takes two steps forwards, then lets out a cry of anguish.

Mandarin Nooooooo!

The Mandarin runs off. The Narrator steps forward.

Narrator It was a very sad time for the people of the province.

The ensemble enters. Music or song: sad, mournful.
All gather round the bodies of Knoon-She and Chang,
as though at a funeral.

The Mandarin, a broken man, disappeared. The rumour
was, he had become a hermit. Living alone in a cave on
the mountain, forever regretting and full of remorse.

The two doves slowly begin to twitch and come to life.

But for Knoon-She and Chang, it wasn't so bad! Their
spirits left their bodies, and transformed into two
beautiful doves. Together they stretched their wings,
and flew off to the Realm of Eternal Happiness.

The two doves fly happily away. The song/music
reaches a crescendo then dies away. Silence.

And that is my story. The moral is clear. They say anger is
a fear of losing control. I say, lose your fear. Control
ain't everything it's cracked up to be.

The funeral song/music is repeated.

End.

Sources of the Quotations

He that is angry is seldom at ease.
Unknown origin

A friend is one who knows everything about you,
and yet still likes you.
Unknown origin

Love is patient, love is kind.
It does not envy, it does not boast, it is not proud.
1 Corinthians 13: 4, 5

Poetry is something that heals oneself.
Unknown origin

He who wears his heart on his sleeve
often looks stupid.
Judith Johnson

To get used to something is something terrible.
Zen master

Happiness is like a perfume: we cannot sprinkle it on
someone else, without a few drops falling on ourselves.
William Shakespeare

Love, and a cough, cannot be hid.
George Herbert

The soul would have no rainbow
if the eyes had no tears.
Indian proverb

All roads lead you astray.
Lonely Planet guidebook

JUDITH JOHNSON

If we do not change direction,
we will probably get to where we are going.
Chinese adage

Without going outside, you may know the whole world.
Lao Tzu

I have my ignorance to thank
for the few things I know.
Sacha Guitry

You have only failed when you have failed to try.
Unknown origin

You can get everything you want in life, if you help
enough other people get what they want.
Unknown origin

Those who think of revenge keep their wounds open.
Francis Bacon

When a man grows angry his reason rides out.
Unknown origin

When wrath speaks, wisdom veils her face.
Unknown origin

When temper rises, reason drops.
Judith Johnson

A Timeless Tale Set in Imaginative Territory

Judith Johnson interviewed by Jim Mulligan

Stone Moon, Judith Johnson's first *Connections* play, produced in 1997, is set in a village in South China, where two women find the strength from their love and friendship to defy convention and leave the community that oppresses them. Since that time she has written four plays, and is now happily engaged in writing episodes for a radio soap, *Westway*, which is transmitted by the BBC World Service and has an enormous following in West Africa

The Willow Pattern, Judith Johnson's second play for *Connections*, is also set in the Far East. It tells the story behind the willow-pattern plates that found their way to Europe in the nineteenth century. Knoon-She is the daughter of a powerful Mandarin. He wants her to marry Ta-Jin, a brainless warrior, but Knoon-She has fallen in love with her father's secretary, Chang, and on the eve of the wedding the lovers elope. As the Narrator says in his opening address: 'But never has there been a man so ruined by anger as the man whose story I'm about to tell.' The Mandarin is so consumed by his rage that he pursues the lovers and burns down their cottage, killing his daughter and her lover as they sleep inside.

> Their souls go up to heaven in the form of two doves, and we are left with the idea that their life continues on a spiritual plane, whereas the Mandarin is unhappy for the rest of his life. My play is pretty close to the original. I've added two characters. There is Min, with a very earthy, cynical kind of humour that I thought was needed to balance the rather starry-eyed

romanticism of the lovers. And there is Ta-Jin's mother, because in my version he is so stupid he can't speak and I created her to be his mouthpiece.

In *The Willow Pattern* the Narrator is full of life and eager to tell his tale. He explodes onto the stage, 'jumps, rolls, runs, glides, skateboards, sky-dives, somersaults, trampolines or even apparates onto the performing space'. His language is that of the music-hall chairman, and he brings a feeling of pantomime to the play, giving it a larger-than-life dimension.

The Narrator was inspired by *Monkey*, a cult TV series from the seventies which in its turn was inspired by the Chinese legend of Monkey and his two spirit friends who help a prince on his spiritual quest. There is slapstick and humour. That is the spirit of the play. Obviously the staging is entirely up to the company, but it is a timeless tale, a journey into imaginative territory.

In the face of her authoritarian father, Knoon-She is manipulative. She has been brought up without a mother and has never had contact with anyone outside the rigorously controlled palace where she lives. She has been spoilt and has had none of the rough edges knocked off her. She is selfish and, if she had been less of an individual, she might have gone along with her father's wishes and there would have been a very different story to tell. As it happens, she falls for Chang, a sensitive poet, without thinking of the consequences. Chang could easily have been executed on the spot when the Mandarin catches him kissing Knoon-She, but Min helps him to escape. She harbours Chang and plans how they can use the confusion of the wedding ceremony to elope. Min and Chang are both virtual slaves and one revealing conversation tells us a good deal about their characters and their dreams.

Chang You are a very wise person, Min.

Min I have my ignorance to thank for the few things I know.

Chang You know you are risking . . . everything by helping us.

Min I promised Knoon-She's mother I would always take care of her and that is what I am going to do.

Chang You are a genuinely good person.

Min And when you and Knoon-She set up your house together, far away from here, I will be with you and I will be free.

But Min is a realist and she does not believe they have an ice cream's chance in Hell of escaping the wrath of the Mandarin.

If young people are looking for issues that concern them in *The Willow Pattern*, it is possible to discern some: the devastating effects of anger on both the victim and the perpetrator; the obsessive control that some parents exercise over their children; arranged or forced marriages; and the possibility of happiness after death. *The Willow Pattern* is a demanding play, with a need for choreography, music, martial arts, elaborate costumes and doves that fly round the space, alight on Knoon-She's shoulders or in some way attach themselves fondly to her. There are some spectacular set pieces such as the fight or the wedding with its drinking, dancing and singing, and where amidst all that action there is a tender moment as Chang removes the wedding garments from Knoon-She.

All plays are demanding in one way or another. I don't think my play is intellectually very demanding. You could approach it as an old legend that has been told for generations or you could bring out the anger that ruined the Mandarin's life or you could focus on forced marriages, which could be a very controversial issue in some of the communities that will be putting the play on. This play is not arguing against arranged marriages, nor is it critical of communities that have them. I want the young people to focus on this despotic father and to realise that in such situations young people will rebel. The play is open to interpretation, but it probably says something about sticking to what you believe in your heart, what you believe your own truth to be. For all her faults, Knoon-She is true to what she believes to be right. And Chang, my favourite character, truly loves Knoon-She, who is inspired by his caring intuition.

Production Notes

The Willow Pattern has eight main characters, including
a very lively Narrator (a part which could be split among
a number of actors). The ensemble, which can be as big or
as small as you like, creates the scenarios and helps to tell
the story, which is based on the legend of 'The Willow
Pattern' told in China a thousand years ago and popularised in this country by the ceramic designs of the late
eighteenth century.

There is a notable contrast between the familiar,
genteel, middle-class associations of the the willow-pattern
design on plates with the epic, passionate, violent, alien
culture that the play portrays. It's exciting to see a
recognisable image torn apart. The pattern on the plates
might suggest the visual style of your production: the
blue-and-white colour scheme could become the palette
you work from.

Despite these Chinese influences in the play, you don't
need to follow these too rigorously: the play borrows
from different cultures, and there are contemporary
western references. These can also be evident in the
design and playing of the piece. Explore as many cultural
influences as possible when researching the play. You may
want to magpie things from a number of places – for
example, turning the percussive use of music in Chinese
culture into something more like 'Stomp' performances.

Screens are a common aspect of Asian design and you
might want to incorporate them in yours. Some of the
characters might burst through them. If you choose to
create a series of tableaux based on the picture on the
plate, then be sure to mark each step on the journey very

clearly, so at the end they are all there. You might consider bringing on a curved frame to put round an image. Also, make sure you get theatrical value from all the scene changes – don't apologise for them. Avoid blackouts.

If you live in an area with a strong ceramic history, why not check it out? There were eighteen centres of willow-pattern manufacture in competition with each other, and your area might have been one of them. You could smash a plate in anger and put it together again as a symbol of hope (Poole Pottery in Dorset has an area where you can smash faulty plates to relieve tension).

STYLE AND USE OF CONVENTIONS

In Chinese theatrical tradition, stage managers remain on stage with the actors. 'Honourably invisible' – the audience and actors ignore them – they are extensions of the actors and carry on props, etc., for them, such as tea or scrolls. You could use lackeys in this way to do everything for the Mandarin to show his status. In Japanese theatre the stage managers wear black, with black masks, and walk with bowed knees. Nobody on stage ever brings anything with them. The Narrator could be such a figure (always look for correspondence between onstage actors and Narrator, there's lots of scope for invention).

The directors at the Keswick retreat watched a video of a moment in *Fosse* as an example of a Kabuki drop. A large red cloth falls from the rear of the stage to cover the whole back wall, and is then pulled forward and down by dancers like a wave rolling over the stage; when completely flat it reveals more dancers behind. You could incorporate this idea in your show to add an element of surprise. It's simple to do: the cloth is suspended by cotton and pulled by two actors on each side of the stage.

The doves could be either puppets or actors. You could use a puppet, a person, or a pantomime-horse-type idea for the donkey. You could have as many donkeys as you like and create a dance routine or even a donkey serenade. Look at the work of Ariane Mnouchkine, who works in a very unusual way based on Bunraku: two actors often work together, one as a puppet, one as the voice and manipulator.

Judith hears the voices in the play as larger than life but *not accented* – definitely not a high-pitched Chinese send-up.

Have the cast watch an episode from the DVD of *Monkey* (the directors in the Keswick workshop watched 'The Foolish Philosopher'), then a snippet from another, then a snippet with sub-titles rather than dubbed.

Certain style elements will jump out at you: it's extremely heightened; it is slapstick at times as in *The Three Stooges*. Surprise is emphasised, with exclamation marks being vocalised; and it involves martial arts and some exciting fight sequences. Also, sound effects are added to make a mime more exciting. Sound is stretched and manipulated. This could be done live and vocally: musicians on stage could use wood blocks to contribute effects, rather in the way sound is used in *Xena, Warrior Princess*.

Try out *status games* for the Mandarin and Knoon-She. Decide who's in charge, work on the proverbs and the humour: analyse what it is that makes *Monkey* funny and do exercises around this. Use characteristics of animals to create bold physical characterisation: go to the zoo, watch nature videos, experiment with masks.

You might vary the playing style from scene to scene – for example, the Mandarin on the rampage could have an almost silent-movie feel, but the scenes between Knoon-

She and Chang should be more real. Look for mixture and contrast. With visual theatre you should *change the picture every three minutes* (attention spans are shortening). Do this with pace, style, scene changes, mood, music. Beware of being inconsistent, however: *connect* the styles you are using to engage the audience.

STYLE INFLUENCES IN MONKEY include English panto-mime (the Water Monster as the Arch Villain; a girl playing Priests, like the principal boy being sensible and wise); slapstick originating in *commedia dell'arte* routines, with stock characters such as masters and servants (servants always being more intelligent, the master never seeing servant pulling faces; servant always being in a good position for upstaging and having relationship with audience).

Also consider: characterisation from animals; special effects using puppets; the use of music intentionally to underscore serious moments; sound effects enhancing fighting and announcing/punctuating the comedy.

Performance style is very *open* and *presentational*. When learning kung fu, you turn out towards the teacher, and this is analogous with Elizabethan theatre: soliloquies are shared with the audience, and arguments are very verbal, antagonists sharing them with the audience before directing them to an opponent.

Without its subtitles, it's less pantomimic – more eastern, less of a send-up, though still exaggerated and theatrical. Physical performances shine through: there's comedy in the facial expressions.

Monkey has an unseen narrator. The narrator in *The Willow Pattern* is more controlling, and characters can interact with him/her (a good humorous conceit). In *Monkey* the narrator still uses quoted words of wisdom, his role being to give us the moral. Judith felt that her Narrator was very like Monkey, so take a look at the Narrator's first entrance, and experiment with making the Monkey connection more explicit. Monkey is irrepressible, cheeky, verbose and pompous. See what happens when the Narrator adopts these characteristics. You don't necessarily have to be serious to tell a serious story, but bring verve and energy to it.

All entrances by the characters are very big. This is the first lesson in old-school acting. You might look at this with the Mandarin.

CHARACTERS

THE MANDARIN AND KNOON-SHE His anger should be genuine and powerful even though it has been written in a humorous way. He has lost his way and hasn't been happy for a long time. He loses his daughter through his own fault, therefore emotionally he has a lot of anger. Judith Johnson admits to tapping into the pantomime villain when creating him. She watched her own little boy's tantrums: his movements were huge but his anger was heart-felt. It can be funny to watch someone lose their temper. Children wind up others with bad tempers for entertainment. Decide if there are moments when Knoon-She winds her father up deliberately. There is a lot of the child in the character of the Mandarin, he has never learned routine or discipline. He's a grown-up spoilt brat. It's perfectly possible Knoon-She would have turned out the same way if she hadn't fallen in love with the poet.

Read the first scene through, and ask the actors these questions:

- Does this happen often? Is it a ritual? (The answer's yes, every morning.)

- Is it the same each time? Is there room for change or spontaneity? (Encourage moments of variety and disruption of patterns.)

- Is it a display for political reasons? (He is asserting his power over her: it's like the test in *King Lear*, for the public to witness.)

- She is standing – she doesn't bow, which might show they are equals; or is this the first time she hasn't done it? She allows him to be powerful in this context, but can wrap him round her little finger.

- What is the tone of her responses? How bored is she? How much of a game are they playing?

- How important is the punctuation to the tone? If you divide the text into sections and name each one, 'The Ritual' could be the name for this section.

Find a sense of progression towards her rebellion later in the play. The Narrator very explicitly sets up a tension in the introduction, so we're expecting a conflict. Surprise comes when they melt into a familiar couple at the end of the scene.

THE MISSING MOTHER is a key character and affects the whole story. There's maybe scope for showing a visual representation of her death: perhaps in flashback without adding any dialogue. Or you could discuss or improvise this piece of back-history, perhaps with the Mandarin, showing exactly what is making him unhappy. (In the pre-show of Matthew Warchus's *Hamlet*, home movies of old King Hamlet playing with Hamlet as a child were screened, which gave the audience an insight into Hamlet's anger at Claudius.)

The wedding day could be acted out in a similar way. The mother's spirit could be present at key moments.

NARRATOR S/he says '*my* story': you can decide whether this implies s/he's telling his/her version or just has a personal connection to it. Read the opening speech of the Narrator. Two phrases are key: 'I myself know this to be true' and 'When life was more definite'. Both need consideration and a response. Decide how s/he knows, why s/he tells us this and whether s/he has a temper too. Look for moments when the Narrator can help to cover the scene changes. (Avoid an empty stage at any time in this fast-moving, narrative theatre.)

Read the opening speech again. Break up the text into four parts (one for each actor) as follows:

HOOOOOOOOOOOORAAAAAAAAAAAAAAAH! HOOPLAAH! AND GREETINGS, MY GOOD FRIENDS! (1) It is written, 'He that is angry is seldom at ease.' (2) I myself know this to be true. (3) And maybe you know this too. (4) But never has there been a man so ruined by anger as the man whose story I'm about to tell. (1) Long ago, in Ancient Times, long before any of you were born. Well, most of you anyway. Way way back when things were different. (2) When things were clearer, (3) when decisions were easier, (4) when life was more definite. And so was death. (1) Back then, there lived a Mandarin. He was the most important man in the province. (2) He was eminent, influential, powerful. (3) He was the chief, the boss, the main man, the king. (4) He was critical, crucial, focal. (1) Of great consequence, (2) of great magnitude, (3) of great worth. (4) You get the picture. (1) Everyone bowed down before him. (2) Everyone except his daughter.

- Re-define the terms in different voices to show the one-upmanship in the lines – a quality of *Monkey*, perhaps?

- Encourage quick pick-ups so there is no need for the speech to slow down.

- One narrator alone seems to know what we know now.

- Note that Number Three is the one who often says the most important thing.

- *Don't* change 'I' to 'we' no matter how many people are reading it; there should still be the sense of *one* consciousness, one character behind it all.

- Make sure that the energy of a single character isn't dissipated by splitting up words in this way.

- You could play it as a 'chorus' of Monkeys: a group of people all playing the same archetype, although in different bodies. Mask-work might be useful to find the consistent physicality.

- Look at tightening rhythms to emphasise short lines.

- Try it with the actors on their feet, reading to the audience in-the-round as a group.

- Try it with the actors at four corners of the room, standing outside the audience circle until they speak, then stepping in.

- Have the actors feel an urgency, a real need to tell the story; step towards people as you speak each line, working the circle.

- Ask the actors to look at each other before speaking in unison to find the timing.

ASPECTS OF STAGING

STREAM/WATER/WASHING The sound of water is very important to the play. The cloth being washed by Min could turn into a representation of water. It could then turn into something else – maybe the tablecloth at the wedding feast (it could be red/blue reversible). The washing doesn't have to be of real garments such as underwear (though there may be comedy mileage in this).

THE BRIDGE Judith imagined it as being made up of human bodies, but it doesn't have to be. It needs to be solid so that it can be fought on. If the bridge is made of people they could join in with the fighting, or if bamboo poles, say, make up the bridge, these could be used as weapons.

If the bridge was made of people you could follow this through and have all solid furniture made of people – throne, table, garden, house, etc.

FIGHTING Judith saw this as stylised, rather as in the film *Crouching Tiger, Hidden Dragon*. You could use the idea of 'bullet time' – i.e., slow motion as in *The Matrix*.

Look at the Tom Cruise movie *The Samurai*. Observe the fights to the death, the big reactions, how holy space is established for fighting in, the exaggeration of vocal and physical responses. Use the film as a basis for working out a style.

The Narrator could fast-forward the boring bits of the fight, playing with speed and rhythm. But it's nevertheless important that the fight is taken seriously dramatically.

Judith feels it's *crucial* that the girls are good or even the best at fighting, like Uma Thurman in *Kill Bill*. They are outnumbered by the warriors, but still miraculously hold

677

them all off. Disparity in numbers could be a source of humour. Check out *Lotus and Sword*, in which Shaolin monks and nuns fought alongside each other in a martial-arts display.

THE JEWEL BOX This is a crucial plot point, and focus must be given to the box for all its appearances. It's vital for the audience to see the transfer of the box to Chang during the fight, so the fight needs to be very controlled: slow motion might help this, with the protagonists moving at a different speed so we focus on them. It is also important that the audience sees the Mandarin see Chang with the box. He pounces on the apparent theft later, and we need to know where this comes from.

MUSIC You could use music as in *Monkey* to punctuate the sound effects, and to create percussive underlining of key moments.

* The style could be epic (look at Ennio Morricone – don't worry about using only Chinese references).

* The Mandarin's story of meeting his wife for the first time seems to cry out for an underscore; you could use a 'Wife's Theme' throughout and affiliate it with the doves.

* A chime tree might be a useful instrument to suggest water.

* You might like to research Kabuki for its use of wood blocks, cymbals, lyre, drums; or Peking Opera, which is more cacophonous, with music revealing emotion, and commenting on stage action.

CHOREOGRAPHY 'Out of stillness comes action' is the basis of martial arts and Asian dance. As an exercise, try to get the actors to do absolutely nothing: to remain impassive despite stimuli. This is very hard. Train them to do as little as possible physically: too much movement can lower status and distract from the text. Having a monarch suggests a theatre of prominent gesture.

Try different styles at different moments: the stag party could have women in dance and be very funny; doves could have a dance with a classical influence; flames might be dancers. Acrobatics should be considered. Use the talents of your cast.

FURTHER REFERENCE

Monkey, the cult Japanese TV series (adapted from the Buddhist text 'The Journey West'), is available on DVD from HMV and other major stores. Four episodes, PG certificate. Ref 5030697005458. Also see the website at www.monkeyheaven.com.

For information on access to Asian culture see the website at www.asiahouse.org.

Type in 'willow pattern' on www.google.co.uk for lots of references to the plate and the story behind it. (The illustrations of the story by children at Sir Robert Hitcham's Primary School are very enjoyable.)

For poems about the willow pattern, see the website at www.netcentral.co.uk/steveb/patterns.willow1.html.

For information on Chinese and Japanese theatre practice go to www.theatrehistory.com/asian/chinese0002.html.

You might also like to look on the web for stills from the Chinese Youth Theatre of Hawaii, who use traditional practices in their productions.

For information on the Chinese tea ceremony (which you might use to show up cultural differences between the UK and China) go to www.holymtn.com/tea/chinatea.html.

JUDITH JOHNSON

The Willow Pattern Story by Alan Drummond is a beautifully illustrated hardback picture book. ISBN: 1558581715.

Crouching Tiger, Hidden Dragon is a martial-arts film directed by Ang Lee, widely available on DVD and video.

The Matrix trilogy of sci-fi martial-arts films pioneered a certain style of film fighting: in slow motion, bodies in the air, pumping techno music soundtrack. Cult and contemporary.

Kill Bill, Part One is the latest film directed by Quentin Tarantino.

based on a workshop led by Wayne Harrison
transcribed by Abigail Anderson

Participating Schools and Companies

The Abbey School, Reading
Aberdeenshire Youth Theatre, Aberdeen
Action Transport Theatre, Ellesmere Port
Albany Interactive Youth Theatre, London
All Saints College, Newcastle
Amery Hill School, Alton
Arnold's In Yer Space, Blackpool
Astor College for the Arts, Dover

Barnwell School, Stevenage (Players and Faces)
Bassingbourn Village College, Royston
Behind the Scenes Youth Theatre, Buckhaven
Best Theatre Arts, St Albans
Bexhill College, Bexhill-on-Sea
Birmingham Rep: Young Rep @ Birmingham Rep, Birmingham
Bishop Luffa School, Chichester
Bishop Perowne CE High School, Worcester
Blue Coat CE Comprehensive School, Walsall
Blyth Community College, Blyth
Boston Spa Comprehensive School, Wetherby
Brentford School for Girls, Brentford
Brewery Arts Centre, Kendal
Brookfield Community School, Southampton
Bungay High School, Bungay

Callington Community College, Callington
Camborne Community College, Camborne
Cap-a-Pie Creative Campus, Dipton
Carlton Junior Television Workshop, Nottingham
Castleford High School Technology College, Castleford
Catteral Hall, Settle
Centerstage Theatre Company, Swansea

Charlton Outreach Theatre Company, Telford
Chellaston School, Derby
Chichester College, Chichester
Chichester Festival Youth Theatre, Chichester
Coedylan Comprehensive School, Pontypridd
Coleg Sir Gar, Llanelli
Cork School of Music Youth Theatre, Cork
Creative Room, Nottingham City Council, Nottingham
Cumberland Youth Theatre, Keswick
Cumbria Institute of the Arts, Carlisle

Dashers Youth Theatre, Monmouth
Dolman Youth Theatre, Newport
Dumont High School Youth Theatre, Dumont

Ealing Hammersmith and West London College, London
East Norfolk Sixth Form College, Great Yarmouth
Edinburgh's Telford College, Edinburgh
Ellowes Hall School, Dudley
EO.45 Theatre, West Suffolk College, Bury St Edmunds

Fallen Angel Project, Nottingham
Ferndale Community School, Rhondda
Fisher More RC High School, Colne
Flintshire Youth Theatre, Mold
Folkestone School for Girls, Folkestone
The Freewheelers, Leatherhead
Freman College, Buntingford
Fulford School, York
Full Circle Children's Theatre Company, Enfield

Gantry Youth Theatre, Bitterne
George Ward School, Melksham
Godalming College, Godalming
Gordonstoun School, Elgin
Gorseinon College, Gorseinon

Hall Green Little Theatre (Youth Section), Solihull
Hall Mead School, Upminster

PARTICIPATING SCHOOLS AND COMPANIES

Harlow College Community Arts Group, Harlow
Headington School, Oxford
Heaton Manor School, Newcastle-upon-Tyne
Hemel Hempstead School, Hemel Hempstead
Hemsworth Arts and Community College, Pontefract
Henbury School, Bristol
Hillcrest School and Community College, Dudley
Hope Valley College, Hope
Hurstpierpoint College, Hassocks

Independent Theatre Workshop, Dublin
International String of Lights

Jigsaw Youth Theatre Company, Barnet
Junior Octagon, Yeovil

Kennet School, Thatcham
Kent Youth Theatre, Faversham
Kidbrooke School, London
Kildare Youth Theatre @ Crooked House, Newbridge
King Edward VI Upper School, Bury St Edmunds
King Henry VIII School, Coventry
The King's School, Peterborough

Lancaster Footlights Youth Theatre, Lancaster
Leicester College, Leicester
Leiston High School, Leiston
Leyton Sixth Form College, London
Lindsey School and Community Arts College, Cleethorpes
Liverpool Hope Youth Theatre, Liverpool
Loft Theatre Group, Exeter
Looe Community School, East Looe
Lyceum Youth Theatre, Edinburgh

Manor College of Technology, Hartlepool
Marshalls Park School, Romford
Methwold High School, Thetford
Morecambe High School, Morecambe

Negus Theatre Company, Plumstead Manor School, London
Nescot College, Epsom
New Bridge Integrated College and Twiglet Theatre Company,
    Banbridge
New College, Durham
New Everyman Youth Theatre, Liverpool
Ninestiles Technology College, Birmingham
North Cumbria Technology College, Carlisle
North Nottinghamshire College, Worksop
North Warwickshire and Hinckley College, Hinckley
Northampton School for Boys, Northampton
Nunthorpe Secondary School, Nunthorpe

Old Hall School, Rotherham
Old Palace School of John Whitgift, Croydon
Oxford Youth Theatre, Oxford

Palace Theatre Watford's Youth Theatre, Watford
Palatine High School, Blackpool
Parsons Mead School, Ashtead
Peele School, Long Sutton, Spalding
Pencoed School, Near Bridgend
Perse School, Cambridge
Pershore High School, Pershore
Pilot Youth Theatre, York
Polka Theatre Company Youth Theatre, London
Ponteland Community High School, London
Portsmouth High School, Southsea
The Princess Helena College

Queen Elizabeth Maridunum School, Carmarthen
Queen Elizabeth School, Kirkby Lonsdale

Reigate School, Reigate
Rickstones School, Witham
Riding Lights Youth Theatre, York
Royal and Derngate Theatres, Northampton
Royal Forest of Dean College, Coleford
Royal School, Haslemere

PARTICIPATING SCHOOLS AND COMPANIES

Rushey Mead Secondary School, Leicester
Ryton Comprehensive School, Ryton

St Bernard's School, Barrow-in-Furness
St George's College of Technology, Sleaford
St Julian's School, Newport
St Martin in the Fields High School for Girls, London
St Mary's Catholic School, Bishop's Stortford
St Mary's Youth Theatre, Leeds
St Monica's High School, Prestwich
St Wilfrid's RC Comprehensive School, South Shields
Silver Street Youth Theatre, London
Sir Frederic Osborn School, Welwyn Garden City
Skelmersdale College, Skelmersdale
Snap Theatre Company, Bishop's Stortford
South Wight Youth Theatre
Southwark College, London
Stafford College, Stafford
Stage 84 Yorkshire School of Performing Arts, Bradford
Stagerite Youth Theatre, York
Stephen Joseph Youth Theatre 'Rounders', Scarborough
Stockton Riverside College, Stockton-on-Tees
Strode College Student Theatre Company, Street
Susi Earnshaw Theatre School, East Barnet Village

Teaterbiten, 65100 Vaasa
Theatre Antidote, Larnaca
Thomas Danby College, Leeds
Tonbridge Grammar School for Girls, Tonbridge
Toonspeak Young People's Theatre, Glasgow
Truro School, Truro
21st century Productions, Amersham

Walton Girls' High School, Grantham
Waterford Youth Drama, Waterford
College of West Anglia, King's Lynn
Westfield School, Gosforth
Westgate School, Winchester
Weydon School, Farnham

Whickham School, Newcastle-upon-Tyne
Whizz Kids Theatre Company, Ely
Winstanley College, Wigan
Wootton Upper School, Wootton

York College, York
York Theatre Royal Young Company, York
The Young Company at Plymouth Theatre Royal, Plymouth
Youth Lyric, Crossgar
Ysgol Aberconwy, Conway